PRECALCULUS

FOR EVERYBODY

Jorge Sáenz

HIPOTENUSA
2023

PRECALCULUS FOR EVERYBODY

Author: Jorge A. Sáenz C.

ISBN: 978-612-48516-2-9

First edition, 2023

Revision March, 2024

Edited by:

Editorial Hipotenusa EIRL

Av. Esteban Campodónico

Lima - Perú

www.hypotenuse.link

Legal Deposit made at Biblioteca Nacional del Perú under number 2023-08737

Printed on demand

A dedication with a bit of disobedience

Back in 1990, my father published one book I consider my favorite above any other book ever written. It wasn't exactly his most ambitious work, nor was it one to which I made any contribution at all; in fact, I was barely a five year old kid. Nevertheless, the frontmatter of this work contains a nearly blank page with a dedication of only two words, "to Roberto". I am certain that if Jorge were alive at the time of writing these words, he would not allow under any circumstances the transgression I am about to perpetrate, as he would consider it almost a crime for a book to be dedicated to its own author. I, the editor, will disregard his will, and take license to perpetrate this infringement. Furthermore, I will do it with pride and, most importantly, with love...

To Jorge

Forever your son and rebellious editor, Roberto.

"No human investigation can be called real science if it cannot be demonstrated mathematically"

—*Leonardo Da Vinci*

1

PRELIMINARIES

Pitágoras Of Samos
(569 - 475 B.C.)

PITÁGORAS was born on the Greek island of Samos about the year 569 B.C. His father was a merchant from Tyre, whom a very young Pythagoras used to join on his frequent business trips. They used to visit Chaldea, Syria, Italy and other regions. During his late teens, he went to Miletus to study with Thales and his student Anaximander, attending lectures on Geometry and Astronomy given by Anaximander.

Pythagoras, a highly educated individual, was skilled in playing the lyre, writing poetry, and reciting Homer's poems. He also demonstrated a strong passion for mathematics, astronomy, philosophy, music, and religion. Around 535 B.C., Pythagoras moved to Egypt to continue his studies, staying for a decade. During this time, he visited many temples and engaged in discussions with numerous priests and scholars until the Persian army invaded Egypt after winning the battle of Pelusium in the Nile Delta. He was taken prisoner and sent to Babylon, which, far from being a tragic experience, allowed him to learn Babylonian mathematics and their sacred rites.

After five years in Babylon, Pythagoras returned to Samos and founded his own school called "Semicircle", nevertheless, his teaching methods were not well appreciated by the Samorians, prompting him of moving to Croton, a Greek colony in the south of Italy around the year 520 B.C.

He founded a scientific, philosophical and religious school in Croton, but this school was no ordinary at all, it was more like a secret society ruled by strict and mysterious principles. The Pythagoreans were vegetarians, and practiced a strict observance of secrecy in matters of doctrine. The most outstanding feature of the Pythagorean doctrine is the principle that *numbers are the essence and basis of the universe.*

They believed that anything can be reduced to numbers, including all the things we can perceive in our daily lives, but the numbers they had in mind were the whole numbers and their ratios (rational).

Later on, they discovered the irrational numbers. Some authors consider this discovery as *one of the most amazing and far-reaching accomplishments of early Greek mathematics*; however, it was a tragedy for the Pythagorean school. The existence of these numbers contradicted the principle under which everything in the universe arises from rational numbers.

The Pythagorean School gained considerable political influence in Croton, earning the opposition of its citizens, who burned down the scholar's house.

Pythagoras was forced into moving to Metapontum(Italy), where he died at the age of eighty (475 B.C.). Yet his school stood for hundreds of years.

AXIOMS AND THEOREMS

Geometry and Algebra are examples of two different mathematical systems. All the propositions of a mathematical system can be classified as **Axioms** and **Theorems**. An axiom is a proposition that is accepted as true without any proof. An axiom is also called a **postulate**.

In contrast, a theorem is a proposition that requires a proof to be admitted as true. In general, a theorem has the next conditional form:

If H, then C

where the antecedent H is the **hypothesis** and C is the conclusion or thesis.

This conditional is an implication. That is, the **hypothesis H implies C**, which is symbolically written as:

$$H \Rightarrow C,$$

A proof of a theorem is a sequence of propositions that ends with the thesis. Each step of the sequence is either an axiom or a previous theorem.

According to the **conditional law** and the **contrapositive law**, we have:

$$H \Rightarrow C \equiv \sim C \vee H \quad \text{and} \quad H \Rightarrow C \equiv \sim C \rightarrow \sim H$$

Other theorems have the **biconditional** form:

A if and only if B. In symbols: $A \Leftrightarrow B$

According to the **biconditional law**, we have the following statements:

- A theorem $A \Leftrightarrow B$ is **equivalent** to the conjunction of the theorems:

  $$A \Rightarrow B \quad \text{and} \quad B \Rightarrow A$$

- To prove $A \Leftrightarrow B$, we must prove the following two implications:

  $$A \Rightarrow B \quad \text{and} \quad B \Rightarrow A$$

- The theorem $B \Rightarrow A$ is the converse of the theorem $A \Rightarrow B$.

QUANTIFIERS

In the sentence "*x is a positive number*", if the variable x is replaced by a specific number, like 5 ($x = 5$), we get the true proposition "5 *is a positive number*"; on the other hand, if x is replaced by -2, we obtain the self-evident false proposition "-2 *is a positive number*".

A sentence like "*x is a positive number*", involving a variable x, that turns into a proposition when you replace the variable with a specific value is called a **propositional function**. Some functional propositions could have more than one variable. For instance, $Q(x, y)\,:\; x + y = 3$ has two variables. A propositional function $P(x)$ may be satisfied by:

1. all values of x. **2. some** values of x **3. only** one value of x.

- The case 1 is denoted by:

$$(\forall \boldsymbol{x})\, \boldsymbol{P(x)} \quad \textbf{or} \quad \forall \boldsymbol{x} \boldsymbol{P(x)}$$

which reads "*for all values of x, $P(x)$ is true*". $\forall$ is called **universal quantifier**. Observe that $\forall$ is an A turned upside down.

- The case 2 is denoted by:

$$(\exists \boldsymbol{x})\, \boldsymbol{P(x)} \quad \textbf{or} \quad \exists \boldsymbol{x} \boldsymbol{P(x)}$$

which reads "*there exist values of x such that $P(x)$ is true*". $\exists$ is called **existential quantifier**. Observe that $\exists$ is an E reversed.

- The case 3 is denoted by:

$$(\exists! \boldsymbol{x})\, \boldsymbol{P(x)} \quad \textbf{or} \quad \exists! \boldsymbol{x} \boldsymbol{P(x)}$$

which reads "*there exists only one value of x such that $P(x)$* is true". $\exists!$ is called **uniqueness existential quantifier**.

Example 1.1.9 Write the following propositions in symbolic form:

1. All mathematical problems are difficult.
2. Some mathematical problems are difficult.
3. Only one mathematical problem is difficult.
4. All mathematical problems are not difficult.
5. Some mathematical problems are not difficult.

Solution

Let $D(x)$: x be a difficult mathematical problem.

1. $(\forall x)\, D(x)$ **2.** $(\exists x)\, D(x)$ **3.** $(\exists! x)\, D(x)$

4. $(\forall x)\, ({\sim} D(x))$ **5.** $(\exists x)\, ({\sim} D(x))$

SECCION 1.2

THE REAL NUMBER SYSTEM

REAL NUMBERS AND COORDINATE LINES

Counting numbers have been a part of human history for thousands of years, with their origins dating back to ancient times. In fact, they were the first numbers ever known. You already know these numbers, they are:

$$0,\ 1,\ 2,\ 3,\ 4,\ 5...$$

The three dots at the end of the list is a notation to indicate that the list keeps going forever. It is worth mentioning that the above list includes a much younger member of the crew, the number **0**, who came into existence several centuries after his peers. The Indian Brahmagupta, in 650 AD, was the first mathematician to formulate arithmetic operations using this number.

The set of **natural numbers**, or **whole numbers**, is the following:

$$\mathbb{N} = \{0, 1, 2, 3, ...\}$$

It is important to note that some authors do not consider zero as an element of this set. Even today, it is an issue that leads to heated debates among mathematicians.

In the work of the Babylonians, about 4.000 years ago, appeared for the first time the **negative numbers**:

$$\ldots, -5, -4, -3, -2, -1$$

Both, the negative and the natural numbers, constitute the **set of integers**:

$$\mathbb{Z} = \{..., -3, -2, -1, 0, 1, 2, 3, ...\}$$

The choice of $\mathbb{Z}$ to represent this set was inspired by the German word "*Zahlen*" that means *number*.

Rational numbers are another important set of numbers, defined as the ratio or quotient of two integers where the denominator is not 0. The following numbers are rational:

$$\frac{1}{2},\quad \frac{-1}{3},\quad \frac{5}{-2},\quad \frac{2}{1} = 2,\quad \frac{-5}{1} = -5$$

Notice that an integer can be represented as a rational number with 1 as the denominator.

In every day use, the word "*rational*" means logical or reasonable. In number theory, this word does not have that meaning. The term "**ratio**nal" comes from the word **ratio**. This set of numbers is denoted by $\mathbb{Q}$. This is:

$$\mathbb{Q} = \left\{ \frac{a}{b} \; / \; a, b \in \mathbb{Z} \text{ y } b \neq 0 \right\}$$

Observe the **decimal representation** of the following rational numbers:

$$\frac{1}{4} = 0.2500\ldots = 0.25\bar{0} \qquad \frac{1}{3} = 0.333\ldots = 0.\bar{3}$$

$$\frac{11}{6} = 1.8333\ldots = 1.8\bar{3}$$

Notice the periodicity of decimal representations delimited by the top bar. Indeed, the next proposition states the most important property of rationals:

A number is rational
if and only if
its decimal representation is periodic.

In the middle of the 5th century B.C., Pythagorean philosopher **Hippasus of Metapontum** discovered that there are numbers that cannot be expressed as a ratio of integers. For this reason, these numbers were called **irrationals**.

This was a transcendental discovery, however, this was tragedy for the Pythagorean school, since it contradicted its doctrine. The legend says that Hippasus was murdered because of this finding.

An **irrational number** is a number whose decimal representation is not periodic. The following numbers are irrational:

$$\sqrt{2} = 1.41415\ldots \qquad \pi = 3.14159\ldots$$

$$\text{The Euler number } \mathbf{e} = 2.7182818284\ldots$$

We denote the set of irrational numbers by $\mathbb{I}$.

The set of real numbers, denoted by $\mathbb{R}$, is the union of the set of rational numbers with the set of irrational numbers:

$$\mathbb{R} = \mathbb{Q} \cup \mathbb{I}$$

The nine field axioms we just discussed imply the forthcoming theorems.

Theorem 1.2.1 $\mathbf{0 \cdot a = 0 = a \cdot 0, \ \forall a \in \mathbb{R}}$

Proof

$$\begin{aligned}
a \cdot 0 &= a \cdot 0 + 0 && (A_3)\\
&= a \cdot 0 + (a + (-a)) && (A_4)\\
&= (a \cdot 0 + a) + (-a) && (A_2)\\
&= (a \cdot 0 \, + \, a \cdot 1) + (-a) && (M_3)\\
&= a(0 + 1) + (-a) && (D_1)\\
&= a \cdot 1 + (-a) && (A_3)\\
&= a + (-a) && (M_3)\\
&= 0 && (A_4)
\end{aligned}$$

On the other hand, we have that $0 \cdot a = a \cdot 0$ by M_1, and we also have that $a \cdot 0 = 0$; therefore $0 \cdot a = 0$.

Theorem 1.2.2 $\boldsymbol{ab = 0 \Leftrightarrow a = 0 \vee b = 0}$

Proof

Since this theorem has a biconditional form, we have to deliver two proofs:

1. $ab = 0 \Rightarrow a = 0 \vee b = 0$, which is symbolized by $(\Rightarrow)$
2. $a = 0 \vee b = 0 \Rightarrow ab = 0$, which is symbolized by $(\Leftarrow)$

$(\Rightarrow)$: Assume that $a \neq 0$. In this case, by M_4, there exists a^{-1}. Now, multiplying $ab = 0$ by a^{-1}, we have:

$$\begin{aligned}
a^{-1}(ab) = a^{-1}0 &\Rightarrow (a^{-1}a)b = 0 && (M_2 \text{ and Theor. } 1.2.1)\\
&\Rightarrow (1)b = 0 && (M_4)\\
&\Rightarrow b = 0 && (M_3)
\end{aligned}$$

$(\Leftarrow)$: Follows from theorem 1.2.1.

Example 1.2.1 Solve the equation $(x-2)(x+3) = 0$

Solution

Applying the previous theorem we have:

$$(x-2)(x+3) = 0 \Leftrightarrow x - 2 = 0 \ \vee \ x + 3 = 0 \Leftrightarrow x = 2 \ \vee \ x = -3$$

Theorem 1.2.3 **Properties of the additive inverse.**

For all $\boldsymbol{a}$ and $\boldsymbol{b}$ in $\mathbb{R}$:

1. $-(-a) = a$

2. $(-1)a = -a$

3. $(-a)b = a(-b) = -(ab)$

4. $(-a)(-b) = ab$

5. $-(a+b) = -a-b$

6. $-(a-b) = -a+b$

Proof

1. By axiom A_4, we have:

$$-(-a) + (-a) = 0 \wedge a + (-a) = 0$$

These results indicate that both $-(-a)$ and a are additive inverses of $-a$. But, A_4 states that the additive inverse is unique. Hence $-(-a) = a$.

2. Let's find out that $(-1)a$ is the additive inverse of a:

$$\begin{aligned} a + (-1)a &= 1 \cdot a + (-1)a && (M_3) \\ &= (1 + (-1))a && (D_1) \\ &= 0 \cdot a && (A_4) \\ &= 0 && (\text{Theor. } 1.2.1) \end{aligned}$$

But, $(-a) + a = 0$. Hence, by the uniqueness of the additive inverse:

$$(-1)a = -a$$

3.

$$\begin{aligned} (-a)b &= ((-1)a)b && (\text{part 2, previous}) \\ &= (-1)(ab) && (M_2) \\ &= -(ab) && (\text{part 2, previous}) \end{aligned}$$

Similarly, $a(-b) = -(ab)$.

4. Applying twice the part 3 and then the part 1, we have:

$$(-a)(-b) = -(a(-b)) = -(-(ab)) = ab$$

5. $-(a+b)$ is the additive inverse of $(a+b)$

Let's find out that $-a-b$ is the additive inverse of $(a+b)$ as well:

$$\begin{aligned} (a+b) + (-a-b) &= (a+b) + (-a + (-b)) && (\text{Def. of difference}) \\ &= (a + (-a)) + (b + (-b)) && (A_2 \text{ and } A_1) \\ &= 0 + 0 = 0 && (A_4 \text{ and } A_3) \end{aligned}$$

Hence, by the uniqueness of the additive inverse of $(a+b)$, we have:

$$-(a+b) = -a-b$$

Example 1.2.6 Solve:

1. $(-2)^3(-2)^4$ 2. $\dfrac{3^7}{3^5}$ 3. $(4^{-3})^{-1}$

4. $((-2)x^2)^4$ 5. $\left(\dfrac{2x^3}{y^2z}\right)^4$ 6. $\left(\dfrac{-2x}{z^2}\right)^{-3}$

Solution

1. $$(-2)^3(-2)^4 = (-2)^{3+4} = (-2)^7 = -128 \qquad \text{(law 1)}$$

2. $$\frac{3^7}{3^5} = 3^{7-5} = 3^2 = 9 \qquad \text{(law 2)}$$

3. $$(4^{-3})^{-1} = 4^{(-3)(-1)} = 4^3 = 64 \qquad \text{(law 3)}$$

4. $$((-2)x^2)^4 = (-2)^4\left(x^2\right)^4 = 16x^{2\times 4} = 16x^8 \qquad \text{(laws 4 and 3)}$$

5. $$\left(\frac{2x^3}{y^2z}\right)^4 = \frac{\left(2x^3\right)^4}{\left(y^2z\right)^4} = \frac{2^4x^{3\times 4}}{y^{2\times 4}z^4} = \frac{16x^{12}}{y^8z^4} \qquad \text{(laws 5, 3 and 4)}$$

6. $$\left(\frac{-2x}{z^2}\right)^{-3} = \left(\frac{z^2}{-2x}\right)^3 = \frac{\left(z^2\right)^3}{(-2x)^3} = \frac{z^{2\times 3}}{(-2)^3x^3} \qquad \text{(laws 6, 3 and 4)}$$
$$= \frac{z^6}{-8x^3} = -\frac{z^6}{8x^3}$$

Example 1.2.7 Simplify: $\left(\dfrac{4}{5b^3}\right)\left(\dfrac{2}{b}\right)^{-3}$

Solution

According to law 6, we have:

$$\left(\frac{4}{5b^3}\right)\left(\frac{2}{b}\right)^{-3} = \left(\frac{4}{5b^3}\right)\left(\frac{b}{2}\right)^3 = \left(\frac{4}{5b^3}\right)\left(\frac{b^3}{2^3}\right) = \frac{(2)^2b^3}{5(2)^3b^3} = \frac{1}{5(2)} = \frac{1}{10}$$

Example 1.2.8 Express with positive exponents and simplify:

$$\frac{12x^4y^{-5}}{-3x^{-2}y^3}$$

Solution

$$\frac{12x^4y^{-5}}{-3x^{-2}y^3} = \frac{12x^4x^2}{-3y^3y^5} = \frac{12x^{4+2}}{-3y^{3+5}} = \frac{12x^6}{-3y^8} = -4\frac{x^6}{y^8} \qquad \text{(laws 7 and 1)}$$

SCIENTIFIC NOTATION

Scientific notation is a way of writing too large or too small numbers using exponential notation. A number x is written in scientific notation if it is expressed in the following form:

$$\boldsymbol{x = a \times 10^n},$$

where:

$$\boldsymbol{1 \leq a < 10} \quad \text{and} \quad \boldsymbol{n} \text{ is an } \textbf{integer}$$

Example 1.2.9 Express the following numbers in scientific notation:

a. $534,000,000$ **b.** 0.000000672

Solution

a. $\underbrace{534,000,000}_{\text{8 places to the left}} = 5.34 \times 10^8$ **b.** $0.\underbrace{000000672}_{\text{7 places to the right}} = 6.72 \times 10^{-7}$

The exponent n in 10^n indicates the number of digits the decimal point will move. If it moves to the left, n is positive. Conversely, if it moves to the right, then n is negative.

Example 1.2.10 **Distance.**

The *Alpha Centauri* is the closest star to our solar system, located 4.22 *light-years* from the sun. A light-year is the distance that light travels in one year, equal to 5.878×10^{12} miles.

Find the distance, in miles, between the Alpha Centauri and the sun, and express its value in scientific notation.

Solution

The distance d from the star to the sun is, in miles:

$$d = 4.22 \times 5.88 \times 10^{12} = 24.8126 \times 10^{12} \text{ miles}$$

$$= 2.48126 \times 10^{13} \text{ miles.}$$

Case 3. $n = 0$.

$$\left(\frac{a}{b}\right)^{-n} = \left(\frac{a}{b}\right)^{-0} = \left(\frac{a}{b}\right)^{0} = 1, \quad \left(\frac{b}{a}\right)^{n} = \left(\frac{b}{a}\right)^{0} = 1$$

$$\text{Hence, } \left(\frac{a}{b}\right)^{-n} = \left(\frac{b}{a}\right)^{n}$$

Problem 1.2.5 **Inconsistency.**

Show that if $0^0 = 1$, then $\left(\frac{1}{0}\right)^0 = 1$.

Solution

$$1 = \frac{1}{1} = \frac{1^0}{0^0} = \left(\frac{1}{0}\right)^0$$

This result is inconsistent because the division by zero is not defined.

EXERCISES 1.2

Evaluate the expressions from 1 to 28 and write the answers in the simplest form.

1. $3(x-1) - x(x-5)$ **2.** $a[5(a-3) - 3(a+1)]$ **3.** $a^{-1}(a+3)$

4. $(2b)^{-1}(2b-8)$ **5.** $(ab)^{-1}(b-a)$ **6.** $(-2ab)^{-1}(4a-10b)$

7. $\left(\frac{8}{15} \times \frac{6}{7}\right) \div \frac{4}{7}$ **8.** $\left(\frac{5a}{12} \times 3b\right) \div \frac{10ab}{4}$ **9.** $12ab \div \left(\frac{3a}{2} \times \frac{4}{3b}\right)$

10. $\left(\frac{8a}{5b} \times \frac{a}{10b}\right) \div \frac{2a}{15b}$ **11.** $\frac{x}{8y} - \frac{x}{3y}$ **12.** $\frac{3}{5x^2} + \frac{1}{2x}$

13. $\frac{x}{a} + \frac{x}{ab}$ **14.** $3\left(\frac{b}{3a} - \frac{2a}{b}\right) - \frac{a^2+b^2}{ab}$ **15.** $-\frac{5}{21} + 1 - \frac{3}{7}$

16. $1 - \left(-\frac{3}{8} + \frac{2}{3}\right)$ **17.** $\left(\frac{1}{5} - 2\right) - \left(\frac{1}{7} - 2\right)$ **18.** $\frac{9}{10}\left(-\frac{5}{6}\right)$

19. $\left(-\frac{3}{4}\right)\left(-\frac{5}{27}\right)\left(-\frac{2}{25}\right)$ **20.** $(-5)\left(-\frac{1}{5}\right)\left(\frac{-3}{4} + \frac{-2}{-3}\right)$ **21.** $\left(\frac{1}{5} - \frac{2}{3}\right) \div \frac{1}{15}$

22. $\left(4 \div \frac{8}{5}\right) - \left(\frac{9}{10} \div \frac{3}{2}\right)$ **23.** $\left(\frac{1}{3} + \frac{2}{5} + \frac{1}{30}\right) \div \frac{23}{30}$

24. $\dfrac{\frac{1}{2} - \frac{3}{4}}{\frac{1}{2} + \frac{3}{4}}$ **25.** $\left(\frac{1}{8} + \frac{3}{4}\right)\left(1 - \frac{5}{12}\right)^{-1}$ **26.** $\dfrac{\frac{4a}{5} - 2a}{\frac{3a}{10} - 3a}$

27. $\dfrac{\frac{1}{5a} - \frac{1}{6a}}{\frac{1}{6b} - \frac{1}{7b}}$ **28.** $\left[\frac{5}{9a} \div \frac{10}{3a} - \frac{1}{4}\right] \div \left[\frac{4y}{5x} - \frac{y}{2x}\right]$

Simplify the expressions from 29 to 50 and write the answers using positive exponents.

29. $(2^2 \times 2^3)^2$ **30.** $\left(\frac{3}{4}\right)^0$ **31.** $\left(\frac{3}{4}\right)^{-1}$ **32.** $5^{-1} \times \left(\frac{5}{6}\right)^2$

33. $\left(\frac{2}{3}\right)^{-4} \div 3^{-3}$ **34.** $\left[\left(\frac{2}{3}\right)^2\right]^3$ **35.** $\left(\frac{4}{5}\right)^1 + \left(\frac{4}{5}\right)^0$ **36.** $\frac{3^{-2} \times 3^3}{2^{-3}}$

37. $\left(\frac{2}{3}\right)^{-2} + \left(\frac{2}{3}\right)^{-1}$ **38.** $\frac{2^3 \times 3^{-4} \times 4^5}{2^5 \times 3^{-5} \times 4^2}$ **39.** $(5^{-2} \times 2^5) \times (2^{-2} \times 5^4)^{-2}$

40. $(3 - 3a^3b^{-2})\,(9a^{-4}b^{-5})$ **41.** $(5x^2y)^0\,(4^2x^{-2}y^{-5})$

42. $(4x^0)^2 \div (-2x^{-1}y^4)^{-3}$ **43.** $\left(\frac{3a^{-3}b^2}{9ab^{-1}}\right)^{-2}$ **44.** $\left(\frac{4xy^{-2}}{2x^{-1}y^2}\right)^{-3}$

45. $\left(\frac{5^3m^0n^{-2}}{4^3m^3n^{-5}}\right)\left(\frac{5^3m^{-1}n}{4^2m^2n^{-2}}\right)^{-1}$ **46.** $(a^{-2} - b^{-2})^{-1}$ **47.** $\frac{3}{7x^{-3}} - \frac{2}{21x^{-1}}$

48. $\left(\frac{x}{2y}\right)^3 \div \left(\frac{4y}{x} \div \frac{2}{3y^3}\right)^{-1}$ **49.** $\left(\frac{2}{x} + 8x^{-1}\right)^{-1} \div 5^{-1}x$

50. $\left(\frac{3}{x^2} - 5x^{-2}\right)^{-1} \div \left(\frac{x^3}{9} + \frac{1}{6x^{-3}}\right)$

51. Write the following numbers using scientific notation.

a. A light year in kilometers: 9,440,000,000,000 km.

b. The electron diameter: 0.0000000000004 cm.

c. The Earth population in 2002: 6,251,000,000 inhabitants.

d. The neutron mass: 0.00000000000000000000000167 Kg.

52. Write the following numbers in standard decimal notation.

a. The distance from the earth to the moon: 4.624×10^5 km.

b. The length of the X ray wave: 4.92×10^{-11} m.

53. Fraction properties. Prove that:

a. $\frac{ac}{bc} = \frac{a}{b}, c \neq 0$ **b.** $\frac{a}{b} = \frac{c}{d} \Rightarrow ad = bc$ **c.** $\frac{-a}{b} = \frac{a}{-b} = -\frac{a}{b}$

54. Exponent laws. If a and b are real numbers; and m, n are integers, prove that:

a. $\frac{a^n}{a^m} = a^{n-m}$ **b.** $(a^n)^m = a^{nm}$ **c.** $(ab)^n = a^nb^n$ **d.** $\frac{a^n}{b^n} = \frac{b^{-n}}{a^{-n}}$

Remark The expressions $a^{\frac{m}{n}}$ and $a^{m/n}$ are equivalent, that is:

$$a^{\frac{m}{n}} = a^{m/n}$$

From now on, we'll alternate both ways of representing these expressions.

Example 1.3.6 Simplify:

1. $(-27)^{1/3} = \sqrt[3]{(-27)} = -3$

2. $(-64)^{2/3} = \left(\sqrt[3]{(-64)}\right)^2 = (-4)^2 = 16$, Another way,

$$(-64)^{\frac{2}{3}} = \sqrt[3]{(-64)^2} = \sqrt[3]{4096} = 16$$

Example 1.3.7 Express the radical in rational exponents.

a. $\sqrt{x^{-3}}$ b. $\dfrac{1}{\sqrt[5]{z^4}}$ c. $\sqrt[3]{(xy)^6}$

Solution

a. $\sqrt{x^{-3}} = x^{-3/2}$ b. $\dfrac{1}{\sqrt[5]{z^4}} = \dfrac{1}{z^{4/5}} = z^{-4/5}$

c. $\sqrt[3]{(xy)^6} = (xy)^{6/3} = (xy)^2$

Example 1.3.8 Simplify:

a. $\left(-216x^6y\right)^{1/3}$ b. $\left(\dfrac{27}{8}\right)^{-2/3} + \left(-\dfrac{32}{243}\right)^{2/5}$

Solution

a. $\left(-216x^6y\right)^{1/3} = (-216)^{1/3}\left(x^6\right)^{1/3}y^{1/3} = \left((-6)^3\right)^{1/3}\left(x^6\right)^{1/3}y^{1/3}$

$$= (-6)^{3/3}x^{6/3}y^{1/3} = -6x^2y^{1/3}$$

b. $$\left(\frac{27}{8}\right)^{-2/3}+\left(-\frac{32}{243}\right)^{2/5}=\frac{8^{2/3}}{(27)^{2/3}}+\frac{(-32)^{2/5}}{243^{2/5}}$$

$$=\frac{\left(8^{1/3}\right)^2}{\left((27)^{1/3}\right)^2}+\frac{\left((-32)^{1/5}\right)^2}{\left((243)^{1/5}\right)^2}$$

$$=\frac{\left(\sqrt[3]{8}\right)^2}{\left(\sqrt[3]{27}\right)^2}+\frac{\left(\sqrt[5]{(-32)}\right)^2}{\left(\sqrt[5]{243}\right)^2}$$

$$=\frac{2^2}{3^2}+\frac{(-2)^2}{3^2}=\frac{4}{9}+\frac{4}{9}=\frac{8}{9}$$

Example 1.3.9 Simplify: $\sqrt[4]{\dfrac{a^8}{81b^4c^{-12}}}$

Solution

$$\sqrt[4]{\frac{a^8}{81b^4c^{-12}}}=\left(\frac{a^8}{81b^4c^{-12}}\right)^{1/4}=\frac{\left(a^8\right)^{1/4}}{\left(81b^4c^{-12}\right)^{1/4}}=\frac{a^{8/4}}{(81)^{1/4}b^{4/4}c^{-12/4}}$$

$$=\frac{a^2}{3b^1c^{-3}}=\frac{a^2c^3}{3b}$$

SOLVED PROBLEMS 1.3

Problem 1.3.1 Simplify: $\dfrac{(64)^{n/6}(49)^{-n/2}}{(27)^{-n/3}}$

Solution

$$\frac{(64)^{n/6}(49)^{-n/2}}{(27)^{-n/3}}=\frac{(64)^{n/6}(27)^{n/3}}{(49)^{n/2}}=\frac{\left(2^6\right)^{n/6}\left(3^3\right)^{n/3}}{\left(7^2\right)^{n/2}}=\frac{2^n3^n}{7^n}$$

$$=\frac{(2\times 3)^n}{7^n}=\frac{6^n}{7^n}=\left(\frac{6}{7}\right)^n$$

Problem 1.3.2 Simplify: $\dfrac{\sqrt{18}-\sqrt{50}}{\sqrt{72}+\sqrt{2}}$

Solution

$$\frac{\sqrt{18}-\sqrt{50}}{\sqrt{72}+\sqrt{2}}=\frac{\sqrt{9\times 2}-\sqrt{25\times 2}}{\sqrt{36\times 2}+\sqrt{2}}=\frac{3\sqrt{2}-5\sqrt{2}}{6\sqrt{2}+\sqrt{2}}=\frac{-2\sqrt{2}}{7\sqrt{2}}=-\frac{2}{7}$$

Example 1.4.3 **Factoring by grouping terms.**

$$\text{Factorise:} \quad 3x^3 - 2xy - 6x^2 + 4y$$

Solution

The four terms of this expression do not have a nontrivial common factor; yet, we can place the terms in two groups, where each group has a common factor as follows:

$$\begin{aligned} 3x^3 - 2xy - 6x^2 + 4y &= \left(3x^3 - 6x^2\right) + \left(-2xy^2 + 4y^2\right) \\ &= 3x^2(x-2) - 2y^2(x-2) = \left(3x^2 - 2y^2\right)(x-2) \end{aligned}$$

FACTORING THE TRINOMIAL $x^2 + bx + c$

To perform this technique we need to find two numbers, r and s, such that:

$$x^2 + bx + c = (x+r)(x+s)$$

But, $(x+r)(x+s) = x^2 + (r+s)x + rs$. Hence, the numbers r and s that we are looking for must satisfy the following two conditions:

$$\boldsymbol{rs = c} \quad \text{and} \quad \boldsymbol{r + s = b}$$

Example 1.4.4 Factorise $x^2 - 2x - 8$

Solution

In this case, $c = -8$, $b = -2$. So r and s must satisfy:

$$rs = -8 \quad \text{and} \quad r + s = -2$$

All the factors of -8, with their corresponding algebraic sum, are:

$r = -1$	$s = 8$	$r + s = 7$
$r = 1$	$s = -8$	$r + s = -7$
$r = -2$	$s = 4$	$r + s = 2$
$r = 2$	$s = -4$	$r + s = -2$

The only numbers that satisfy both conditions are:

$$r = 2 \quad \text{and} \quad s = -4$$

Hence:

$$x^2 - 7x + 12 = (x-3)(x-4)$$

Example 1.4.5 Factorise $x^2 - 7cx + 12c^2$

Solution

We are looking for r and s such that $rs = 12c^2$ and $r + s = -7c$. The factors of $12c^2$, with their corresponding algebraic sum, are:

$r = c, \quad s = 12c, \quad r + s = 13c \qquad r = -c, \quad s = -12c, \quad r + s = -13c$

$r = 2c, \quad s = 6c, \quad r + s = 8c \qquad r = -2c \quad s = -6c, \quad r + s = -8c$

$r = 3c, \quad s = 4c, \quad r + s = 7c \qquad r = -3c, \quad s = -4c, \quad r + s = -7c$

The numbers that satisfy the above two conditions are $r = -3c$ and $s = -4c$

Therefore:

$$x^2 - 7cx + 12c^2 = (x - 3c)(x - 4c)$$

FACTORING THE TRINOMIAL $ax^2 + bx + c$

We can factor this polynomial in the same way as we did with the one of the form $x^2 + bx + c$. We just need to introduce a pre-factoring step to transform it into the latter.

For this purpose, multiply and divide the trinomial by the coefficient a, then make the change $y = ax$:

$$\frac{a\left(ax^2 + bx + c\right)}{a} = \frac{(ax)^2 + b(ax) + ac}{a} = \frac{y^2 + by + ac}{a}$$

The numerator of this expression is the same trinomial $x^2 + bx + c$ we have dealt with before, that means we are now able to factorise it as usual.

Example 1.4.6 Factorise $5x^2 - 7x - 6$

Solution

We multiply and divide by 5, and make the change $y = 5x$:

$$\frac{5\left(5x^2 - 7x - 6\right)}{5} = \frac{(5x)^2 - 7(5x) - 30}{5} = \frac{(5x - 10)(5x + 3)}{5}$$

$$= \left(\frac{5x - 10}{5}\right)(5x + 3) = (x - 2)(5x + 3)$$

Example 1.4.7 Factorise $12x^2 - 5ax - 2a^2$

Solution

We multiply and divide by 12, and make the change $y = 12x$:

$$\frac{12\left(12x^2 - 5ax - 2a^2\right)}{12} = \frac{(12x)^2 - 5a(12x) - 24a^2}{12} = \frac{(12x - 8a)(12x + 3a)}{4 \times 3}$$

$$= \left(\frac{12x - 8a}{4}\right)\left(\frac{12x + 3a}{3}\right) = (3x - 2a)(4x + a)$$

SPECIAL FACTORING FORMULAS

1. Difference of two squares

$$a^2 - b^2 = (a + b)(a - b)$$

2. Perfect square trinomial

$$a^2 \pm 2ab + b^2 = (a \pm b)^2$$

3. Difference of two cubes

$$a^3 - b^3 = (a - b)(a^2 + ab + b^2)$$

4. Sum of two cubes

$$a^3 + b^3 = (a + b)(a^2 - ab + b2)$$

5. Difference of two nth powers

$$a^n - b^n = (a - b)(a^{n-1} + a^{n-2}b + a^{n-3}b^2 + \cdots + ab^{n-2} + b^{n-1})$$

The formulas 1 and 2 are special product formulas written in reverse order. Formulas 3, 4, and 5 can be proved by multiplying out.

Example 1.4.8 **Difference of squares and difference of cubes.**

Factorise: **a.** $x^2 - 36$ **b.** $16x^4 - 81y^2$ **c.** $8x^3 - 27$

Solution

a. By formula 1:

$$x^2 - 36 = x^2 - 6^2 = (x + 6)(x - 6)$$

b. By formula 1:

$$16x^4 - 81y^2 = (4x^2)^2 - (9y)^2 = (4x^2 + 9y)(4x^2 - 9y)$$

c. By formula 3:

$$8x^3 - 27 = (2x)^3 - (3)^3 = (2x-3)\left((2x)^2 + (2x)(3) + 3^2\right)$$
$$= (2x-3)\left(4x^2 + 6x + 9\right)$$

Example 1.4.9 **Perfect square.**

Factorise: **a.** $40x^2 + 25x^4 + 16$ **b.** $9x^2 - 3xy + \frac{y^2}{4}$

Solution

Prior to applying the formulas 2 or 3 we must verify that the trinomial is a perfect square. First, we order the trinomial according to the degree of the variable, or to one variable if there is more than one. Now:

1. Verify that the first and the third term have square root.
2. Verify that the second term is equal to $\pm$ twice the product of the square roots of the first and third term.

a. Rearranging $40x^2 + 25x^4 + 16$: $25x^4 + 40x^2 + 16$

Square root of $25x^4$: $\mathbf{5x^2}$

Square root of 16 : **4**

Twice the product of the two roots:

$$2(5x^2)(4) = 40x^2 = \text{second term}$$

Therefore, $25x^4 + 40x^2 + 16 = (5x^2 + 4)^2$

b. $9x^2 - 3xy + \frac{y^2}{4}$ is already arranged according to the variable x.

Square root of $9x^2$: $\mathbf{3x}$

Square root of $\dfrac{y^2}{4}$: $\mathbf{\dfrac{y}{2}}$

Twice the product of the two roots with negative signal:

$$-2(3x)\left(\frac{y}{2}\right) = -3xy = \text{second term}$$

Therefore, $9x^2 - 3xy + \dfrac{y^2}{4} = \left(3x - \dfrac{y}{2}\right)^2$

Example 1.4.10 **Difference of nth powers.**

$$\text{Factorise:} \quad 2x^5 - 64a^5$$

Solution

We factorise the common term 2, then apply the formula 5:

$$\begin{aligned} 2\left(x^5 - 32a^5\right) &= 2\left(x^5 - (2a)^5\right) \\ &= 2(x-2a)\left(x^4 + x^3(2a) + x^2(2a)^2 + x(2a)^3 + (2a)^4\right) \\ &= 2(x-2a)\left(x^4 + 2ax^3 + 4a^2x^2 + 8a^3x + 16a^4\right) \end{aligned}$$

FRACTIONAL EXPRESSIONS

A **fractional expression** is a quotient of two algebraic expressions. As a special case, a quotient of two polynomials is a fractional expression called **rational expression**. The following expressions are fractional ones, where only the first is a rational expression:

1. $\dfrac{2x^3 - 3x^2 + 5}{x^2 - 4x + 3}$ **2.** $\dfrac{3x + 1}{x - \sqrt{2x}}$ **3.** $\dfrac{\sqrt{2x - 3}}{x + 5}$

The variables contained in a fractional expression represent real numbers, therefore they follow the same rules as the fractions of real numbers given on theorem 1.2.6.

SIMPLIFYING FRACTIONAL EXPRESSIONS

To simplify a fractional expression factorise both, numerator and denominator, and then cancel the common factors. This procedure follows from this property of fractions:

$$\frac{ac}{bc} = \frac{a}{b}, \quad c \neq 0$$

Example 1.4.11 Simplify:

a. $\dfrac{6x^2 - 3xy}{4x^2 - y^2}$ b. $\dfrac{2x^3 - 54}{4x^2 - 32x + 60}$

Solution

a. $\dfrac{6x^2 - 3xy}{4x^2 - y^2} = \dfrac{3x(2x - y)}{(2x - y)(2x + y)} = \dfrac{3x}{2x + y}$

b. $$\frac{2x^3-54}{4x^2-32x+60}=\frac{2\left(x^3-27\right)}{4\left(x^2-8x+15\right)}=\frac{2\left(x^3-3^3\right)}{4\left(x^2-8x+15\right)}$$

$$=\frac{2(x-3)\left(x^2+3x+9\right)}{4(x-3)(x-5)}=\frac{x^2+3x+9}{2(x-5)}$$

MORE ABOUT RATIONALIZING

In this part we will focus on rationalizing denominators and numerators with two terms. We will now present two cases.

Case 1. Denominator or numerator is of the form:

$$\boldsymbol{a \pm b\sqrt{d}} \quad \text{or} \quad \boldsymbol{a\sqrt{c} \pm b\sqrt{d}}$$

- Multiply numerator and denominator by the corresponding **conjugate**.
- The conjugate of $\boldsymbol{a \pm b\sqrt{d}}$ is $\boldsymbol{a \mp b\sqrt{d}}$ (the sign changes).
- Similarly, the conjugate of $\boldsymbol{a\sqrt{c} \pm b\sqrt{d}}$ is $\boldsymbol{a\sqrt{c} \mp b\sqrt{d}}$.

This strategy follows from the special product formula:

$$\boldsymbol{(a+b)(a-b)=a^2-b^2}$$

Example 1.4.12 Rationalize the denominator: $\dfrac{2}{4+5\sqrt{2}}$

Solution

The conjugate of $4+5\sqrt{2}$ is $4-5\sqrt{2}$. Hence:

$$\frac{2}{4+5\sqrt{2}}=\frac{2\left(4-5\sqrt{2}\right)}{\left(4+5\sqrt{2}\right)\left(4-5\sqrt{2}\right)}=\frac{2\left(4-5\sqrt{2}\right)}{4^2-\left(5\sqrt{2}\right)^2}=\frac{2\left(4+5\sqrt{2}\right)}{16-50}$$

$$=\frac{2\left(4-5\sqrt{2}\right)}{-34}=\frac{4-5\sqrt{2}}{-17}=\frac{5\sqrt{2}-4}{17}$$

Example 1.4.13 Rationalize the denominator: $\dfrac{5}{\sqrt{2}+3\sqrt{3}}$

Solution

$$\frac{5}{\sqrt{2}+3\sqrt{3}} = \frac{5}{\sqrt{2}+3\sqrt{3}}\,\frac{\sqrt{2}-3\sqrt{3}}{\sqrt{2}-3\sqrt{3}} = \frac{5\left(\sqrt{2}-3\sqrt{3}\right)}{\left(\sqrt{2}\right)^2-\left(3\sqrt{3}\right)^2}$$

$$= \frac{5\left(\sqrt{2}-3\sqrt{3}\right)}{2-27} = \frac{5\left(\sqrt{2}-3\sqrt{3}\right)}{-25} = \frac{\sqrt{2}-3\sqrt{3}}{-5}$$

$$= \frac{3\sqrt{3}-\sqrt{2}}{5}$$

Example 1.4.14 Rationalize the numerator: $\dfrac{\sqrt{x+h}-\sqrt{x}}{h}$

Solution

The conjugate of $\sqrt{x+h}-\sqrt{x}$ is $\sqrt{x+h}+\sqrt{x}$. Hence:

$$\frac{\sqrt{x+h}-\sqrt{x}}{h} = \frac{\sqrt{x+h}-\sqrt{x}}{h}\,\frac{\sqrt{x+h}+\sqrt{x}}{\sqrt{x+h}+\sqrt{x}} = \frac{\left(\sqrt{x+h}\right)^2-\left(\sqrt{x}\right)^2}{h\left(\sqrt{x+h}+\sqrt{x}\right)}$$

$$= \frac{x+h-x}{h\left(\sqrt{x+h}+\sqrt{x}\right)} = \frac{h}{h\left(\sqrt{x+h}+\sqrt{x}\right)}$$

$$= \frac{1}{\left(\sqrt{x+h}+\sqrt{x}\right)}$$

Case 2. Denominator or numerator is of the form $\sqrt[3]{a} \pm \sqrt[3]{b}$

If the denominator or numerator has the form $\sqrt[3]{a}+\sqrt[3]{b}$, we multiply and divide by the following expression:

$$\boldsymbol{\sqrt[3]{a^2}-\sqrt[3]{a}\sqrt[3]{b}+\sqrt[3]{b^2}}$$

The above statement is based on the special factoring formula:

$$\boldsymbol{a^3+b^3=(a+b)(a^2-ab+b^2)}$$

As a result, we have:

$$\left(\sqrt[3]{a}+\sqrt[3]{b}\right)\left(\sqrt[3]{a^2}-\sqrt[3]{a}\sqrt[3]{b}+\sqrt[3]{b^2}\right) = \left(\sqrt[3]{a}\right)^3+\left(\sqrt[3]{b}\right)^3$$

$$= a+b$$

Similarly, if the denominator or numerator has the form $\sqrt[3]{a} - \sqrt[3]{b}$, we multiply and divide by:

$$\boldsymbol{\sqrt[3]{a^2} + \sqrt[3]{a}\sqrt[3]{b} + \sqrt[3]{b^2}}$$

The above statement is based on the special factoring formula:

$$\boldsymbol{a^3 - b^3 = (a - b)(a^2 + ab + b^2)}$$

As a result, we have:

$$\begin{aligned}\left(\sqrt[3]{a} - \sqrt[3]{b}\right)\left(\sqrt[3]{a^2} + \sqrt[3]{a}\sqrt[3]{b} + \sqrt[3]{b^2}\right) &= \left(\sqrt[3]{a}\right)^3 - \left(\sqrt[3]{b}\right)^3 \\ &= a - b\end{aligned}$$

Example 1.4.15 Rationalize the denominator:

$$\frac{16}{\sqrt[3]{5} + \sqrt[3]{3}}$$

Solution

$$\frac{16}{\sqrt[3]{5} + \sqrt[3]{3}} = \frac{16\left(\sqrt[3]{5^2} - \sqrt[3]{5}\sqrt[3]{3} + \sqrt[3]{3^2}\right)}{\left(\sqrt[3]{5} + \sqrt[3]{3}\right)\left(\sqrt[3]{5^2} - \sqrt[3]{5}\sqrt[3]{3} + \sqrt[3]{3^2}\right)} = \frac{16\left(\sqrt[3]{5^2} - \sqrt[3]{5}\sqrt[3]{3} + \sqrt[3]{3^2}\right)}{\left(\sqrt[3]{5}\right)^3 + \left(\sqrt[3]{3}\right)^3}$$

$$= \frac{16\left(\sqrt[3]{5^2} - \sqrt[3]{5}\sqrt[3]{3} + \sqrt[3]{3^2}\right)}{5 + 3} = 2\left(\sqrt[3]{25} - \sqrt[3]{15} + \sqrt[3]{9}\right)$$

Example 1.4.16 Rationalize the denominator:

$$\frac{6}{3 - \sqrt[3]{3}}$$

Solution

$$\frac{6}{3 - \sqrt[3]{3}} = \frac{6\left(3^2 + 3\sqrt[3]{3} + \sqrt[3]{3^2}\right)}{\left(3 - \sqrt[3]{3}\right)\left(3^2 + 3\sqrt[3]{3} + \sqrt[3]{3^2}\right)} = \frac{6\left(9 + 3\sqrt[3]{3} + \sqrt[3]{9}\right)}{(3)^3 - \left(\sqrt[3]{3}\right)^3}$$

$$= \frac{6\left(9 + 3\sqrt[3]{3} + \sqrt[3]{9}\right)}{27 - 3} = \frac{6\left(9 + 3\sqrt[3]{3} + \sqrt[3]{9}\right)}{24}$$

$$= \frac{9 + 3\sqrt[3]{3} + \sqrt[3]{9}}{4}$$

Problem 1.4.4 Rationalize the denominators:

a. $\dfrac{9-a}{\sqrt[3]{\sqrt{a}-\sqrt{3}}}$ **b.** $\dfrac{x+y}{\sqrt[3]{x^2}-\sqrt[3]{xy}+\sqrt[3]{y^2}}$

Solution

a.
$$\frac{9-a}{\sqrt[3]{\sqrt{a}-\sqrt{3}}}=\frac{(9-a)\sqrt[3]{(\sqrt{a}-3)^2}}{\left(\sqrt[3]{\sqrt{a}-3}\right)\left(\sqrt[3]{(\sqrt{a}-3)^2}\right)}$$

$$=\frac{(9-a)\sqrt[3]{(\sqrt{a}-3)^2}}{\sqrt{a}-3}=\frac{(9-a)\sqrt[3]{(\sqrt{a}-3)^2}\,(\sqrt{a}+3)}{(\sqrt{a}-3)(\sqrt{a}+3)}$$

$$=\frac{(9-a)\sqrt[3]{(\sqrt{a}-3)^2}\,(\sqrt{a}+3)}{a-9}=-(\sqrt{a}+3)\sqrt[3]{(\sqrt{a}-3)^2}$$

b.
$$\frac{x+y}{\sqrt[3]{x^2}-\sqrt[3]{xy}+\sqrt[3]{y^2}}=\frac{(x+y)\left(\sqrt[3]{x}+\sqrt[3]{y}\right)}{\left(\sqrt[3]{x^2}-\sqrt[3]{xy}+\sqrt[3]{y^2}\right)\left(\sqrt[3]{x}+\sqrt[3]{y}\right)}$$

$$=\frac{(x+y)\left(\sqrt[3]{x}+\sqrt[3]{y}\right)}{\left(\sqrt[3]{x}\right)^3+\left(\sqrt[3]{y}\right)^3}=\frac{(x+y)\left(\sqrt[3]{x}+\sqrt[3]{y}\right)}{x+y}$$

$$=\sqrt[3]{x}+\sqrt[3]{y}$$

Problem 1.4.5 Simplify $\dfrac{x}{1-\dfrac{1}{1+\dfrac{x}{y}}}$

Solution

$$\frac{x}{1-\dfrac{1}{1+\dfrac{x}{y}}}=\frac{x}{1-\dfrac{1}{\dfrac{y+x}{y}}}=\frac{x}{1-\dfrac{y}{y+x}}=\frac{x}{\dfrac{y+x-y}{y+x}}$$

$$=\frac{x}{\dfrac{x}{y+x}}=\frac{x(y+x)}{x}$$

$$=y+x$$

Problem 1.4.6 Simplify $\dfrac{\dfrac{1}{x+1}+\dfrac{1}{x-1}}{\dfrac{x+1}{x-1}-\dfrac{x-1}{x+1}}$

Solution

$$\frac{\dfrac{1}{x+1}+\dfrac{1}{x-1}}{\dfrac{x+1}{x-1}-\dfrac{x-1}{x+1}} = \left(\frac{1}{x+1}+\frac{1}{x-1}\right) \div \left(\frac{x+1}{x-1}-\frac{x-1}{x+1}\right)$$

$$= \left(\frac{x-1+x+1}{(x+1)(x-1)}\right) \div \left(\frac{(x+1)(x+1)-(x-1)(x-1)}{(x-1)(x+1)}\right)$$

$$= \left(\frac{2x}{(x+1)(x-1)}\right) \div \left(\frac{(x^2+2x+1)-(x^2-2x+1)}{(x-1)(x+1)}\right)$$

$$= \left(\frac{2x}{(x+1)(x-1)}\right) \div \left(\frac{4x}{(x-1)(x+1)}\right)$$

$$= \frac{2x}{(x+1)(x-1)} \cdot \frac{(x-1)(x+1)}{4x} = \frac{1}{2}$$

EXERCISES 1.4

In the exercises 1 through 16, use the Special Product Formulas to find each product.

1. $\left(2x+\sqrt{5}\right)\left(2x-\sqrt{5}\right)$

2. $\left(2\sqrt{x}+\sqrt{y}\right)\left(2\sqrt{x}-\sqrt{y}\right)$

3. $\left(3x^2+4y^3\right)\left(3x^2-4y^3\right)$

4. $\left(\sqrt{h+1}+1\right)\left(\sqrt{h+1}-1\right)$

5. $\left(\sqrt{x}+\frac{1}{y}\right)\left(\sqrt{x}-\frac{1}{y}\right)$

6. $(a+b+c)(a+b-c)$

7. $(4x+5)^2$

8. $(2x-5y)^2$

9. $\left(x-x^{-1}\right)^2$

10. $\left(x^3-x^{-3}\right)^2$

11. $(4x+y)^3$

12. $\left(a^2+b^2\right)^3$

13. $\left(x^2-y\right)^3$

14. $\left(\sqrt[3]{x}+\sqrt[3]{y}\right)^3$

15. $(x-5)^2(x+5)^2$

16. $(2x-y)(2x+y)\left(4x^2+y^2\right)$

In the exercises 17 through 56, factorise the expression.

17. $7x^3-63x^2$

18. $8x^2y^2z^3-24xy^3z^2-4x^3y^4z^3$

19. x^3-2x^2-4x+8

20. $4y^2+16y+12xy+48x$

21. $x^2y^2-y^2-4x+4$

22. $2a^2x-5a^2y+15by-6bx$

23. $x^2+2x-48$

24. x^2-4x-5

25. $y^2+28y-29$

26. $x^2+15x-216$

27. x^4-2x^2-80

28. $a^2b^2+ab-12$

29. $3x^2+7x+4$

30. $5y^2+10y-75$

31. $5a^2x^2+4ax-12$

32. $9x^2-15x-50$

33. $4x^2y^2+11xy^2+6y^2$

34. $25x^4-10x^2+1$

35. $25x^2-36y^4$

36. $63x^4-7x^2$

37. $45x^2y^2-5x^4$

38. $\frac{x^2}{36}-\frac{y^2}{25}$

39. $16x^{2n}-\frac{1}{49}$

40. $(a-b)^2-9$

41. $(a+b)^2-(a-b)^2$

42. $(x-1)^2-(y-2)^2$

43. x^2-y^2-6y-9

44. $9(a-b)^2-4(a+b)^2$

45. a^4-2a^2+1

46. $16x^2-24xy+9y^2$

47. $400x^4+40x^2+1$

48. $\frac{x^2}{9}+\frac{2x}{3}+1$

49. $\frac{4x^2}{25}-\frac{x}{5}+\frac{1}{16}$

50. $8x^3-y^3$

51. $27a^3+64b^3$

52. $5x^3y^3+5$

53. x^5-125x^2

54. $(x+y)^3-1$

55. $(x-y)^3-8$

56. $(x+1)^3-(x-2)^3$

In the exercises 57 through 68, simplify the given fraction.

57. $\frac{60a^3b^2-45a^2b}{15a^2b}$

58. $\frac{x^2-3x}{3-x}$

59. $\frac{a^2-1}{a+1}$

60. $\frac{x^2-x-20}{x^2+2x-8}$

61. $\frac{2x^2+x-6}{2x-3}$

62. $\frac{x^2+x-2}{2x^2+6x+4}$

63. $\frac{x^2-y^2}{x^2+2xy+y^2}$

64. $\frac{x^2-4xy+4y^2}{x^3-8y^3}$

65. $\frac{(3-a)^2}{27-a^3}$

66. $\frac{x^3+1}{x^4-x^3+x-1}$

67. $\frac{y+8y^2+16y^3}{6y^2+25y^3+4y^4}$

68. $\frac{x^2-y^2}{x^2-6y-xy+6x}$

In the exercises 69 through 80, rationalize the denominator.

69. $\frac{2}{1-\sqrt{2}}$

70. $\frac{h}{\sqrt{3+h}-\sqrt{3}}$

71. $\frac{2a}{\sqrt{a+1}-\sqrt{a-1}}$

72. $\frac{3\sqrt{2}}{7\sqrt{2}-6\sqrt{3}}$

73. $\frac{\sqrt{x}+\sqrt{a}}{\sqrt{x}+2\sqrt{a}}$

74. $\frac{5}{\sqrt{x-3}-\sqrt{x-13}}$

75. $\frac{3}{\sqrt[3]{7}+\sqrt[3]{2}}$

76. $\frac{16x-2}{2\sqrt[3]{x}-1}$

77. $\frac{70x-16}{2\sqrt[3]{x-1}+3\sqrt[3]{x}}$

78. $\frac{3x-9y}{\sqrt[3]{x^2}+\sqrt[3]{3xy}+\sqrt[3]{9y^2}}$

79. $\frac{8-x}{\sqrt{2-\sqrt[3]{x}}}$

80. $\frac{2x-1}{\sqrt{2\sqrt{x}+\sqrt{2}}}$

In the exercises 81 through 83, rationalize the numerator.

81. $\dfrac{3+\sqrt{5}}{4}$ **82.** $\dfrac{\sqrt{a+2}-\sqrt{a}}{2}$ **83.** $\dfrac{\sqrt{a-1+h}-\sqrt{a-1}}{h}$

In the exercises 84 through 104, perform the given operations and simplify.

84. $\dfrac{3a}{a+1}+\dfrac{2a}{a-1}$ **85.** $\dfrac{x+y}{x-y}-\dfrac{x-y}{x+y}$ **86.** $\dfrac{12}{x^2-9}-\dfrac{2}{x-3}+1$

87. $\dfrac{x-2}{x^2-x-2}-\dfrac{2}{x^2-1}$ **88.** $\dfrac{1}{x+1}+\dfrac{2}{x-1}-\dfrac{1}{x^2-1}$

89. $\frac{x+5}{x^2+2x+1}+\frac{x}{x^2-4x-5}+\frac{1}{x-5}$ **90.** $\frac{x}{x^2-x-2}-\frac{6}{x^2+5x-14}-\frac{1}{x^2+8x+7}$

91. $\dfrac{x^2}{y^2-x^2}\times\dfrac{xy-x^2}{xy}$ **92.** $\dfrac{x^2+4x}{3x-2}\times\dfrac{9x^2-4}{x^2-16}$

93. $\dfrac{x^3-8}{a^3-1}\times\dfrac{a^2+a+1}{x^2+2x+4}$ **94.** $\frac{x^2+xy-2y^2}{x^2-2xy-8y^2}\times\frac{x^2+2xy}{x^2+4xy}\times\frac{x^2-16y^2}{x+2y}$

95. $\dfrac{a^2-ab-6b^2}{b^2+ab}\div\dfrac{a^2-4b^2}{a^2+ab}$ **96.** $\dfrac{x^4-x}{x^2+6x+8}\div\dfrac{2x^2-x-1}{2x^2+9x+4}$

97. $\frac{25x^3-x}{25x^2-10x+1}\div\frac{6x^2+13x+6}{15x^2+7x-2}$ **98.** $\left(\frac{x+1}{3x-3}\times\frac{6x-6}{2x+4}\right)\div\frac{x^2+x}{x^2+x-2}$

99. $\frac{3x^2+3}{2x-4}\div\left(\frac{3x+6}{2x-6}\times\frac{x^3+x}{3x-6}\right)$ **100.** $\left(1-\frac{a^3}{b^3}\right)\left(b+\frac{ab}{b-a}\right)$

101. $\left(x+\frac{4x^2+20x}{x^2-25}\right)\left(x+2-\frac{28}{x-1}\right)$ **102.** $\left(\frac{x^2}{x^2-y^2}-1\right)\left(\frac{x}{y}-1\right)\left(\frac{y}{x}+1\right)$

103. $\left(\frac{x^2}{x+1}-x+1\right)\div\left(\frac{2}{x^2-1}+1\right)$ **104.** $\left(\frac{2a+1}{a^2+2}-a\right)\div\left(\frac{a+1}{a}-a^2-1\right)$

Simplify the given compound fractions.

105. $\dfrac{\frac{1}{x}-x^2}{\frac{1}{x}-1}$ **106.** $\dfrac{\frac{a}{b^2}-\frac{b}{a^2}}{\frac{1}{b^2}-\frac{1}{a^2}}$ **107.** $a-\dfrac{b}{\frac{a}{b}+\frac{b}{a}}$

108. $1-\dfrac{1}{1-\dfrac{1}{1-\dfrac{1}{x^2}}}$ **109.** $\dfrac{1-\dfrac{1}{a-2}}{a+3-\dfrac{24}{a+1}}$

SECCION 1.5

POLYNOMIAL EQUATIONS

A polynomial of **degree n** in the variable x is an expression of the form:

$$p(x) = a_n x^n + a_{n-1}x^{n-1} + \cdots + a_1 x + a_0 \tag{1}$$

where:

- n is a natural number.
- $a_n, a_{n-1}, \ldots, a_1$ and a_0 are real numbers.
- $a_n \neq 0$.

The numbers $a_n, a_{n-1}, \ldots, a_1$ and a_0 are the coefficients, where a_n is the **leading coefficient** and a_0 is the **constant term**.

A **polynomial equation of degree n** is an equation of the form:

$$a_n x^n + a_{n-1}x^{n-1} + \cdots + a_1 x + a_0 = 0 \tag{2}$$

A **zero** of a polynomial $p(x)$ is a number c such that $p(c) = 0$. That is, c is a **root** or a **solution** of the polynomial equation (2).

LINEAR EQUATION

The simplest polynomial equation is the **linear equation $ax + b = 0$**, and its root or solution is $x = -\frac{b}{a}$.

A fascinating example of a polynomial equation can be found on a grave marker. The Epitaph of Diophantus is a poem written in his tomb by one of his disciples.

Example 1.5.1 **The Epitaph of Diophantus**

Traveler!
This tomb holds Diophantus. Ah, how great a marvel!
the tomb tells scientifically the measure of his life.
God granted him to be a boy for the sixth part of his life,
and adding a twelfth part to this, he clothed his cheeks with down;
He lit him the light of wedlock after a seventh part,
and five years after his marriage He granted him a son.
Alas! late-born wretched child;
after attaining the measure of half his father's life, chill Fate took him.
After consoling his grief by this science of numbers for four years
he ended his life.
Tell me traveler, how old was Diophantus when he died?

Solution

Let x be the number of years that Diophantus lived. Mathematically, the epitaph says:

$$\frac{x}{6}+\frac{x}{12}+\frac{x}{7}+5+\frac{x}{2}+4=x$$

Let's solve the equation.

- The Least Common denominator (LCD) is 84.
- Multiplying each term of the equation by 84:

$$\begin{aligned}84\left(\frac{x}{6}\right)+84\left(\frac{x}{12}\right)+84\left(\frac{x}{7}\right)+84(5)+84\left(\frac{x}{2}\right)+84(4)=84x\\ \Leftrightarrow 14x+7x+12x+420+42x+336=84x\\ \Leftrightarrow 14x+7x+12x+42x-84x=-336-420\\ \Leftrightarrow -9x=-756\\ \Leftrightarrow x=\frac{-756}{-9}=84\end{aligned}$$

The traveler answered: "*Diophantus was 84 years old when he died*".

Did you know this?

DIOPHANTUS OF ALEXANDRIA (200-284 BC)

The Alexandrian Greek mathematician, Diophantus, is the author of a renowned series of 13 books called ***Arithmetica****, which stands as the most prominent work on algebra in Greek mathematics. He is often regarded as the* ***father of algebra****, although very little is known about his life.*

Arithmetica deals with solving algebraic equations and number theory. Though many of this books are now lost, the work of Diophantus influenced the subsequent evolution of algebra and number theory for centuries.

QUADRATIC EQUATIONS

A **quadratic equation** is a polynomial equation of degree 2:

$$\boldsymbol{ax^2+bx+c=0},$$

where a, b and c are real numbers, and $a\neq 0$.

There are two common ways of solving quadratic equations:

By Factoring **By the Quadratic Formula**

SOLVING QUADRATIC EQUATIONS BY FACTORING

This method is based on the theorem 1.2.2, which states:

$$\boldsymbol{ab = 0 \Leftrightarrow a = 0 \vee b = 0}$$

Example 1.5.2 Solve the equation:

$$2x^2 - 3x - 20 = 0$$

Solution

We must factorise the trinomial, and then apply the theorem 1.2.2:

$$2x^2 - 3x - 20 = 0 \Leftrightarrow (2x+5)(x-4) = 0$$

(factorise the trinomial $ax^2 + bx + c$)

$$\Leftrightarrow 2x + 5 = 0 \ \vee \ x - 4 = 0 \qquad \text{(theorem 1.2.2)}$$

$$\Leftrightarrow 2x = -5 \ \vee \ x = 4$$

$$\Leftrightarrow x = -\frac{5}{2} \ \vee \ x = 4$$

SOLVING QUADRATIC EQUATIONS BY THE QUADRATIC FORMULA

The solutions for a quadratic equation $\boldsymbol{ax^2 + bx + c = 0}$ are given by the **quadratic formula**, well known since Babylonian times:

$$\boldsymbol{x = \frac{-b \pm \sqrt{b^2 - 4ac}}{2a}} \tag{3}$$

The sub-radical expression $\boldsymbol{\Delta = b^2 - 4ac}$ is called the **discriminant** of the quadratic equation $ax^2 + bx + c = 0$, of which we can state the following:

If $\boldsymbol{\Delta = b^2 - 4ac > 0}$, the equation has **two distinct real solutions.**

If $\boldsymbol{\Delta = b^2 - 4ac = 0}$, the equation has exactly **one real solution.** (a repeated root)

If $\boldsymbol{\Delta = b^2 - 4ac < 0}$, the equation **does not have real solutions.** (it has two complex roots)

Example 1.5.3 Solve the equation: $\dfrac{x(x+4)}{2} - \dfrac{x^2}{4} = \dfrac{3x}{2} - \dfrac{1}{12}$

Solution

The LCD is 12. So, multiplying each term of the equation by 12:

$$\begin{aligned}\frac{x(x+4)}{2} - \frac{x^2}{4} = \frac{3x}{2} - \frac{1}{12} &\Leftrightarrow 12\frac{x(x+4)}{2} - 12\frac{x^2}{4} = 12\frac{3x}{2} - 12\frac{1}{12}\\ &\Leftrightarrow 6x(x+4) - 3x^2 = 18x - 1\\ &\Leftrightarrow 6x(x+4) - 3x^2 - 18x + 1 = 0\\ &\Leftrightarrow 6x^2 + 24x - 3x^2 - 18x + 1 = 0\\ &\Leftrightarrow 3x^2 + 6x + 1 = 0\end{aligned}$$

Now, we use the quadratic formula with $a = 3$, $b = 6$ and $c = 1$:

$$\begin{aligned}x = \frac{-b \pm \sqrt{b^2 - 4ac}}{2a} = \frac{-6 \pm \sqrt{6^2 - 4(3)(1)}}{2(3)} = \frac{-6 \pm \sqrt{24}}{6} &= \frac{-6 \pm 2\sqrt{6}}{6}\\ &= -1 \pm \frac{\sqrt{6}}{3}\end{aligned}$$

The solutions, or roots, are: $x_1 = -1 + \dfrac{\sqrt{6}}{3}$ and $x_2 = -1 - \dfrac{\sqrt{6}}{3}$

Example 1.5.4 Considering that m is a positive constant, solve:

$$\frac{x^2}{2m} - \frac{3x}{4} = \frac{m}{2}$$

Solution

The LCD is $4m$. So, when multiplying each term of the equation by $4m$:

$$\begin{aligned}\frac{x^2}{2m} - \frac{3x}{4} = \frac{m}{2} &\Leftrightarrow (4m)\left(\frac{x^2}{2m}\right) - (4m)\left(\frac{3x}{4}\right) = (4m)\left(\frac{m}{2}\right)\\ &\Leftrightarrow 2x^2 - 3mx = 2m^2 \Leftrightarrow 2x^2 - 3mx - 2m^2 = 0\end{aligned}$$

Now, let's make use of the quadratic formula with $a = 2$, $b = -3m$ and $c = -2m^2$:

$$\begin{aligned}x = \frac{-b \pm \sqrt{b^2 - 4ac}}{2a} &= \frac{-(-3m) \pm \sqrt{(-3m)^2 - 4(2)(-2m^2)}}{2(2)}\\ &= \frac{3m \pm \sqrt{9m^2 + 16m^2}}{4} = \frac{3m \pm \sqrt{25m^2}}{4}\\ &= \frac{3m \pm 5m}{4}\end{aligned}$$

Theorem 1.5.2 **The factor theorem.**

$$x - c \text{ is a factor of the polynomial } p(x) \Leftrightarrow p(c) = 0$$

Proof

($\Rightarrow$) If $x - c$ is a factor of $p(x)$, then $p(x) = (x - c)q(x)$.

Setting $x = c$:

$$p(c) = (c - c)q(c) = (0)q(c) = 0$$

($\Leftarrow$) By the previous theorem:

$$p(x) = (x - c)q(x) + p(c) = (x - c)q(x) + 0 = (x - c)q(x)$$

So, $x - c$ is a factor of $p(x)$.

Remark

We can conclude from the previous theorem that the following propositions have the same meaning:

1. $x - c$ is a factor of $p(x)$ **2.** $p(c) = 0$

3. c is a zero of $p(x)$ **4.** c is a root of the equation $p(x)$

5. c is a solution of the equation $p(x) = 0$

Example 1.5.10 **Factoring a polynomial using the factor theorem.**

Given the polynomial: $p(x) = x^3 - 4x^2 - 11x + 30.$

a. Prove that -3 is a zero of $p(x)$.

b. Use the part **a** to factorise the polynomial $p(x)$.

Solution

a. We have:

$$p(-3) = (-3)^3 - 4(-3)^2 - 11(-3) + 30 = -27 - 36 + 33 + 30 = 0$$

Hence, by the factor theorem, -3 is a zero of $p(x)$.

b. We must divide the polynomial $p(x)$ by $x-(-3)=x+3$. In this regard, we better use **synthetic division**:

$$x^3-4x^2-11x+30=(x-(-3))\left(x^2-7x+10\right)$$

$$=(x+3)\left(x^2-7x+10\right)$$

	1	-4	-11	30
-3		-3	21	-30
	1	-7	10	0

But, $x^2-7x+10=(x-2)(x-5)$. Hence:

$$x^3-4x^2-11x+30=(x+3)(x-2)(x-5)$$

THE FUNDAMENTAL THEOREM OF ALGEBRA

The fundamental theorem of algebra was proved by C.F. Gauss in 1799. We need advanced knowledge to understand the proof of this theorem; that's why we will define it without presenting its corresponding proof.

Theorem 1.5.3 **The Fundamental Theorem of Algebra.**

Every polynomial $p(x)$, with complex coefficients of degree $n \geq 1$, has at least one complex zero.

Since every real number is a complex number with a zero imaginary part, this theorem also applies to polynomial with real coefficients.

Let $p(x)$ be a polynomial of degree $n \geq 1$. By the fundamental theorem of algebra, there is a complex number c_1 such that c_1 is a zero of $p(x)$. Hence, by the factor theorem:

$$p(x)=(x-c_1)q_1(x),$$

where the degree of $q_1(x)$ is $n-1$. If $n-1 \geq 1$, we apply again the fundamental theorem of algebra to $q_1(x)$ for obtaining c_2, a zero of $q_1(x)$. Hence:

$$p(x)=(x-c_1)(x-c_2)q_2(x),$$

where the degree of $q_2(x)$ is $n-2$. After n iterations of this procedure, we obtain n zeros for $p(x): c_1, c_2, \ldots c_n$, and a polynomial $q_n(x)$ of degree 0 (a constant), such that:

$$p(x)=(x-c_1)(x-c_2)\cdots(x-c_n)q_n(x) \tag{4}$$

These results are synthesized in the next theorem.

Theorem 1.5.4 **Complete Factorization Theorem.**

If $p(x)$ is a polynomial of degree $n \geq 1$, with a_n as leading coefficient, then there exist n complex numbers c_1, c_2,... c_n, which are zeros of $p(x)$, such that:

$$\boldsymbol{p(x) = a_n(x - c_1)(x - c_2)\cdots(x - c_n)} \qquad (5)$$

Proof

We only need to prove that $q_n(x) = a_n$ in (4).

Performing the multiplication in (4) we get only one term of degree n, which is $q_n(x)x^n$. But, the term of degree n for $p(x)$ is an x_n. Hence:

$$\boldsymbol{q_n(x) = a_n}$$

The n zeros c_1, c_2, ... c_n are not necessarily different. If the factor $x - c_i$ appears k times, we say that c_i is zero of **multiplicity** $\boldsymbol{k}$.

THE RATIONAL ZEROS OF A POLYNOMIAL

Our interest in this course is focused on real functions, particularly, we are interested in the real zeros of a polynomial. Hopefully, the next theorem and its corollary provide an approach to find rational zeros for any polynomial.

Theorem 1.5.5 **The rational zero theorem.**

Given the polynomial:

$$p(x) = a_n x^n + a_{n-1}x^{n-1} + \cdots + a_1 x + a_0,$$

If the coefficients are integers and the rational $\frac{h}{k}$, reduced to lowest terms, is a zero of $p(x)$, then:

1. h divides the constant term a_0.

2. k divides the leading coefficient a_n.

Proof

See the solved problem 2.

Corolary

If the leading coefficient of the polynomial is $a_n = 1$, that is:

$$p(x) = x^n + a_{n-1}x^{n-1} + \cdots + a_1 x + a_0,$$

then, every rational zero of $p(x)$ is an **integer** that divides a_0.

Proof

If $\frac{h}{k}$ is a zero of $p(x)$, then, by the previous theorem, k divides $a_n = 1$; hence:

$$k = 1 \text{ or } k = -1 \qquad \textbf{and} \qquad \frac{h}{k} = h \text{ or } \frac{h}{k} = -h$$

That is, the rational zero $\frac{h}{k}$ is the integer h or the integer $-h$.

STRATEGY TO FIND THE RATIONAL ZEROS OF A POLYNOMIAL

Step 1. List all the possible rational zeros using the rational zero theorem. From this list, identify which are really zeros, verifying that $p(c) = 0$, where c is on the list.

Step 2. Let c be one zero obtained in step 1. Divide $p(x)$ by $x - c$ using synthetic division, and get the quotient $q(x)$.

$$p(x) = (x - c)q(x)$$

Step 3. Repeat the steps 1 and 2 taking $q(x)$ as dividend to get another quotient. Continue this process until the quotient is a quadratic polynomial, which could be factorised using the quadratic formula, or by any other technique.

Example 1.5.11 Solve the following equation by factorising.

$$x^3 - 3x^2 - 5x + 15 = 0$$

Solution

Step 1. The roots of this equation are the zeros of $p(x) = x^3 - 3x^2 - 5x + 15$.

Since the leading coefficient is 1, by the previous corollary, the candidates to be rational zeros are the divisors of 15:

$$1,\ -1,\ 3,\ -3,\ 5,\ -5,\ 15 \text{ and } -15$$

We apply the factor theorem to these candidates.

$$p(1) = 8, \quad p(-1) = 16, \quad p(3) = 0 \quad p(-3) = -24$$
$$p(5) = 40, \quad p(-5) = -150 \quad p(15) = 2,640 \quad p(-15) = -3,960$$

We have only one rational zero, the integer 3.

Step 2. Dividing the polynomial by synthetic division, we have:

$$\left(p(x) = x^3 - 3x^2 - 5x + 15\right) \div (x - 3)$$

	1	-3	-5	15
3		3	0	-15
	1	0	-5	0

Then,

$$x^3 - 3x^2 - 5x + 15 = (x - 3)(x^2 - 5) = 0$$

Step 3. The quotient $q(x) = x^2 - 5$ is a quadratic polynomial, which can be easily factorised as a difference of squares as follows:

$$x^2 - 5 = \left(x - \sqrt{5}\right)\left(x + \sqrt{5}\right)$$

Hence:

$$x^3 - 3x^2 - 5x + 15 = (x - 3)\left(x - \sqrt{5}\right)\left(x + \sqrt{5}\right) = 0$$

The roots are: 3, $\sqrt{5}$ and $-\sqrt{5}$; that is, one integer and two irrationals.

Example 1.5.12 Solve the equation and factorise the polynomial:

$$2x^4 + x^3 - 9x^2 + 16x - 6 = 0$$

Solution

Step 1. The possible numerators are the factors of -6: $\pm 1, \pm 2, \pm 3, \pm 6$.

The possible denominators are the factors of 2: $\pm 1, \pm 2$

The candidates for rational zeros are:

$$\pm 1, \quad \pm 2, \quad \pm 3, \quad \pm 6, \quad \pm\frac{1}{2}, \quad \pm\frac{2}{2}, \quad \pm\frac{3}{2}, \quad \pm\frac{6}{2}$$

Simplifying and taking out the equivalent candidates:

$$\pm 1, \quad \pm 2, \quad \pm 3, \quad \pm 6, \quad \pm\frac{1}{2}, \quad \pm\frac{3}{2}$$

Now, if $p(x) = 2x^4 + x^3 - 9x^2 + 16x - 6$, then:

$$p(1) = 4, \quad p(-1) = -30, \quad p(2) = 30, \quad p(-2) = -50$$

$$p(3) = 150, \quad p(-3) = 0, \quad p\left(\frac{1}{2}\right) = 0, \quad p\left(-\frac{1}{2}\right) = -\frac{65}{4}$$

$$p\left(\frac{3}{2}\right) = \frac{45}{4}, \quad p\left(-\frac{3}{2}\right) = -\frac{87}{2}$$

As we can see, $p(x)$ has only two rational zeros: -3 and $\frac{1}{2}$.

Steps 2 and 3. Dividing the polynomial $p(x) = 2x^4 + x^3 - 9x^2 + 16x - 6$ by $(x + 3)$, and the resulting quotient by $\left(x - \frac{1}{2}\right)$, we have:

	2	1	-9	16	-6
-3		-6	15	-18	6
	2	-5	6	-2	0

	2	-5	6	-2
$\frac{1}{2}$		1	-2	2
	2	-4	4	0

$$p(x) = (x + 3)(2x^3 - 5x^2 + 6x - 2); \qquad 2x^3 - 5x^2 + 6x - 2 = \left(x - \frac{1}{2}\right)(2x^2 - 4x + 4)$$

Now, we have that:

$$p(x) = (x + 3)\left(x - \frac{1}{2}\right)(2x^2 - 4x + 4)$$

The polynomial $2x^2 - 4x + 4$ is quadratic, that means we can find its zeros using the quadratic formula:

$$x = \frac{-(-4) \pm \sqrt{(-4)^2 - 4(2)(4)}}{2(2)} = \frac{4 \pm 4\sqrt{-1}}{4} = 1 \pm i$$

By the complete factorization theorem:

$$2x^2 - 4x + 4 = 2(x - (1 + i))(x - (1 - i)) = 2(x - 1 - i)(x - 1 + i)$$

Finally, we have:

$$2x^4 + x^3 - 9x^2 + 16x - 6 = 2(x + 3)\left(x - \frac{1}{2}\right)(x - 1 - i)(x - 1 + i)$$

The equation has four roots:

- Two rational roots: -3 and $\frac{1}{2}$
- Two complex roots: $1 + i$ and $1 - i$

Example 1.5.13 Solve the equation and factorise the polynomial:

$$4x^3 - 16x^2 + 11x + 10 = 0$$

Solution

Step 1.

The possible numerators are the factors of 10. These are:

$$\pm 1 \qquad \pm 2 \qquad \pm 5 \qquad \pm 10$$

The possible denominators are the factors of 4. These are:

$$\pm 1 \qquad \pm 2 \qquad \pm 4$$

The candidates for rational zeros are:

$$\begin{array}{cccccc} \pm 1, & \pm 2, & \pm 5, & \pm 10, & \pm \frac{1}{2}, & \pm \frac{2}{2}, \\ \pm \frac{5}{2}, & \pm \frac{10}{2}, & \pm \frac{1}{4}, & \pm \frac{2}{4}, & \pm \frac{5}{4}, & \pm \frac{10}{4} \end{array}$$

Simplifying and taking out the equivalent candidates:

$$\pm 1, \quad \pm 2, \quad \pm 5, \quad \pm 10, \quad \pm \frac{1}{2}, \quad \pm \frac{5}{2}, \quad \pm \frac{1}{4}, \quad \pm \frac{5}{4}$$

Replacing these candidates in $p(x) = 4x^3 - 16x^2 + 11x + 10$, we have:

$$\begin{array}{llll} p(1) = 9, & p(-1) = 21, & p(2) = 0, & p(-2) = -108 \\ p(5) = 165, & p(-5) = -945, & p(10) = 2,520, & p(-10) = -2,500 \end{array}$$

$$p\left(\frac{1}{2}\right) = 12, \quad p\left(-\frac{1}{2}\right) = 0, \quad p\left(\frac{1}{4}\right) = \frac{189}{16}, \quad p\left(-\frac{1}{4}\right) = \frac{99}{16}$$

$$p\left(\frac{5}{2}\right) = 0, \quad p\left(-\frac{5}{2}\right) = -125, \quad p\left(\frac{5}{4}\right) = \frac{105}{16}, \quad p\left(-\frac{5}{4}\right) = -\frac{805}{16}$$

The equation has 3 rational roots: $-\frac{1}{2}$, 2 and $\frac{5}{2}$.

This is a third-degree equation. Since we already know three of its roots, the complete factorization theorem allows us to skip steps 2 and 3.

$$\begin{aligned} 4x^3 - 16x^2 + 11x + 10 &= 4\left(x + \frac{1}{2}\right)(x-2)\left(x - \frac{5}{2}\right) \\ &= (2x+1)(x-2)(2x-5) \end{aligned}$$

Did you know this?

*Polynomials are very useful in Cybersecurity, specifically, in **Encryption**. Encryption is a security system that consists of encoding messages between a sender and a receiver, as protection in case a third party manages to intercept the channel through which the message is sent. One of the most popular encryption systems, **RSA** (Rivest-Shamir-Adleman), implements polynomials to encode its messages, in fact, the strength of its algorithm is based on the difficulty of factoring polynomials of long extension.*

SOLVED PROBLEMS 1.5

Problem 1.5.1

Solve the equation, factorise the polynomial and determine the multiplicity of each root:

$$x^5 + x^4 - 2x^3 - 2x^2 + x + 1 = 0$$

Solution

Let $p(x) = x^5 + x^4 - 2x^3 - 2x^2 + x + 1$. Since the leading coefficient is 1, the candidates to rational roots are the divisors of the constant term 1. Hence, the candidates are 1 and -1.

$$p(1) = 1 + 1 - 2 - 2 + 1 + 1 = 0 \quad p(-1) = -1 + 1 + 2 - 2 - 1 + 1 = 0$$

Both, 1 and -1, are roots. Let's divide $p(x)$ by $(x - 1)$, and the quotient $q_1(x)$ by $(x + 1)$:

	1	1	-2	-2	1	1
1		1	2	0	-2	-1
	1	2	0	-2	-1	0
-1		-1	-1	1	1	
	1	1	-1	-1	0	

$$x^5 + x^4 - 2x^3 - 2x^2 + x + 1 = (x - 1)(x + 1)(x^3 + x^2 - x - 1)$$

If 1 is a multiple root, then 1 must be also a root of the quotient. Similarly, if -1 is a multiple root, then -1 must be also a root of the quotient:

$$q_2(x) = x^3 + x^2 - x - 1$$

We have:

$$q_2(1) = 1 + 1 - 1 - 1 = 0 \qquad q_2(-1) = -1 + 1 + 1 - 1 = 0$$

These results indicate that 1 and -1 are roots of $q_2(x)$. Now, we divide $q_2(x)$ by $(x - 1)$, and the quotient $q_3(x)$ by $(x + 1)$:

	1	1	-1	-1
1		1	2	1
	1	2	1	**0**
-1		-1	-1	
	1	1	**0**	

$$x^3 + x^2 - x - 1 = (x-1)(x+1)(x+1)$$

Hence:

$$\begin{aligned} x^5 + x^4 - 2x^3 - 2x^2 + x + 1 &= (x-1)(x+1)(x-1)(x+1)(x+1) \\ &= (x-1)^2(x+1)^3 \end{aligned}$$

Finally, the roots are: 1, with multiplicity 2; and -1, with multiplicity 3.

Problem 1.5.2 Prove the rational zero theorem (theorem 1.5.5)

Given a polynomial:

$$p(x) = a_n x^n + a_{n-1}x^{n-1} + \cdots + a_1 x + a_0,$$

If the coefficients of $p(x)$ are integers and the rational $\frac{h}{k}$, reduced to lowest terms, is a zero of $p(x)$, then:

1. h divides the constant term a_0
2. k divides the leading coefficient a_n

Solution

If $\frac{h}{k}$ is a zero of $p(x)$, then:

$$a_n \left(\frac{h}{k}\right)^n + a_{n-1}\left(\frac{h}{k}\right)^{n-1} + \cdots + a_1\left(\frac{h}{k}\right) + a_0 = 0$$

Multiplying by k^n:

$$a_n h^n + a_{n-1}h^{n-1}k + \cdots + a_1 h k^{n-1} + a_0 k^n = 0 \quad \text{(i)}$$

1. Transposing $a_0 k^n$ in (i) and factorising:

$$h\left(a_n h^{n-1} + a_{n-1}h^{n-2}k + \cdots + a_1 k^{n-1}\right) = -a_0 k^n$$

This equality indicates that h divides $a_0 k^n$. Since h does not divide k, h does not divide k^n either. Hence, h divides a_0.

2. Transposing $a_n h^n$ in (i) and factorising:

$$k\left(a_{n-1}h^{n-1} + \cdots + a_1 h k^{n-2} + a_0 k^{n-1}\right) = -a_n h^n$$

This equality indicates that k divides $a_n h^n$. Since k does not divide h, k does not divide h^n either. Hence, k divides a_n.

Did you know this?

The ancient Babylonians already knew the quadratic formula for finding the roots of the second degree equation $ax^2 + bx + c = 0$, that is:

$$x = \frac{-b \pm \sqrt{b^2 - 4ac}}{2a}$$

As we have witnessed, this formula outputs the roots of the equation in terms of radicals.

For many centuries mathematicians had looked for a formula, similar to the quadratic, to solve the cubic equation $\boldsymbol{ax^3 + bx^2 + cx + d = 0}$.

The formula was finally achieved during the Renaissance in the early 16th century, with four mathematicians playing outstanding roles in this triumph: ***Scipione del Ferro**, **Nicolo Fontana**(Tartaglia), **Giroldamo Cardano** and **Ludovico Ferrari**.*

***SCIPIONE DEL FERRO** (1465-1526) was a lecturer of arithmetic and geometry at the University of Bologna from 1496 to 1526. In 1515, he discovered the solution of the particular cubic equation called the **depressed cubic equation** (without the quadratic term):*

$$x^3 + px + r = 0, \quad \textit{where } p \textit{ and } r \textit{ are integers}$$

*Scipione is recognized as a great algebraist. He never published his work, but he divulged it to a small select group of friends, specially to his disciples, **Anniballe della Nave** and **Antonio Maria Flore**.*

***NICOLO FONTANA** (1499-1557) better known by the nickname **Tartaglia** (meaning "the stammered"), was born in Brescia, Italy.*

Tartaglia

In 1512, the French army invaded Brescia and massacred its inhabitants. Twelve-year-old Nicolo, along with his mother and many others, sought refuge in the cathedral.

The invaders stormed into the temple, leaving devastation in their wake. Nicolo endured a sword cut to his jaw and palate, nearly fatal and almost leaving him for dead. Miraculously, he survived the fatal injury but was left with a lifelong stutter.

About 1535, Nicolo announced that he found the formula to solve the cubic equation. Tartaglia found the general solution for the cubic equations:

$$x^3 + bx^2 + r = 0 \quad \textit{and} \quad x^3 + px + r, \textbf{ the depressed cubic equation}$$

*In Bologna, **Antonio del Fiore**, a disciple of Scipione del Ferro, accused Tartaglia of being an impostor. He claimed that his master was the true discoverer of the formula 20 years earlier. Fiore challenged Tartaglia to a public contest, which Tartagia accepted and ultimately won.*

GIROLDAMO CARDANO *(1501-1526) was an important eccentric and confrontational mathematician from Milan. While he was a student of medicine at the University of Padua, he covered his expenses by gambling, in which he became very proficient. His experience in this field helped him to write the book **Liber de ludo aleae** (Book of Games of Chance), which was a groundbreaking work on the topic of probability.*

Cardano

Cardano finished his university studies in 1526, obtaining a doctorate in medicine. He became one of the most famous physicians of his time.

In 1539, he took advantage of Tartaglia's respect for him and persuaded him to reveal his solution for the cubic equation. Tartaglia initially refused, but eventually showed it to Cardano after the later swore not to make it public.

*In 1545, Cardano published his book **Ars Magna, sive de regulis algebraicis** (concerning the rules of algebra), which contained the solution to the cubic equation without fully crediting its creator. This naturally upset Tartaglia greatly.*

*Tartaglia was challenged by Cardano to a public debate, which he refused. However, his brilliant disciple **Ludovico Ferrari** (1522-1565) stepped in and challenged Tartaglia to another public debate that took place in 1548. By that time, Ludovico had mastered both the cubic and quartic equation, causing Tartaglia to withdraw from the debate before it concluded.*

LUDOVICO FERRARI *(1522-1565) was born in Bologna, Italy. In his early years, he served as a assistant to Cardano. An exceptionally bright student, he mastered Latin, Greek and mathematics while attending Cardano's lectures. After achieving proficiency in mathematics, Ludovico collaborated with Cardano on research involving cubic and quartic equations.*

At the age of twenty, in 1540, he succeeded Cardano as a public lecturer in Milan. Following his debate with Tartaglia, Ferrari gained the reputation of being one of Italy's finest mathematicians.

After holding several well-paid positions, Ferrari returned to his hometown in 1565, where he lived a comfortable life before dying of arsenic poisoning.

In the book ***Ars Magna*** *also appears the formula for solving the cubic equation:* $\boldsymbol{ax^3 + bx^2 + cx + d = 0}$.

The change of variable $\boldsymbol{x = z - \frac{b}{3a}}$ *transforms this equation into another one of the form:*

$$\boldsymbol{x^3 + qx + r = 0,}$$

whose final solution is given by the formula:

$$x = \left[-\frac{r}{2} + \sqrt{\frac{r^2}{4} + \frac{q^3}{27}}\right]^{1/3} + \left[-\frac{r}{2} - \sqrt{\frac{r^2}{4} + \frac{q^3}{27}}\right]^{1/3}$$

EXERCISES 1.5

Solve the equations provided in exercises 1 to 14.

1. $5(x-3) = 3(x+7) + x$

2. $y - (6 - 2y) = 8(y - 2)$

3. $\frac{1}{2}(2x - 1) = 3\left(x + \frac{1}{4}\right)$

4. $\frac{x}{4} - \frac{x}{3} = \frac{7}{6} - \frac{4x}{3}$

5. $\frac{2x-1}{5} = \frac{2+x}{3}$

6. $\frac{7z+1}{6} + \frac{3}{2} = \frac{3z}{4}$

7. $\frac{x-1}{3} - \frac{2-3x}{14} = \frac{4x-3}{7}$

8. $\frac{x-3}{6} - \frac{2x-1}{5} = -1$

9. $\frac{x+1}{5} + \frac{x+2}{6} = \frac{x-1}{4} + \frac{x+7}{10}$

10. $\frac{5x-2}{3} - \frac{1}{2}(3x-1) = \frac{9x+7}{6} - \frac{2}{9}(5x-1)$

11. $(x-3)^2 = (x-1)^2$

12. $(x-5)(x+1) = (x+2)(x-3) + 13$

13. $(2x-5)(x-1) + x^2 = (3x-1)(x+2) + 1$

14. $8x(x+2)(x-1) = (2x+1)^3 - (2x+3)^2$

In exercises 15 through 22, solve the equations for the variable x.

15. $5(5x - a) = a^2(x - 1)$

16. $a(x+b) + x(b-a) = 2b(2a - x)$

17. $x^2 + b^2 + b(b-1) = (x+b)^2$

18. $(x+a)^3 - 2x^3 = 12a^3 - (x-a)$

19. $\frac{x-a}{b} + \frac{x-b}{a} = 2$

20. $\frac{x-3m}{m^2} + \frac{x-2m}{mn} = -\frac{1}{m}$

21. $\frac{a-x}{a} - \frac{b-x}{b} = \frac{2(a-b)}{ab}$

22. $\frac{x-a}{a+b} + \frac{a+b}{a-b} = \frac{x+b}{a+b} + \frac{x-b}{a-b}$

In exercises 23 to 26, solve the equations for the indicated variable in terms of the remaining variables.

23. $A = \pi(r^2 + rs),\ s$

24. $S = a\frac{1-r^n}{1-r},\ a$

25. $S = \frac{f}{H-h},\ h$

26. $\frac{1}{x} + \frac{1}{y} = \frac{1}{a},\ x$

Solve the equations from 27 to 40 by factorising.

27. $x^2 - 4x - 12 = 0$

28. $x^2 - 6x + 9 = 0$

29. $x^2 + 24 = -11x$

30. $2x^2 - 3x + 1 = 0$

31. $9x^2 - 17x - 2 = 0$

32. $(2x - 1)^2 - (x + 5)^2 = -19$

33. $(x-5)^2 - (x-4)^2 = (2x+3)^2 + 12$

34. $(x - 2)^3 - (x + 1)^3 = -x(3x + 4) - 24$

35. $6x^2 - \frac{5x}{2} = -\frac{1}{4}$

36. $\frac{2(x+5)}{5} + \frac{x-4}{4} = \frac{x^2-53}{5}$

37. $x^4 - 17x^2 + 16 = 0$

38. $6y^4 = \frac{y^2}{2} + \frac{1}{4}$

39. $x^{2/3} + x^{1/3} - 6 = 0$

40. $2x^{2/3} + 3x^{1/3} - 2 = 0$

Solve the equations from 41 to 46 using the quadratic formula.

41. $9(x - 1)^2 = 5$

42. $4\sqrt{3}x - 3 = 4x^2$

43. $2x(2x - 3) = -1$

44. $(x + 15)^2 = 6x(x + 5)$

45. $x^2 - 2x - (a^2 + 2a) = 0$

46. $\frac{x^2}{2a} - \frac{a+2}{2a}x + 1 = 0$

In the exercises 47 to 60, solve the given equations.

47. $\frac{x-6}{x} = \frac{x+6}{x-6} + \frac{6}{x}$

48. $\frac{x}{x+2} - \frac{x}{x-2} = \frac{x-15}{x^2-4}$

49. $\frac{1}{3x-3} + \frac{1}{4x+4} = \frac{1}{12x-12}$

50. $\frac{4x+1}{4x-1} = \frac{4x-1}{4x+1} + \frac{6}{16x^2-1}$

51. $\frac{1}{x} + \frac{1}{4-x} = 1$

52. $\frac{x}{1+x} + \frac{1}{1-x} = 0$

53. $\frac{3y-2}{3y+2} = \frac{2y+3}{4y-1}$

54. $\frac{x+5}{(x-1)(x+2)} = \frac{2x}{x+2}$

55. $\frac{1}{x-1} - \frac{1}{x-2} = \frac{1}{x-3}$

56. $\frac{3x}{x-2} - \frac{1}{x^2-4} = 2$

57. $\frac{1}{x^2} + \frac{2}{x} - 15 = 0$

58. $\frac{12}{x-1} + \frac{12}{x} = 10$

59. $\frac{2x}{x-1} = \frac{8}{x-1} - \frac{5}{x}$

60. $\frac{1}{x^2-4} + \frac{2x+3}{x+2} + \frac{x+3}{x-2} = 0$

In exercises 61 to 76, solve the equations and eliminate any extraneous solutions.

61. $5 - \sqrt{2x + 3} = 0$

62. $\sqrt{\frac{x}{18} + 1} = \frac{2}{3}$

63. $(5x - 1)^{1/2} = 7$

64. $(y + 9)^{3/2} = 4^3$

65. $\sqrt{x^2 - 5} = 5 - x$

66. $\sqrt{z + 7} - \sqrt{z} = 1$

67. $\sqrt{9x^2 - 10x} = 3x - 2$

68. $\sqrt{\frac{1}{x}} - \sqrt{\frac{8}{4x+1}} = 0$

69. $\sqrt{4x+1} + 1 = 2x$

70. $\sqrt{x^2+5} = 2x - 1$

71. $\sqrt{x+5} = 2\sqrt{x} - 1$

72. $\sqrt{x} + \sqrt{x-3} = \sqrt{x+5}$

73. $\sqrt{x + \sqrt{x+8}} = 2\sqrt{x}$

74. $\sqrt{3x-2} = \sqrt{2x-3} + \sqrt{x-1}$

75. $\sqrt{x+1} + \sqrt{x} + \frac{1}{\sqrt{x+1} - \sqrt{x}} = 4$

76. $\frac{x}{2} = \frac{\sqrt{x+2} - \sqrt{x-2}}{\sqrt{x+2} + \sqrt{x-2}}$

In exercises 77 to 78, solve the equations using a change of variable.

77. $\left(\frac{3x}{x+1}\right)^2 - \frac{6x}{x+1} = 8$

78. $\sqrt[3]{\frac{5x+4}{x-1}} + \sqrt[3]{\frac{x-1}{5x+4}} = \frac{5}{2}$

In exercises 79 to 80, use the remainder theorem to find the remainders.

79. $3x^4 - 5x^3 - 4x^2 + 3x - 2$, by $(x-2)$

80. $x^3 - 6x^2 + 11x - 6$, by $(x+2)$

In exercises 81 to 88, find the roots of the equations and factorise the polynomials.

81. $x^3 + 2x^2 - x - 2 = 0$

82. $x^3 - 3x^2 + 2 = 0$

83. $4x^3 - 7x^2 + 3 = 0$

84. $2x^3 - 2x^2 - 11x + 2 = 0$

85. $x^4 - x^3 - 5x^2 + 3x + 6 = 0$

86. $3x^4 + 5x^3 - 5x^2 - 5x + 2 = 0$

87. $x^5 - 3x^4 - 5x^3 + 15x^2 + 4x - 12 = 0$

88. $x^5 + 4x^4 - 4x^3 - 34x^2 - 45x - 18 = 0$

In the exercises 89 to 91, use the factor theorem to prove:

89. $x - a$ is a factor of $x^n - a^n$, where n is positive integer.

90. $x + a$ is a factor of $x^n - a^n$, where n is positive even integer.

91. $x + a$ is a factor of $x^n + a^n$, where n is positive odd integer.

SECCION 1.6

ORDER AXIOMS AND INEQUATIONS

ORDER AXIOMS

Let a and b be real numbers. If $\boldsymbol{a < b}$, we say that $\boldsymbol{a}$ **is less than** $\boldsymbol{b}$. The order axioms describe the properties of the relation "$<$" as follows:

O_1. Trichotomy Law: For any $\boldsymbol{a}$, $\boldsymbol{b} \in \mathbb{R}$, exactly one of the relations holds:

$$\boldsymbol{a = b}, \quad \boldsymbol{a < b}, \quad \text{or} \quad \boldsymbol{b < a}$$

O_2. Transitive Law:

$$a < b \ \wedge \ b < c \Rightarrow a < c$$

O_3. Additive Law:

$$a < b \Rightarrow a + c < b + c, \ \forall \ c \in \mathbb{R}$$

O_4. Multiplicative Law:

$$a < b \ \wedge \ c > 0 \Rightarrow ac < bc$$

SOME IMPORTANT PROPERTIES OF INEQUALITIES

The next definition remarks three relations in terms of "$<$".

Definition We say that:

1. $\boldsymbol{a}$ **is greater than** $\boldsymbol{b}$, and write $\boldsymbol{a > b}$ if $\boldsymbol{b < a}$.

2. $\boldsymbol{a}$ **is less or equal to** $\boldsymbol{b}$, and write $\boldsymbol{a \leq b}$ if $\boldsymbol{a < b \vee a = b}$.

3. $\boldsymbol{a}$ **is greater or equal to** $\boldsymbol{b}$, and write $\boldsymbol{a \geq b}$ if $\boldsymbol{a > b \vee a = b}$.

The symbols "$<$", "$\leq$", "$>$" and "$\geq$" are called the **inequality signs**, and the expressions constructed with these symbols, such as $a < b$, $a \leq b$, $a > b$ or $a \geq b$, are called **inequalities**.

Definition

1. A number $\boldsymbol{a}$ is **negative** if $\boldsymbol{a < 0}$, and is **positive** if $\boldsymbol{a > 0}$.

2. Two numbers have **equal signs** if both are negative or both are positive. Conversely, two numbers have **opposite signs** if one is negative and the other one is positive.

Theorem 1.6.1 $\boldsymbol{a < b \wedge c < d \Rightarrow a + c < b + d}$

Proof

$$a < b \Rightarrow a + c < b + c \qquad (O_3)$$
$$c < d \Rightarrow b + c < b + d \qquad (O_3 \text{ and } A_1)$$

Applying O_2 to the above results, we get:

$$a < b \wedge c < d \Rightarrow a + c < b + d$$

Corolary

The sum of two positive numbers is a positive number. Likewise, the sum of two negative numbers is a negative number.

Proof

Let a and b be positive. Hence,

$$0 < a \quad \vee \quad 0 < b$$

Applying the theorem 1.6.1:

$$0 + 0 < a + b. \text{ This is } 0 < a + b.$$

Hence, $a + b$ is positive.

Proceed similarly in the case of negative numbers.

Theorem 1.6.2 $a < b \Rightarrow -a > -b$

Proof

$$\begin{aligned} a < b &\Rightarrow a + [(-a) + (-b)] < b + [(-a) + (-b)] && (O_3) \\ &\Rightarrow [a + (-a)] + (-b) < [b + (-b)] + (-a) && (A_1 \text{ and } A_2) \\ &\Rightarrow 0 + (-b) < 0 + (-a) && (A_4) \\ &\Rightarrow -b < -a && (A_3) \\ &\Rightarrow -a > -b && (\text{Definition of "}>\text{"}) \end{aligned}$$

Theorem 1.6.3 $a < b \wedge c < 0 \Rightarrow ac > bc$

Proof

$$
\begin{aligned}
c < 0 &\Rightarrow -c > 0 && \text{(Theorem 1.6.2)}\\
a < b \wedge -c > 0 &\Rightarrow a(-c) < b(-c) && (O_4)\\
&\Rightarrow -(ac) < -(bc) && \text{(Theorem 1.2.3 part 3)}\\
&\Rightarrow -(-(ac)) > -(-(bc)) && \text{(Theorem 1.6.2)}\\
&\Rightarrow ac > bc && \text{(Theorem 1.2.3 part 1)}
\end{aligned}
$$

INTERVALS

Let $\boldsymbol{a}$ and $\boldsymbol{b}$ be two numbers on the real number line. The expression $\boldsymbol{a < b}$ indicates that the point corresponding to $\boldsymbol{a}$ is located to the left of the point that corresponds to $\boldsymbol{b}$.

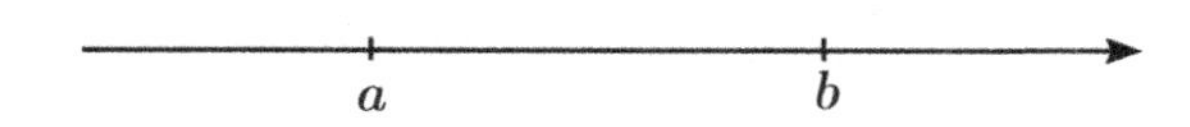

Definition

Let $\boldsymbol{a}$ and $\boldsymbol{b}$ be two real numbers such that $a \leq b$:

The Closed Interval from a to b is the set:

$[a,\, b] = \{x \in \mathbb{R} / a \leq x \leq b\}$

The Open Interval from a to b is the set:

$(a,\, b) = \{x \in \mathbb{R} / a < x < b\}$

In the above definitions, $\boldsymbol{a}$ is the **left endpoint**, and $\boldsymbol{b}$ is the **right endpoint** of the interval. Observe that both endpoints fit inside the closed interval $[a,\, b]$, but they do not fit inside the open interval $(a,\, b)$. That is:

$$a, b \in [a,\, b] \quad \text{and} \quad a, b \notin (a,\, b)$$

Half-open or half-closed Intervals

$[a,\, b) = \{x \in \mathbb{R} / a \leq x < b\}$

$(a,\, b] = \{x \in \mathbb{R} / a < x \leq b\}$

Infinite Intervals

We use the symbol $+\infty$ or ∞ to indicate that there are no boundaries in the positive direction. Conversely, the symbol $-\infty$ is used to indicate that there are no boundaries in the negative direction. It is important to clarify that $+\infty$ and $-\infty$ are not real numbers.

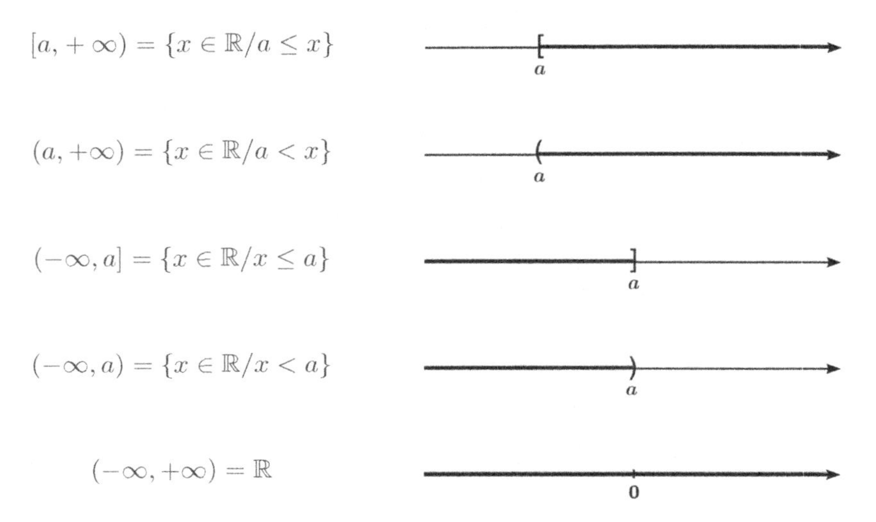

The infinite intervals shown above are all **rays**, except for the last one. This one represents the entire real number line.

INEQUATIONS

Everyday language often treats an **inequation** and an inequality as the same, but in mathematics, an inequation specifically refers to inequalities that involve variables. An inequation may contain one or more variables; also, it may be **linear, quadratic**, **cubic**, etc. In this part, we are interested on inequations of **one variable**. A solution to a one-variable inequation is a number that, when substituted for the variable, results in a true proposition. The **solution set** of an inequation is the set of all solutions.

Linear inequations are the simplest type of inequations, involving degree 1 polynomials. These inequations can be easily solved by using the basic properties of the inequalities. To solve inequations expressed in terms of polynomials of degree greater than 1, or in terms of quotients of polynomials (rational functions), we will make use of the **Sturm Method**.

LINEAR INEQUATIONS

An inequation is linear if the highest power of the variable is 1. As previously mentioned, these inequations are easy to solve using the basic properties of inequalities, as demonstrated in the following example:

Example 1.6.1 Solve the inequation: $5x - 15 < 2x$

Solution

$$\begin{aligned} 5x - 15 < 2x &\Leftrightarrow 5x < 2x + 15 && (O_3, \text{ adding 15 on both sides}) \\ &\Leftrightarrow 3x < 15 && (O_3, \text{ adding } -2x \text{ on both sides}) \\ &\Leftrightarrow x < \frac{15}{3} && (O_4, \text{multiplying by } \tfrac{1}{3} \text{ on both sides}) \\ &\Leftrightarrow x < 5 \end{aligned}$$

The solution set of the inequation is the interval $(-\infty, 5)$

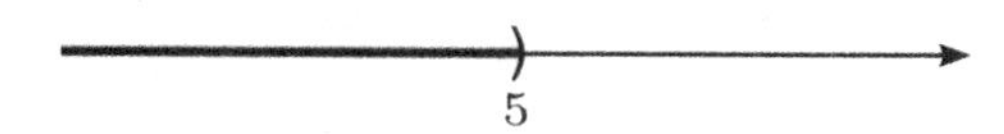

Remark

From now on, the transpositions will be performed without being mentioned.

Example 1.6.2 Solve: $\dfrac{x-1}{6} + 2 \leq \dfrac{x-3}{2} + \dfrac{x}{3}$

Solution

We multiply both sides by the LCD (6) to eliminate the denominators:

$$\begin{aligned} 6\left(\frac{x-1}{6} + 2\right) \leq 6\left(\frac{x-3}{2} + \frac{x}{3}\right) &\Leftrightarrow (x-1) + 12 \leq 3(x-3) + 2x \\ &\Leftrightarrow x - 1 + 12 \leq 3x - 9 + 2x \\ &\Leftrightarrow -4x \leq 1 - 12 - 9 \\ &\Leftrightarrow -4x \leq -20 \\ &\Leftrightarrow x \geq \frac{-20}{-4} = 5 \end{aligned}$$

The solution set of the inequation is the interval $[5, +\infty)$

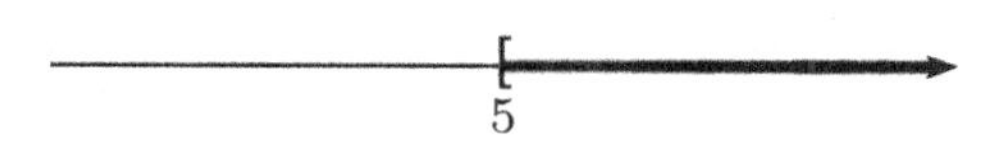

Example 1.6.3 Solve: $4 \leq \dfrac{5x+1}{4} < 9$

Solution

There are two inequations in this expression:

$$4 \leq \frac{5x+1}{4} \quad \textbf{and} \quad \frac{5x+1}{4} < 9$$

We will solve them separately.

1. $4 \leq \dfrac{5x+1}{4}$

$$4 \leq \frac{5x+1}{4} \Leftrightarrow 16 \leq 5x+1 \Leftrightarrow 16-1 \leq 5x \Leftrightarrow 15 \leq 5x \Leftrightarrow 3 \leq x$$

The solution set of this inequation is the interval $[3, +\infty)$.

2. $\dfrac{5x+1}{4} < 9$

$$\frac{5x+1}{4} < 9 \Leftrightarrow 5x+1 < 36 \Leftrightarrow 5x < 35 \Leftrightarrow x < 7$$

The solution set of this inequation is the interval $(-\infty, 7)$.

The solution of the original inequation must also be a solution for the two previous inequations; hence, the solution set of the original inequation is the intersection of both solution sets. This is:

$$[3, +\infty) \cap (-\infty, 7) = [3, 7)$$

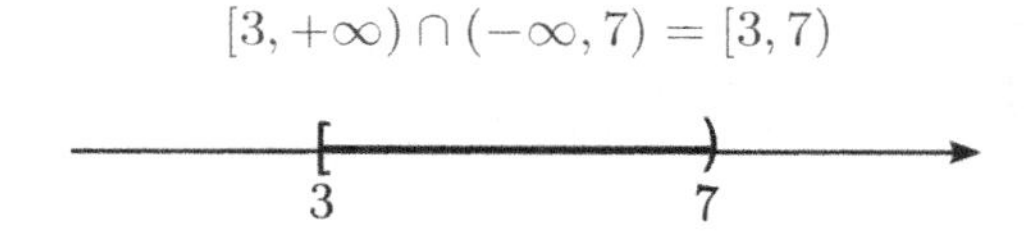

THE STURM METHOD

In general, the inequations of degree greater than 1 are not easy to solve, that is why we have such practical methodologies as the **Sturm method**.

This method is based on the fact that *the sign of a polynomial remains constant within each interval formed by two consecutive zeros.*

This procedure consists of three steps.

Step 1. Transpose terms to turn the inequation into one of the following:

1. $p(x) < 0$ **2.** $p(x) > 0$ **3.** $p(x) \leq 0$ **4.** $p(x) \geq 0$,

where $p(x)$ is a polynomial of degree greater than 1.

Step 2. Find all the rational rots of $p(x) = 0 : r_1,\ r_2,\ r_3, \dots r_n$ and factorise:

$$p(x) = (x-r_1)(x-r_2)(x-r_3)\cdots(x-r_n), \text{ where } r_1 < r_2 < r_3 < \cdots < r_n$$

Divide the real number line in the interval determined by the roots. These are called **test intervals**.

$$(-\infty, r_1), (r_1, r_2), (r_2, r_3), \dots, (r_{n-1}, r_n), (r_n, +\infty)$$

The sign of the polynomial remains constant in each of these intervals.

Take any number in the interval and find the value of the polynomial for that number. This will be called **test value**.

Write down the sign of the value across the entire interval.

Step 3. The real line provides the solution set. If the inequation in step 1 is expressed by "$<$" or "$>$", then all the intervals of the solution set are **open**. On the other hand, if the inequation is expressed by "$\geq$" or "$\leq$", then all the intervals of the solution set are **closed**.

Example 1.6.4 Solve the inequation: $x^2 - 2 < 3x + 8$

Solution

Step 1. Transposing and factorizing:

$$x^2 - 2 < 3x + 8 \Leftrightarrow x^2 - 3x - 10 < 0 \Leftrightarrow (x+2)(x-5) < 0$$

Step 2. The roots of $p(x) = (x+2)(x-5) = 0$ are -2 and 5. The test intervals are:

$$(-\infty, -2), \quad (-2, 5) \quad \text{and} \quad (5, +\infty)$$

Let's determine the sign of $p(x) = (x+2)(x-5)$ in each test interval.

In $(-\infty, -2)$, if we take $x = -3$, we obtain the test value:

$$p(-3) = (-3+2)(-3-5) = +8 \Rightarrow \text{ sign of } p(x) \text{ in } (-\infty, -2) \text{ is } (+)$$

In $(-2,\ 5)$, if we take $x = 0$, we obtain the test value:

$$p(0) = (0+2)(0-5) = -10 \Rightarrow \text{ sign of } p(x) \text{ in } (-2, 5) \text{ is } (-)$$

In $(5, +\infty)$, if we take $x = 6$, we obtain the test value:

$$p(6) = (6+2)(6-5) = +12 \Rightarrow \text{ sign of } p(x) \text{ in } (5, +\infty) \text{ is } (+)$$

Now, we proceed to write the roots and the signs on the test intervals in the real number line:

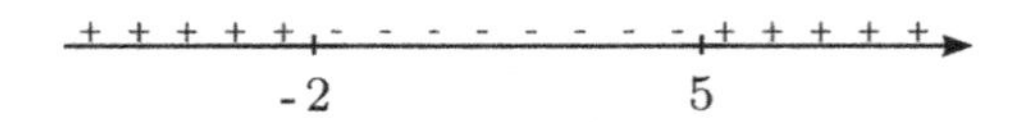

Step 3. The figure shows that $p(x) < 0$ in the interval $(\mathbf{-2,\ 5})$.

Hence, the solution set is the interval $(\mathbf{-2,\ 5})$

Convention

For brevity's sake, the above steps won't be mentioned in the upcoming examples. Instead, all the work done will be synthesized in a figure as follows:

$$p(x) = (x + 2)(x - 5) < 0$$

+ + + + + +	-2 - - - - - -	5 + + + + +
$x = -3$	$x = 0$	$x = 7$
$p(-3) = (-3 + 2)(-3 - 5)$	$p(0) = (0 + 2)(0 - 5)$	$p(7) = (7 + 2)(7 - 5)$
$= +8$	$= -10$	$= +18$

Example 1.6.5 Solve: $(x - 1)(2 - 3x) \leq (2x + 7)(x - 2) - 4$

Solution

$(x - 1)(2 - 3x) \leq (2x + 7)(x - 2) - 4$

$$\Leftrightarrow 2x - 3x^2 - 2 + 3x \leq 2x^2 - 4x + 7x - 14 - 4$$

$$\Leftrightarrow -3x^2 + 5x - 2 \leq 2x^2 + 3x - 18$$

$$\Leftrightarrow -5x^2 + 2x + 16 \leq 0$$

$$\Leftrightarrow 5x^2 - 2x - 16 \geq 0$$

$$\Leftrightarrow (5x + 8)(x - 2) \geq 0$$

Let's find the roots of $p(x) = (5x + 8)(x - 2) = 0$:

$$(5x + 8)(x - 2) = 0 \Leftrightarrow 5x + 8 = 0 \text{ or } x - 2 = 0 \Leftrightarrow x = -\frac{8}{5} \text{ or } x = 2$$

Hence, the test intervals are: $\left(-\infty, -\frac{8}{5}\right)$, $\left(-\frac{8}{5}, 2\right)$, and $(2, +\infty)$

$$p(x) = (5x+8)(x-2) \geq 0$$

$+ + + + + +$	$-\frac{8}{5}$ $- - - - - -$	2 $+ + + + +$
$x = -3$	$x = 0$	$x = 3$
$p(-3) = (5(-3)+8)(-3-2)$	$p(0) = (5(0)+8)(0-2)$	$p(3) = (5(3)+8)(3-2)$
$= +35$	$= -16$	$= +23$

The solution set is $\left(-\infty, -\frac{8}{5}\right] \cup [2, +\infty)$.

Example 1.6.6 Solve: $3x^3 - 6x > 7x^2$

Solution

$$3x^3 - 6x > 7x^2 \Leftrightarrow 3x^3 - 7x^2 - 6x > 0$$
$$\Leftrightarrow x(3x^2 - 7x - 6) > 0 \Leftrightarrow x(3x+2)(x-3) > 0$$

Let's find the roots of $p(x) = x(3x+2)(x-3) = 0$:

$$x(3x+2)(x-3) = 0 \Leftrightarrow x = 0,\ 3x+2 = 0 \text{ or } x - 3 = 0$$
$$\Leftrightarrow x = 0,\ x = -\frac{2}{3} \text{ or } x = 3$$

Hence, the test intervals are:

$$\left(-\infty, -\frac{2}{3}\right), \left(-\frac{2}{3}, 0\right), (0, 3) \text{ y } (3, +\infty)$$

$$p(x) = x(3x+2)(x-3) > 0$$

$- - - - -$	$-\frac{2}{3}$ $+ + + + +$	0 $- - - - -$	3 $+ + + +$
$x = -1$	$x = -\frac{1}{3}$	$x = 1$	$x = 4$
$p(-1) = (-1)[3(-1)+2] \times [(-1)-3]$	$p\left(-\frac{1}{3}\right) = \left(-\frac{1}{3}\right)\left[3\left(-\frac{1}{3}\right)+2\right] \times \left[\left(-\frac{1}{3}\right)-3\right]$	$p(1) = (1)[3(1)+2] \times [(1)-3]$	$p(4) = (4)[3(4)+2] \times [(4)-3]$
$p(-1) = -4$	$p\left(-\frac{1}{3}\right) = +\frac{10}{9}$	$p(1) = -10$	$p(4) = +56$

The solution set is $\left(-\frac{2}{3}, 0\right) \cup (3, +\infty)$.

RATIONAL INEQUATIONS

A rational inequation is an inequation that involves rational expressions. To solve these expressions using the Sturm method, follow the next three steps. This process is similar to the given method for solving polynomial inequations, but now we have to deal with a numerator and a denominator.

Step 1. Transform the inequation to adopt one of the four following forms, where the polynomials, $p(x)$ and $q(x)$, are factorised:

$$\frac{p(x)}{q(x)} > 0, \quad \frac{p(x)}{q(x)} \geq 0, \quad \frac{p(x)}{q(x)} < 0, \quad \frac{p(x)}{q(x)} \leq 0$$

Step 2. Find the roots of $p(x) = 0$ and $q(x) = 0$.

Step 3. Write down these roots on the real number line, as well as the signs of $\frac{p(x)}{q(x)}$ across the intervals determined by the roots. As with non-rational inequations, use test values to determine these signs.

Determine the solution set by checking the sign on the real number line. If the inequation in step 1 is expressed by "$<$" or "$>$", then the intervals of the solution set are open. On the other hand, if the inequation is expressed by "$\geq$" or "$\leq$", then the intervals of the solution set are closed in the endpoints corresponding to the roots of the numerator, and they are open in the endpoints corresponding to the roots of the denominator.

Example 1.6.7 Solve: $\dfrac{x+3}{1-x} \geq -3$

Solution

Step 1. Transposing and factorising:

$$\frac{x+3}{1-x} \geq -3 \Leftrightarrow \frac{x+3}{1-x} + 3 \geq 0 \Leftrightarrow \frac{x+3+3(1-x)}{1-x} \geq 0 \Leftrightarrow \frac{2(x-3)}{x-1} \geq 0$$

Step 2. Find the roots of the numerator and the denominator.

$$2(x-3) = 0 \ \wedge \ x - 1 = 0 \Leftrightarrow x = 3 \ \wedge x = 1$$

Step 3. The test intervals are: $(-\infty, 1)$, $(1, 3)$ and $(3, +\infty)$.

$$\boldsymbol{p(x) = \frac{2(x-3)}{x-1} \geq 0}$$

+ + + + + +	1 - - - - - -	3 + + + + +
$x = 0$	$x = 2$	$x = 5$
$p(0) = \frac{2[(0)-3]}{(0)-1} = +6$	$p(2) = \frac{2[(2)-3]}{(2)-1} = -2$	$p(5) = \frac{2[(5)-3]}{(5)-1} = +1$

The solution set is $(-\infty, 1) \cup [3, +\infty)$.

Keep in mind that the interval $[3, +\infty)$ is closed in 3 because the inequality relation is "$\geq$", and 3 is a root of the numerator. On the other hand, the interval $(-\infty, 1)$ is open in 1, because 1 is a root of the denominator.

Example 1.6.8 Solve: $\dfrac{3x+1}{x-1} \leq \dfrac{2x+7}{x+2}$

Solution

As stated in the last agreement, we will not reference the steps for the sake of brevity.

$$\begin{aligned} \frac{3x+1}{x-1} \leq \frac{2x+7}{x+2} &\Leftrightarrow \frac{3x+1}{x-1} - \frac{2x+7}{x+2} \leq 0 \\ &\Leftrightarrow \frac{(x+2)(3x+1)-(x-1)(2x+7)}{(x-1)(x+2)} \leq 0 \\ &\Leftrightarrow \frac{x^2+2x+9}{(x-1)(x+2)} \leq 0 \end{aligned}$$

Let's find the roots of the numerator x^2+2x+9. As we can see, this is a 2nd degree polynomial. Its **discriminant** is $b^2-4ac = (2)^2 - 4(1)(9) = -32$, which is negative. That means the numerator does not have real roots.

Now, we just need to find the roots of the denominator $(x-1)(x+2)$, which are clearly -2 and 1. Hence, the test intervals are:

$$(-\infty, -2), \quad (-2, 1) \quad \text{and} \quad (1, -\infty)$$

Therefore:

$$f(x) = \frac{x^2+2x+9}{(x-1)(x+2)} \leq 0$$

+ + + + + +	-2	- - - - - -	1	+ + + + +
$x=-3$		$x=0$		$x=2$
$f(-3) = \frac{(-3)^2+2(-3)+9}{[(-3)-1][(-3)+2]}$		$f(0) = \frac{(0)^2+2(0)+9}{[(0)-1][(0)+2]}$		$f(2) = \frac{(2)^2+2(2)+9}{[(2)-1][(2)+2]}$
$= +3$		$= -\frac{9}{2}$		$= +\frac{17}{4}$

The solution set is $(-2,\ 1)$.

Example 1.6.9 Solve: $\dfrac{4}{x} < x \leq \dfrac{20}{x-1}$

Solution

There are two inequations in this expression:

$$\frac{4}{x} < x \quad \text{and} \quad x \leq \frac{20}{x-1}$$

Solution of $\dfrac{4}{x} < x$

$$\frac{4}{x} < x \Leftrightarrow \frac{4}{x} - x < 0 \Leftrightarrow \frac{4-x^2}{x} < 0 \Leftrightarrow \frac{(2-x)(2+x)}{x} < 0$$

The roots are: -2, 0 and 2. Using test values we get:

The solution set of this inequation is $(-2,\ 0) \cup (2,\ +\infty)$.

Solution of $x \leq \dfrac{20}{x-1}$

$$x \leq \frac{20}{x-1} \Leftrightarrow x - \frac{20}{x-1} \leq 0 \Leftrightarrow \frac{x(x-1)-20}{x-1} \leq 0$$

$$\Leftrightarrow \frac{x^2-x-20}{x-1} \leq 0 \Leftrightarrow \frac{(x-5)(x+4)}{x-1} \leq 0$$

The roots are: -4, 1 and 5. Using test values we get:

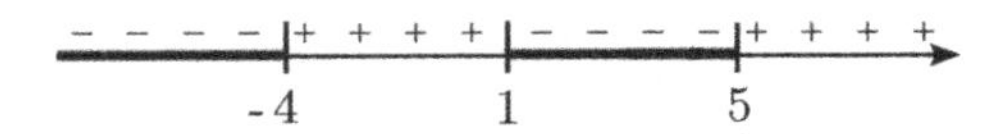

The solution set of this inequation is $(-\infty, -4] \cup (1,\ 5]$.

Final Solution.

The final solution set is the intersection of the partial solution sets:

$$\big[(-2,0) \cup (2,+\infty)\big] \cap \big[(-\infty,-4] \cup (1,5]\big] = \mathbf{(2,\ 5]}$$

Example 1.6.10 **Temperature.**

In certain day, the Celsius temperature of a city changed according to the interval $25 \leq C \leq 40$. In what interval, in Fahrenheit degree (F), did the temperature change on that day? Consider the following Celsius formula to find the result:

$$C = \frac{5}{9}(F - 32)$$

Solution

$$\begin{aligned}
25 \leq C \leq 40 \quad &\Rightarrow \quad 25 \leq \frac{5}{9}(F - 32) \leq 40 \\
&\Rightarrow \quad 25(9) \leq 5(F - 32) \leq 40(9) \quad \Rightarrow \quad 225 \leq 5F - 160 \leq 360 \\
&\Rightarrow \quad 225 + 160 \leq 5F \leq 360 + 160 \Rightarrow \quad 385 \leq 5F \leq 520 \\
&\Rightarrow \quad \frac{385}{5} \leq F \leq \frac{520}{5} \quad \Rightarrow \quad 77 \leq F \leq 104
\end{aligned}$$

Did you know this?

JACQUES CHARLES FRANÇOIS STURM *(1803-1855)*

Sturm was born in Geneva, Switzerland, where he studied mathematics at the Geneva Academy.

In 1833, he became a French citizen and three years later, he was admitted to the Academie des Sciences of Paris, where he maintained close relationship with many leading scientific figures, such as Laplace, Poisson, Fourier and Ampere.

Jacques Sturm

In 1829 Sturm published one of his most famous papers, ***Mémoires sur la resolutión des equations numériques****, in which he developed his famous method described in this section.*

SOLVED PROBLEMS 1.6

Problem 1.6.1 Solve: $x^3 - 5x^2 + 3x + 9 > 0$

Solution

Let's Factorize $p(x) = x^3 - 5x^2 + 3x + 9$.

The possible integer zeros of $p(x)$ are the factors of 9. These are:

$$\pm\mathbf{1} \qquad \pm\mathbf{3} \qquad \pm\mathbf{9}$$

Then:

$$P(-1) = 0 \qquad P(1) = 8 \qquad P(-3) = -72$$

$$P(3) = 0 \qquad P(-9) = -1,152 \qquad P(9) = 360$$

Clearly $p(x)$ has two integer zeros: -1 and 3. We must divide $x^3 - 5x^2 + 3x + 9$ by $x - (-1) = x + 1$:

	1	-5	3	9
-1		-1	6	-9
	1	-6	9	0

Now, we have:

$$p(x) = x^3 - 5x^2 + 3x + 9 = (x+1)(x^2 - 6x + 9) = (x+1)(x-3)^2$$

That is:

$$p(x) = (x+1)(x-3)^2$$

From what we can see, the root $x = 3$ has multiplicity 2. Now, we apply the Sturm method. The test intervals are:

$$(-\infty, -1), \quad (-1, 3) \quad \text{y} \quad (3, +\infty)$$

Therefore:

$$p(x) = (x+1)(x-3)^2 > 0$$

$-\ -\ -\ -\ -\ -$	-1 $+\ +\ +\ +\ +\ +$	3 $+\ +\ +\ +\ +$
$x = -2$	$x = 0$	$x = 4$
$p(-2) = (-2+1)(-2-3)^2$ $= -25$	$p(0) = (0+1)(0-3)^2$ $= +9$	$p(4) = (4+1)(4-3)^2$ $= +5$

The solution set is: $\mathbf{(-1, 3) \cup (3, +\infty)}$.

Problem 1.6.2

One machine produces open metal boxes using rectangular sheets of metal as raw material. Each sheet is 40 *cm.* long and 30 *cm.* wide.

The machine cuts equal-sized squares from each corner of the sheets, with sides of x *cm*. Then the machine shapes the metal into an open box by folding the sides up. Find the highest possible length x of the side of the squares if the area of the base of each box is at least 600 cm^2.

Solution

If x is the length of the size of the square to be cut out, then:

- Length of the base of the box: $40 - 2x$
- Width of the base of the box: $30 - 2x$
- Area of the base: $(40 - 2x)(30 - 2x)$

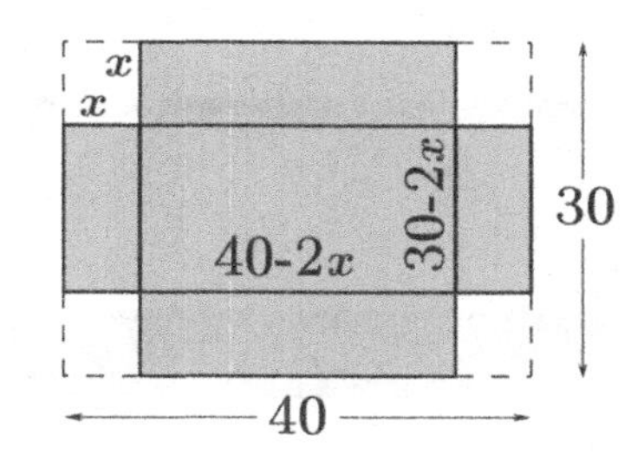

We have that:

$$(40 - 2x)(30 - 2x) \geq 600$$

Let's solve this inequation.

$$\begin{aligned}(40 - 2x)(30 - 2x) \geq 600 &\Leftrightarrow 1,200 - 140x + 4x^2 \geq 600\\ &\Leftrightarrow 4x^2 - 140x + 600 \geq 0\\ &\Leftrightarrow x^2 - 35x + 150 \geq 0\\ &\Leftrightarrow (x - 5)(x - 30) \geq 0\end{aligned}$$

The roots of $(x - 5)(x - 30) = 0$ are $x = 5$ and $x = 30$. Using test values we get:

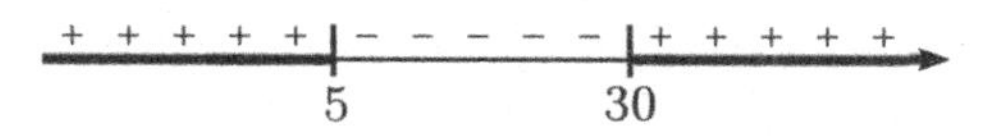

Then, the solution set is: $(-\infty, 5] \cup [30, +\infty)$.

Any solution in the interval $[30, +\infty)$ gives rise to negative values for the width of the base. Thus, for $x = 30$, the width of the base is $30 - 2(30) = -30$; for this reason we must ignore the solutions of this interval.

Hence, the solution set for our problem is $(\mathbf{0},\ \mathbf{5}]$. As expected, the highest possible value of x in this interval is 5, so, the highest length x of the side of the squares is 5 cm.

Jokes in the era of Science

9x-7i > 3(3x-7u)

9x-7i > 9x-21u

-7i > -21u

7i < 21u

i <3u

Inequations can also be romantic

EXERCISES 1.6

In the exercises 1 through 21, solve the inequation. Construct the graph of the solution set.

1. $4x - 5 < 2x + 3$

2. $2(x - 5) - 3 > 5(x + 4) - 1$

3. $\frac{2x-5}{3} - 3 > 1$

4. $\frac{5x-1}{4} - \frac{x+1}{3} \leq \frac{3x-13}{10}$

5. $8 \geq \frac{2x-5}{3} - 3 > 1 - x$

6. $5 < \frac{x-1}{-2} < 10$

7. $(x - 3)(x + 2) < 0$

8. $x^2 - 1 < 0$

9. $x^2 + 2x - 20 \geq 0$

10. $2x^2 + 5x - 3 > 0$

11. $9x - 2 < 9x^2$

12. $(x-2)(x-5) < -2$

13. $(x + 2)(x - 1)(x + 3) \geq 0$

14. $\frac{x-2}{x+2} \leq 0$

15. $\frac{2}{x} \leq -\frac{3}{5}$

16. $\frac{2}{x-1} \leq -3$

17. $\frac{x}{2} + \frac{1}{x} \leq \frac{3}{x}$

18. $\frac{1}{x+1} - \frac{x-2}{3} \geq 1$

19. $\frac{x-1}{x+3} < \frac{x+2}{x}$

20. $\frac{x+1}{1-x} < \frac{x}{2+x}$

21. $\frac{4-2x}{x^2+2} > 2 - \frac{x}{x-3}$

22. One day, the Celsius temperature of a city changed according to the interval $5 \leq C \leq 20$. In what interval did the Fahrenheit temperature change on that day?

23. One day, the Fahrenheit temperature of a city changed according to the interval $59 \leq F \leq 95$. In what interval did the Celsius temperature change on that day?

24. (**Highest length**) One machine produces open boxes using rectangular sheets of metal as raw material. The length and width of each sheet are 52 cm. and 42 cm. respectively.

The machine cuts equal-sized squares with sides of length x cm from each corner of the sheets. Then the machine shapes the metal into an open box by folding the sides up. Find the highest length x of the side of the squares if the area of the base of the box is at least 1200 cm^2.

In the exercises, from 24 to 30, prove the proposition.

25. $a < b \wedge c > d \Rightarrow a - c < b - d$ **26.** $a \neq 0 \Rightarrow a^2 > 0$

27. $a > 1 \Rightarrow a^2 > a$ **28.** $0 < a < 1 \Rightarrow a^2 < a$

29. $0 < a < b \wedge 0 < c < d \Rightarrow ac < bd$

30. $a \neq 0 \Rightarrow a$ and a^{-1} have the same sign (both positive or negative).

31. The **arithmetic mean** of two numbers, a and b, is the number $\frac{a+b}{2}$. Prove that the arithmetic mean of two numbers falls between them. This is, prove that:

$$a < b \Rightarrow a < \frac{a+b}{2} < b$$

32. The **geometric mean** of two positive numbers, a and b, is the number $\sqrt{ab}$. Prove that the geometric mean of two positive numbers is falls between them. This is, prove that:

$$0 < a < b \Rightarrow a < \sqrt{ab} < b$$

33. Prove that $\sqrt{ab} \leq \frac{a+b}{2}$, where $a \geq 0$ and $b \geq 0$. Hint: $0 \leq (a-b)^2$.

SECCION 1.7

ABSOLUTE VALUE

Definition

The **absolute value** of the real number $\boldsymbol{x}$, denoted by $|\boldsymbol{x}|$, is the following real number:

$$|x| = \begin{cases} x, & \text{if } x \geq 0 \\ -x, & \text{if } x < 0 \end{cases}$$

This is, if x is nonnegative ($x \leq 0$), the absolute value of x is the number itself. On the other side, if x is negative ($x < 0$), the absolute value of x is its additive opposite. Since $\sqrt{x^2}$ is the positive square root of x^2, we have that:

$$\boldsymbol{\sqrt{x^2} = |x|}$$

Example 1.7.1 Solve:

1. $|0|$ **2.** $|8|$ **3.** $|-5|$ **4.** $|\sqrt{2}-3|$

Solution

1. $|0| = 0$ **2.** $|8| = 8$ **3.** $|-5| = -(-5) = 5$

4. $|\sqrt{2}-3| = -\left(\sqrt{2}-3\right) = 3-\sqrt{2}$, since $\sqrt{2}-3 < 0$

The next theorem follows from the above definition.

Theorem 1.7.1

1. $|x| \geq 0,\ \forall x \in \mathbb{R}$ **2.** $|x| = |-x|$ **3.** $|x| = 0 \Leftrightarrow x = 0$

4. $-|x| \leq x \leq |x|,\ \forall x \in \mathbb{R}$

5. If $\boldsymbol{a \geq 0}$, then $\boldsymbol{|x| = a \Leftrightarrow x = a}$ ó $\boldsymbol{x = -a}$

Example 1.7.2 Solve the equation: $|x-3| = 1$

Solution

By the property 5 of the theorem 1.7.1, we have:

$$|x-3| = 1 \Leftrightarrow x-3 = 1 \quad \text{or} \quad x-3 = -1 \Leftrightarrow x = 4 \quad \text{or} \quad x = 2$$

Example 1.7.3 Solve the equations:

a. $\mid 2x-3 \mid = 3x-6$ **b.** $\mid 2x-3 \mid = 6-3x$

Solution

a. Since $|2x-3|$ is nonnegative, the expression $3x-6$ must be nonnegative:

$$3x-6 \geq 0 \Leftrightarrow 3x \geq 6 \Leftrightarrow x \geq 2$$

Now, according to property 4 of the previous theorem, we have:

$$2x-3 = 3x-6 \quad \text{or} \quad 2x-3 = -(3x-6) \Leftrightarrow -x = -3 \quad \text{or} \quad 5x = 9$$
$$\Leftrightarrow \quad x = 3 \quad \text{or} \quad x = \frac{9}{5}$$

We discard the solution $x = \frac{9}{5}$ because it does not satisfy the condition $x \geq 2$. Hence, the equation has only one solution, that is $x = 3$.

b. First of all, we must have that:

$$6-3x \geq 0 \Leftrightarrow 6 \geq 3x \Leftrightarrow 2 \geq x \Leftrightarrow x \leq 2$$

Now, according to property 5 of the previous theorem, we have:

$$2x-3 = 6-3x \quad \text{or} \quad 2x-3 = -(6-3x) \Leftrightarrow 5x = 9 \quad \text{or} \quad -x = -3$$
$$\Leftrightarrow \quad x = \frac{9}{5} \quad \text{or} \quad x = 3$$

We discard the solution $x = 3$ because it does not satisfy the condition $x \leq 2$. Hence, the equation has only one solution, that is $x = \frac{9}{5}$.

DISTANCE BETWEEN POINTS ON THE REAL LINE

If $\boldsymbol{a}$ and $\boldsymbol{b}$ are real numbers, then the **distance** between the points a and b in the real line is:

$$\boldsymbol{d(a,\, b) = \mid b - a \mid}$$

Referring back to property 2 of the theorem 1.7.1, we have that:

$$\boldsymbol{d(a,\, b) = \mid b - a \mid = \mid a - b \mid = d(b,\, a)},$$

which confirms what we expected, the distance from a to b is the same as the distance from b to a.

Considering that $\mid x \mid = \mid x - 0 \mid$, we can tell that the number x is located $\mid x \mid$ units away from 0 to the right if $x > 0$, and to the left if $x < 0$.

Example 1.7.4 The distance between 2 and 3 is:

$$d(-2,\, 3) = |3 - (-2)| = 5$$

Theorem 1.7.2 **Properties of absolute value.**

1. If $a > 0$, then $\mid x \mid < a \Leftrightarrow -a < x < a$

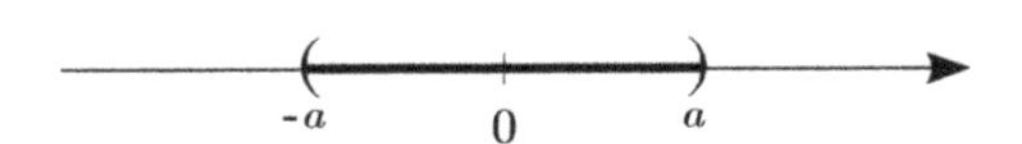

2. If $a \geq 0$, then $\mid x \mid \leq a \Leftrightarrow -a \leq x \leq a$

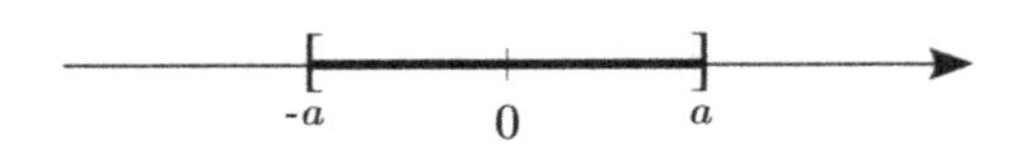

3. $\mid x \mid > a \Leftrightarrow x < -a \;$ or $\; x > a$

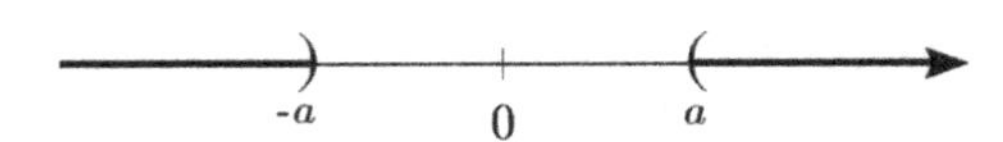

4. $\mid x \mid \geq a \Leftrightarrow x \leq -a \;$ or $\; x \geq a$

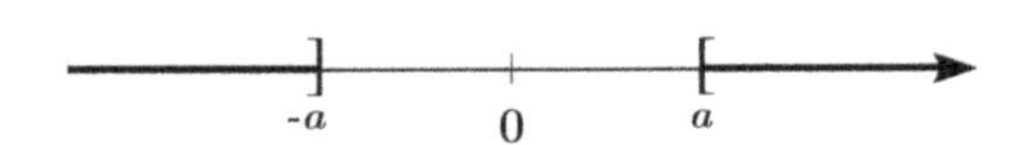

Proof

See the solved problem 1.7.3.

Example 1.7.5 Solve the inequation $\mid 2x - 3 \mid < 5$

Solution

According to property 1 of the theorem 1.7.2, we have:

$$\mid 2x - 3 \mid < 5 \Leftrightarrow -5 < 2x - 3 < 5 \Leftrightarrow -2 < 2x < 8 \Leftrightarrow -1 < x < 4$$

Therefore, the solution set is the interval $(-1,\, 4)$.

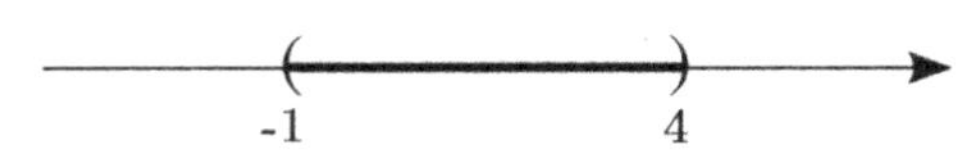

Example 1.7.6 Solve the inequation: $\left|\dfrac{x}{3}-2\right|>4$

Solution

According to part 3 of the theorem 1.7.2, we have:

$$\left|\frac{x}{3}-2\right|>4 \Leftrightarrow \frac{x}{3}-2<-4 \quad \text{or} \quad \frac{x}{3}-2>4 \Leftrightarrow \frac{x}{3}<-2 \quad \text{or} \quad \frac{x}{3}>6$$

$$\Leftrightarrow x<-6 \quad \text{or} \quad x>18$$

Therefore, the solution set is $(-\infty,-6)\cup(18,+\infty)$.

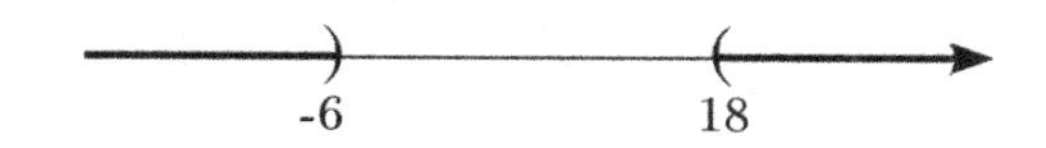

Example 1.7.7 Solve the inequation: $\mid 7x-2 \mid \leq 3x+6$

Solution

Firstly, we must have that:

$$3x+6\geq 0 \Rightarrow x\geq -2 \tag{1}$$

Now, according to property 2 of the theorem 1.7.2, we have:

$$\mid 7x-2 \mid \leq 3x+6 \Leftrightarrow -(3x+6)\leq 7x-2\leq 3x+6$$

$$\Leftrightarrow -3x-6\leq 7x-2 \quad \wedge \quad 7x-2\leq 3x+6$$

$$\Leftrightarrow \quad -10x\leq 4 \quad \wedge \quad 4x\leq 8$$

$$\Leftrightarrow \quad x\geq -\frac{2}{5} \quad \wedge \quad x\leq 2 \tag{2}$$

The solutions of the inequation must satisfy three conditions:

$$x>-2, \quad x\geq -\frac{2}{5} \quad \text{and} \quad x\leq 2$$

Hence, the solution set is the interval $\left[-\frac{2}{5},\,2\right]$.

OTHER IMPORTANT PROPERTIES OF THE ABSOLUTE VALUE

Theorem 1.7.3

If x and y are real numbers, and n is a natural number, then:

1. $| xy |=| x || y |$ **2.** $\left|\frac{x}{y}\right| = \frac{|x|}{|y|},\ y \neq 0$

3. $| x^n |=| x |^n$ **4.** $| x |<| y | \Leftrightarrow x^2 < y^2$

5. Triangle Inequality: $| x + y |\leq| x | + | y |$

Proof

See the solved problem 1.7.4.

Example 1.7.8 Solve the inequation: $\left|\dfrac{x+4}{x-3}\right| < 1$

Solution

Applying the property 2 of the theorem 1.7.3:

$$\left|\frac{x+4}{x-3}\right| < 1 \Leftrightarrow \frac{| x+4 |}{| x-3 |} < 1 \Leftrightarrow | x+4 |<| x-3 |$$

Now, according to property 4 of the theorem 1.7.3, we have:

$$\begin{aligned} | x+4 |<| x-3 | &\Leftrightarrow (x+4)^2 < (x-3)^2 \qquad \text{(property 4)} \\ &\Leftrightarrow x^2 + 8x + 16 < x^2 - 6x + 9 \\ &\Leftrightarrow 14x < -7 \Leftrightarrow x < -\frac{1}{2} \end{aligned}$$

Hence, the solution set is: $\left(-\infty, -\frac{1}{2}\right)$.

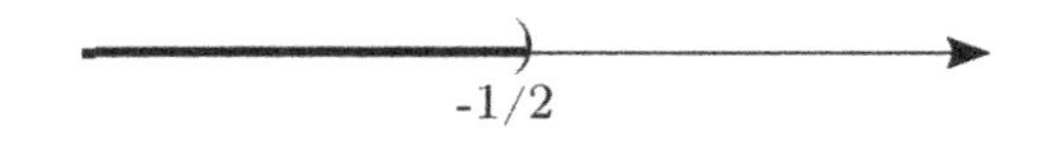

DIVIDE AND CONQUER

We will now introduce a technique that allows us to solve inequations getting rid of the absolute value symbols. You will soon understand the reason behind our decision to give it this name.

This procedure consists of the following steps:

Step 1: Divide the real line by the intervals determined by the zeros of the expressions enclosed by absolute values.

Step 2: Solve the inequation on each interval.

Step 3: Join the above solutions. The solution set of the inequation is the **union** of the partial solution sets obtained in each interval.

Example 1.7.9 Solve the inequation:

$$|\, x+3 \,| < 1 + |\, x-4 \,|$$

Solution

Step 1

We divide the real line in intervals. The zeros of the expressions inside the absolute values are:

$$x+3=0 \ \wedge \ x-4=0 \Leftrightarrow x=-3 \ \wedge \ x=4$$

These zeros divide the real line in the intervals:

$$(-\infty,-3), \quad [-3,4) \quad \text{and} \quad [4,+\infty)$$

-3 4

Step 2

Now, we proceed to solve the inequation in each of these intervals.

In the interval $(-\infty,-3)$: we have $x+3<0 \ \wedge \ x-4<0$.

Therefore:

$$|\, x+3 \,| < 1 + |\, x-4 \,| \Leftrightarrow -(x+3) < 1-(x-4)$$

$$\Leftrightarrow -x-3 < 1-x+4$$

$$\Leftrightarrow -3 < 5 \Leftrightarrow x \in (-\infty,+\infty)$$

The solution set in the interval $(-\infty,-3)$ is:

$$(-\infty,-3) \cap (-\infty,+\infty) = \mathbf{(-\infty,-3)}$$

In the interval $[-3,\ 4)$: we have $x+3 \geq 0 \ \wedge \ x-4<0$.

Therefore:

$$
\begin{aligned}
\mid x+3 \mid < 1+ \mid x-4 \mid &\Leftrightarrow x+3<1-(x-4) \Leftrightarrow x+3<1-x+4 \\
&\Leftrightarrow 2x<2 \Leftrightarrow x<1 \\
&\Leftrightarrow x \in (-\infty, 1)
\end{aligned}
$$

The solution set in the interval $[-3,4)$, is:

$$[-3,4) \cap (-\infty,1) = \mathbf{[-3,1)}$$

In the interval $[4,+\infty)$: we have $x+3>0 \ \wedge \ x-4 \geq 0$.

Therefore:

$$
\begin{aligned}
\mid x+3 \mid < 1+ \mid x-4 \mid &\Leftrightarrow x+3<1+x-4 \Leftrightarrow 3<-3 \\
&\Leftrightarrow x \in \varnothing
\end{aligned}
$$

The solution set in the interval $[4,+\infty)$, is:

$$[4,+\infty) \cap \varnothing = \varnothing$$

Step 3

The **final solution set** is the union of the partial solution sets:

$$(-\infty,-3) \cup [-3,1) \cup \varnothing = \mathbf{(-\infty,1)}$$

1

Example 1.7.10 Find a number M such that:

$$\mid x-2 \mid < 1 \Rightarrow \mid x^2+4x-6 \mid < M$$

Solution

Applying the triangle inequality (theorem 1.7.3):

$$
\begin{aligned}
\mid x^2+4x-6 \mid &< \mid x^2 \mid + \mid 4x-6 \mid \\
&< \mid x^2 \mid + \mid 4x \mid + \mid -6 \mid = \mid x \mid^2 + 4 \mid x \mid + 6
\end{aligned}
$$

This is:

$$| x^2 + 4x - 6 | < | x |^2 + 4 | x | + 6 \tag{1}$$

On the other hand,

$$| x - 2 | < 1 \Rightarrow -1 < x - 2 < 1 \Rightarrow 1 < x < 3 \Rightarrow | x | < 3$$

$$\Rightarrow | x |^2 < 9 \quad \wedge \quad 4 | x | < 12$$

From these inequalities, and the inequality (1), we have:

$$| x - 2 | < 1 \Rightarrow | x^2 + 4x - 6 | < 9 + 12 + 6 = 27$$

The number $M = 27$ meets the required condition.

SOLVED PROBLEMS 1.7

Problem 1.7.1 Solve the equation: $\left| \dfrac{3x-2}{x-2} \right| = 2$

Solution

According to the property 5 of theorem 1.7.1, we have:

$$\begin{aligned}
\left| \frac{3x-2}{x-2} \right| = 2 \quad &\Leftrightarrow \quad \frac{3x-2}{x-2} = 2 \quad &&\text{or} \quad \frac{3x-2}{x-2} = -2 \\
&\Leftrightarrow \quad 3x - 2 = 2(x-2) &&\text{or} \quad 3x - 2 = -2(x-2) \\
&\Leftrightarrow \quad 3x - 2 = 2x - 4 &&\text{or} \quad 3x - 2 = -2x + 4 \\
&\Leftrightarrow \quad x = -2 &&\text{or} \quad 5x = 6 \\
&\Leftrightarrow \quad x = -2 &&\text{or} \quad x = \frac{6}{5}
\end{aligned}$$

Problem 1.7.2 Solve the inequation: $| 3x - 2 | > 2x + 12$

Solution

According to the property 3 of theorem 1.7.2, we have:

$$\begin{aligned}
| 3x - 2 | > 2x + 12 \quad &\Leftrightarrow \quad 3x - 2 < -(2x + 12) \quad &&\text{or} \quad 3x - 2 > 2x + 12 \\
&\Leftrightarrow \quad 5x < -10 &&\text{or} \quad x > 14 \\
&\Leftrightarrow \quad x < -2 &&\text{or} \quad x > 14
\end{aligned}$$

Hence, the solution is $(-\infty, -2) \cup (14, +\infty)$.

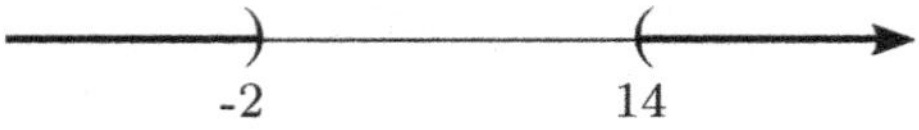

$$\longleftarrow\!\!\!-\!\!\!\rangle_{-2} \qquad \langle_{14}\!\!\!-\!\!\!\longrightarrow$$

Problem 1.7.3 Prove theorem 1.7.2:

1. If $a > 0$, then, $|\, x \,| < a \Leftrightarrow -a < x < a$
2. If $a > 0$, then, $|\, x \,| \leq a \Leftrightarrow -a \leq x \leq a$
3. $|\, x \,| > a \Leftrightarrow x < -a$ or $x > a$
4. $|\, x \,| \geq a \Leftrightarrow x \leq -a$ or $x \geq a$

Solution

1. Since $-x \leq |\, x \,| \;\wedge\; x \leq |\, x \,|$, we have:

$$|\, x \,| < a \Leftrightarrow -x < a \;\wedge\; x < a \Leftrightarrow -a < x \;\wedge\; x < a \Leftrightarrow -a < x < a$$

2. Similar to 1.

3. Since $|\, x \,| = -x \;\vee\; |\, x \,| = x$, we have:

$$|\, x \,| > a \Leftrightarrow -x > a \quad \text{ó} \quad x > a \Leftrightarrow x < -a \quad \text{ó} \quad x > a$$

4. Similar to 3.

Problem 1.7.4 Prove theorem 1.7.3:

If $\boldsymbol{x}$ and $\boldsymbol{y}$ are real numbers, and $\boldsymbol{n}$ is a natural number, then:

1. $|\, xy \,| = |\, x \,||\, y \,|$
2. $\left|\frac{x}{y}\right| = \frac{|x|}{|y|}$, $y \neq 0$
3. $|\, x^n \,| = |\, x \,|^n$
4. $|\, x \,| < |\, y \,| \Leftrightarrow x^2 < y^2$
5. **Triangle inequality:** $|\, x + y \,| \leq |\, x \,| + |\, y \,|$

Solution

1. $|\, xy \,| = \sqrt{(xy)^2} = \sqrt{x^2y^2} = \sqrt{x^2}\sqrt{y^2} = |\, x \,||\, y \,|$

2. Let $\dfrac{x}{y} = z$. Then:

$$x = yz \Rightarrow |\, x \,| = |\, yz \,| \Rightarrow |\, x \,| = |\, y \,||\, z \,| \Rightarrow \frac{|\, x \,|}{|\, y \,|} = |\, z \,| = \left|\frac{x}{y}\right|$$

3. If $n = 0$, then $|x^0| = |1| = 1$ and $|x|^0 = 1$. So, $|x^0| = |x|^0$

$$\text{If } n > 0, \quad |x^n| = |\underbrace{xx x \cdots x}_{n}| = \underbrace{|x||x||x|\cdots|x|}_{n} = |x|^n$$

4. $(\Rightarrow)$

$$|x| < |y| \Rightarrow |x||x| < |x||y| \quad \text{and} \quad |x||y| < |y||y| \qquad (O_4)$$

$$\Rightarrow |x|^2 < |y|^2 \Rightarrow x^2 < y^2$$

$(\Leftarrow)$

$$x^2 < y^2 \Rightarrow |x|^2 < |y|^2 \Rightarrow |x|^2 - |y|^2 < 0$$

$$\Rightarrow (|x| - |y|)(|x| + |y|) < 0$$

$$\Rightarrow |x| - |y| < 0 \Rightarrow |x| < |y|$$

5. We have that:

$$-|x| \leq x \leq |x| \quad \text{and} \quad -|y| \leq y \leq |y|$$

Adding these inequalities:

$$-(|x| + |y|) \leq x + y \leq |x| + |y|$$

Applying theorem 1.7.2 (part 2), we obtain:

$$|x + y| \leq |x| + |y|$$

Problem 1.7.5 Find a number M such that:

$$|x - 1| < \frac{1}{4} \Rightarrow \frac{|x+3|}{\left|x - \frac{1}{4}\right|} < M$$

Solution

$$|x - 1| < \frac{1}{4} \Rightarrow -\frac{1}{4} < x - 1 < \frac{1}{4} \Rightarrow \frac{3}{4} < x < \frac{5}{4}$$

But,

$$\frac{3}{4} < x < \frac{5}{4} \quad \Rightarrow \quad \frac{3}{4} + 3 < x + 3 < \frac{5}{4} + 3 \quad \wedge \quad \frac{3}{4} - \frac{1}{4} < x - \frac{1}{4} < \frac{5}{4} - \frac{1}{4}$$

$$\Rightarrow \quad \frac{15}{4} < x + 3 < \frac{17}{4} \quad \wedge \quad \frac{1}{2} < x - \frac{1}{4} < 1$$

$$\Rightarrow \quad |x + 3| < \frac{17}{4} \quad \wedge \quad \frac{1}{2} < \left|x - \frac{1}{4}\right|$$

Now, we have:

$$|x - 1| < \frac{1}{4} \Rightarrow \frac{|x+3|}{\left|x - \frac{1}{4}\right|} < \frac{\frac{17}{4}}{\frac{1}{2}} = \frac{17}{2} = M$$

EXERCISES 1.7

In the exercises 1 through 9, solve the equation.

1. $|x-5|=4$ **2.** $|2x+1|=x+3$ **3.** $|x-2|=3x-9$

4. $|x-2|=9-3x$ **5.** $|x+4|=|2-x|$ **6.** $|x-1|=|2x-4|$

7. $\left|\frac{3x-2}{2}\right|=|x-4|$ **8.** $\left|5-\frac{2}{x}\right|=3$ **9.** $\left|\frac{x-5}{2x-3}\right|=1$

In the exercises 10 through 26, solve the inequation.

10. $|x-4|<3$ **11.** $|3x+1|<15$ **12.** $\left|\frac{2x}{3}-1\right|<2$

13. $|-3x-2|\leq 4$ **14.** $|5x+2|\geq 1$ **15.** $|-4x-3|>1$

16. $\left|\frac{2x}{5}-2\right|\geq 3$ **17.** $|x^2-5|\geq 4$ **18.** $1<|x|\leq 4$

19. $0<|x-3|<1$ **20.** $|x-1|<|x|$ **21.** $\left|\frac{3-2x}{1+x}\right|\leq 1$

22. $\left|\frac{1}{1-2x}\right|\geq\frac{1}{3}$ **23.** $|x-1|+|x-2|>1$ **24.** $|x-1|+|x+1|\leq 4$

25. $\left|\frac{1}{2+x}\right|<\frac{1}{|x|}$ **26.** $|3x-5|\leq|2x-1|+|2x+3|$

In the exercises 27 through 29, find a number M that satisfies the given inequality.

27. $|x+2|<1\Rightarrow|x^3-x^2+2x+1|<M$

28. $|x-3|<1/2\Rightarrow\dfrac{|x+2|}{|x-2|}<M$

29. $|x-1/4|<1/8\Rightarrow\dfrac{|16x+4|}{1+x^2}<M$

30. Prove:

a. $|x-y|\geq|x|-|y|$.

Suggestion: Apply the triangle inequality to $x=(x-y)+y$.

b. $|x-y|\geq|y|-|x|$ **c.** $||x|-|y||\leq|x-y|$

2

THE CARTESIAN PLANE AND THE LINE

René Descartes (1596 - 1650)

DESCARTES was a French philosopher, mathematician, physicist and writer, widely regarded as one of the great geniuses of the 17th century. He is the author of the famous philosophical statement "*I think, therefore I am*", but is also credited as the father of **Analytic Geometry**.

Enrolling at the Jesuit college La Flèche when he was just eight years old, he quickly distinguished himself as a very bright boy, despite being physically weak. The school authorities allowed him to stay in bed studying during the coldest days of winter to protect his fragile health. Descartes took full advantage of those days to discover the fundamental concepts of Analytic Geometry.

These concepts were also discovered in parallel by his compatriot Pierre de Fermat (1601-1665). Despite this coincidence, it was Descartes who made Analytic Geometry worldwide famous with his book *La Géométrie.*

Descartes moved to Holland in 1628, where he lived 21 years. During this time he wrote the books *Principles of Philosophy, The Discourse on the Method* and *The Meditations on First Philosophy.*

In 1649 Descartes moved to Stockholm, Sweden, to become the philosophy tutor of the vigorous and young Queen Christina. The classes were scheduled at 5 a.m. which unfortunately prejudiced his health. He died of pneumonia one year after his arrival to Stockholm.

NOTEWORTHY SIDE EVENTS

During the life of René Descartes the following important events took place in America: In 1609, the Peruvian chronicler Inca Garcilazo de la Vega, son of an Inca princess and a Spanish conqueror, published *Los Comentarios Reales de los Incas.* In this famous work, he provided accurate historical accounts of the Incas history. In 1630, puritan colonist from England founded Boston. The Harvard University, the oldest institution of higher education in the United States, is founded in 1636 in Cambridge, a town close to Boston.

SECCION 2.1

THE CARTESIAN PLANE

Descartes's greatest achievement was providing a geometric representation for the set $\mathbb{R}^2$, which consists of all ordered pairs (a, b) of real numbers. This is now referred to as **Analytic Geometry**. The set $\mathbb{R}^2$ is represented as follows:

$$\mathbb{R}^2 = \{(a, b)/a, b \in \mathbb{R}\}$$

Observe the geometric representation of an ordered pair (x, y) of $\mathbb{R}^2$ on the figure. The first step in obtaining this representation is to start with an empty plane.

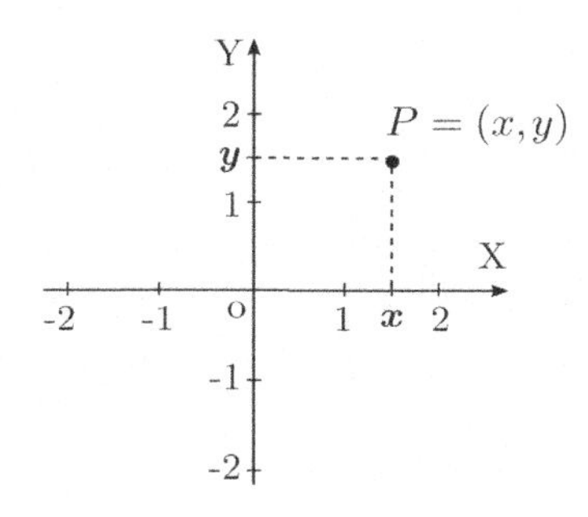

Draw two real perpendicular lines on this empty plane, which are called **Coordinate Axes**. One of this axes will be horizontal, the other vertical. Both intersect at point zero, also called the **Origin**.

Same length is typically used for both lines of the coordinate axes. With that, we have successfully constructed a **Coordinate Plane**.

The horizontal line is often referred to as the **X-axis** and the vertical line as the **Y-axis**. The entire plane is also called a **XY-plane**. The coordinate axes divide the plane in four parts called quadrants, labeled with Roman numbers as **first**(I), **second**(II), **third**(III) and **fourth**(IV).

Now, we establish a one-to-one correspondence between the coordinate plane and $\mathbb{R}^2$. Consider any point $\boldsymbol{P}$ in the XY-plane. If the vertical and horizontal lines through P intersect the X and Y axes at the points with the coordinates a and b, respectively, then P is assigned the ordered pair (a, b).

- The number a is called the **X-coordinate** or **abscissa** of P.
- The number b is called the **Y-coordinate** or **ordinate** of P.
- (a, b) are the **coordinates** of the point P.

We identify P with its coordinates, and write $P = (a, b)$. The **origin** is the point $\text{O} = (0, 0)$.

This coordinate system is called **Rectangular** Coordinate System or **Cartesian** Coordinate System, in honor to René Descartes, its creator. A plane with this coordinate system is called **Cartesian Plane**.

Example 2.1.1 Let $P_1 = (3, 2)$:

a. Find the point P_2 symmetric to the point P_1 with respect to the X-axis.

b. Find the point P_3 symmetric to the point P_1 with respect to the Y-axis.

c. Find the point P_4 symmetric to the point P_1 with respect to the origin.

Solution

a. $P_2 = (3, -2)$

b. $P_3 = (-3, 2)$

c. $P_4 = (-3, -2)$

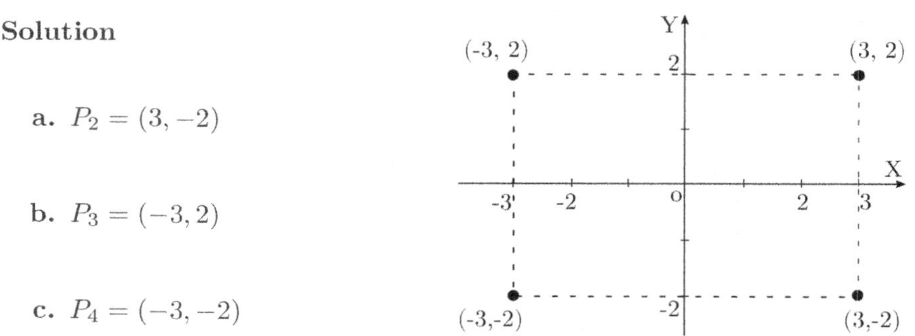

THE DISTANCE FORMULA

Theorem 2.1.1 **The Distance Formula**

Given two points, $P_1 = (x_1, y_1)$ and $P_2 = (x_2, y_2)$ in the plane, the distance between P_1 and P_2 is:

$$\boldsymbol{d(P_1, P_2) = \sqrt{(x_2 - x_1)^2 + (y_2 - y_1)^2}}$$

Proof

If Q is the point at which the horizontal line passing through P_1 intersects the vertical line passing through P_2, then:

$$Q = (x_2, y_1)$$

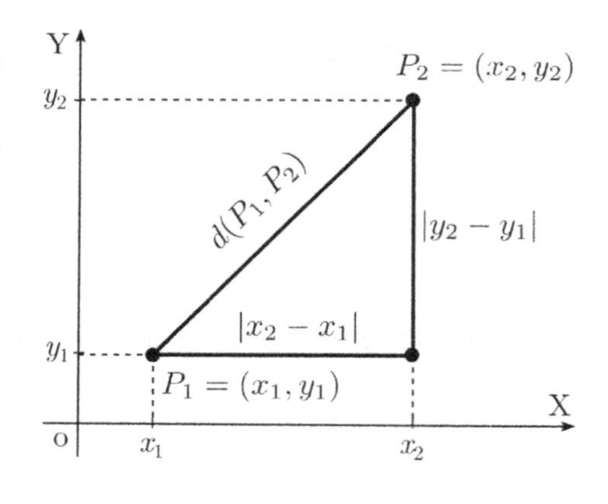

Now, we have:

$$d(P_1, Q) = | x_2 - x_1 |$$

and

$$d(Q, P_2) = | y_2 - y_1 |$$

Since P_1, Q and P_2 are vertices of a right triangle, by the Pythagorean theorem we have:

$$(d(P_1, P_2))^2 = (d(p_1, Q))^2 + (d(Q, p_2))^2$$

$$= | x_2 - x_1 |^2 + | y_2 - y_1 |^2$$

Hence:

$$d(P_1, P_2) = \sqrt{(x_2 - x_1)^2 + (y_2 - y_1)^2}$$

Example 2.1.2

Given the the points $A = (1, 1)$, $B = (3, 0)$ and $C = (4, 7)$, prove that they form a right triangle by using the distance formula.

Solution

We have:

$$d(A, B) = \sqrt{(3-1)^2 + (0-1)^2} = \sqrt{2^2 + 1^2} = \sqrt{5}$$

$$d(A, C) = \sqrt{(4-1)^2 + (7-1)^2} = \sqrt{3^2 + 6^2} = \sqrt{45}$$

$$d(B, C) = \sqrt{(4-3)^2 + (7-0)^2} = \sqrt{1^2 + 7^2} = \sqrt{50}$$

We also have that:

$$d(A, B)^2 + d(A, C)^2 = 5 + 45 = 50 = d(B, C)^2,$$

Then, by the converse of the Pythagorean Theorem, we can assure that $\triangle ABC$ is a right triangle.

THE MIDPOINT FORMULA

Theorem 2.1.2

The midpoint of the line segment with endpoints $P_1 = (x_1, y_1)$ and $P_2 = (x_2, y_2)$ is given by:

$$M = \left(\frac{x_1 + x_2}{2}, \frac{y_1 + y_2}{2} \right)$$

Proof

- Assume that:

$$x_2 > x_1 \text{ and } y_2 > y_1$$

- Let $M = (x, y)$ be the midpoint of $\overline{P_1 P_2}$.
- Cast $\overline{P_1 P_2}$ over the axes.

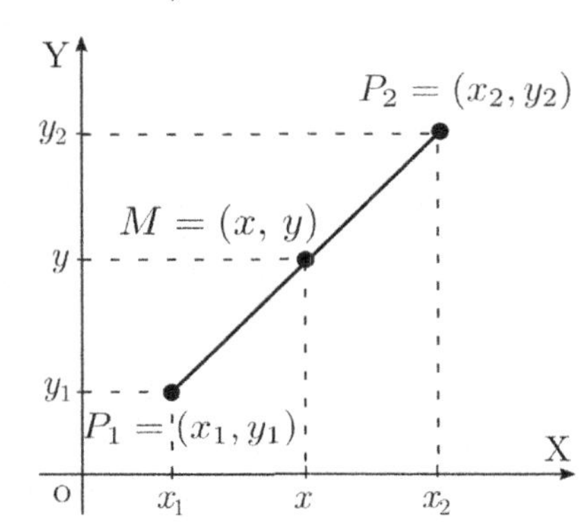

Since $M = (x, y)$ is the midpoint, then x and y are the midpoints of the intervals $[x_1, x_2]$ and $[y_1, y_2]$, respectively. Hence:

$$
\begin{array}{lccc}
 & x - x_1 = x_2 - x & \wedge & y - y_1 = y_2 - y \\
\Rightarrow & 2x = x_1 + x_2 & \wedge & 2y = y_1 + y_2 \\
\Rightarrow & x = \dfrac{x_1 + x_2}{2} & \wedge & y = \dfrac{y_1 + y_2}{2}
\end{array}
$$

Example 2.1.3

Find the midpoint of the line with endpoints $(-3, 0)$ and $(1, 2)$.

Solution

$$M = \left(\frac{-3+1}{2}, \frac{0+2}{2}\right)$$
$$= (-1, 1)$$

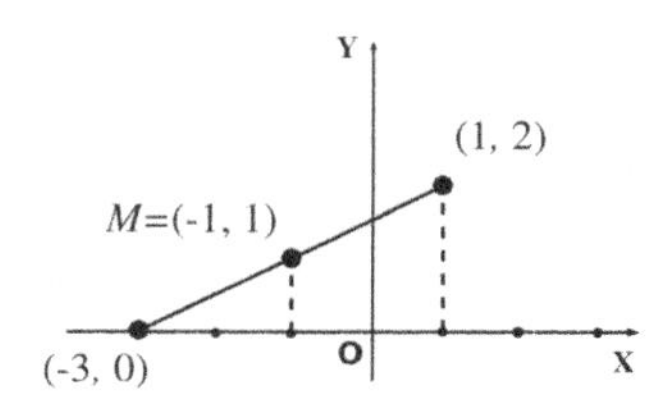

Example 2.1.4

Prove that the midpoint of the hypotenuse in a right triangle is equidistant from the vertices.

Solution

We can take any right triangle. Since the distance between points doesn't vary with translations and reflections, we can assume that one vertex of the right angle is the origin and the cathetus(leg) extends along the positive axes, as shown in the figure.

- One vertex is **O**$= (0, 0)$.
- Let $A = (a,\ 0)$ and $B = (0,\ b)$ be the other two vertices.
- The midpoint of the hypotenuse is:

$$M = \left(\frac{a+0}{2}, \frac{0+b}{2}\right) = \left(\frac{a}{2}, \frac{b}{2}\right)$$

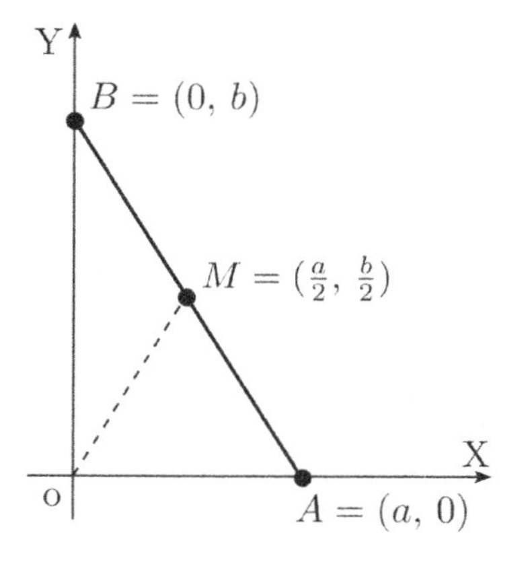

Now, we calculate the distances between M and the three vertices:

$$d(M,A) = \sqrt{\left(a-\frac{a}{2}\right)^2+\left(0-\frac{b}{2}\right)^2} = \sqrt{\left(\frac{a}{2}\right)^2+\left(-\frac{b}{2}\right)^2} = \frac{1}{2}\sqrt{a^2+b^2}$$

$$d(M,B) = \sqrt{\left(0-\frac{a}{2}\right)^2+\left(b-\frac{b}{2}\right)^2} = \sqrt{\left(-\frac{a}{2}\right)^2+\left(\frac{b}{2}\right)^2} = \frac{1}{2}\sqrt{a^2+b^2}$$

$$d(M,\mathbf{O}) = \sqrt{\left(0-\frac{a}{2}\right)^2+\left(0-\frac{b}{2}\right)^2} = \sqrt{\left(-\frac{a}{2}\right)^2+\left(-\frac{b}{2}\right)^2} = \frac{1}{2}\sqrt{a^2+b^2}$$

Clearly, the distances are equal, so the midpoint is equidistant from all the vertices.

Did you know this?

Although, René Descartes is the most prominent name in Analytic Geometry, it was Pierre de Fermat the first to discover the principles of this field. Fermat was a lawyer by trade and also a family man, for whom mathematics was only a pleasant pastime. His works were not formally published, nevertheless, due to its scientific genius, they were widely spread by the French scientific community.

Fermat

Descartes

On the other hand, Descartes was a prominent member of the scientific community, exclusively committed to produce and publish research papers of high content on philosophy and mathematics. Descartes discovered the principles of Analytic Geometry independently of Fermat's work, and formalized his research in 1637, in his book "La Géométrie", almost 8 years after the completion of Fermat's own research.

By then, Descartes was not even aware of the existence of Fermat, who eventually became his mathematical adversary.

SOLVED PROBLEMS 2.1

Problem 2.1.1

Using the distance formula, prove that the three points $A = (-1, 1)$, $B = (3, 9)$ and $C = (5, 13)$ are collinear (lie along the same line).

Solution

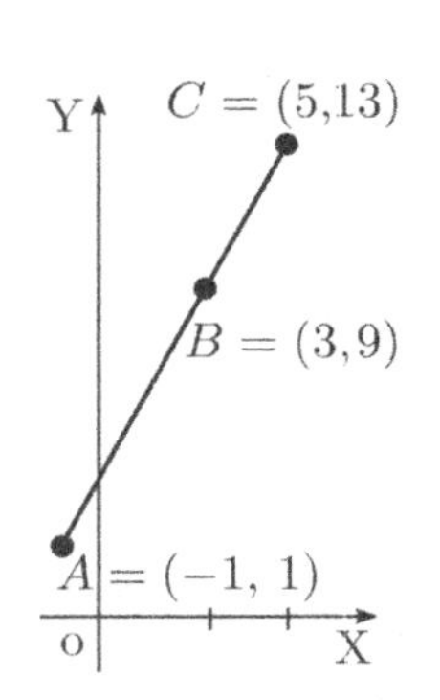

$$d(A, B) = \sqrt{(3+1)^2 + (9-1)^2} = \sqrt{80} = 4\sqrt{5}$$

$$d(B, C) = \sqrt{(5-3)^2 + (13-9)^2} = \sqrt{20} = 2\sqrt{5}$$

$$d(A, C) = \sqrt{(5+1)^2 + (13-1)^2} = \sqrt{180} = 6\sqrt{5}$$

We have that: $d(A, B) + d(B, C) = d(A, C)$.

Hence the three points A, B and C are collinear.

Problem 2.1.2

Let x and y be two variables.

Find an equation that relates both variables, satisfied by the coordinates of all points $P = (x, y)$ equidistant from points $A = (1, 2)$ and $B = (5, -1)$.

Solution

We have that:

$$d(P, A) = d(P, B),$$

then:

$$d(P, A)^2 = d(P, B)^2$$

That is:

$$\begin{aligned}
& (1-x)^2 + (y-2)^2 = (5-x)^2 + (1+y)^2 \\
\Leftrightarrow \quad & 1 - 2x + x^2 + y^2 - 4y + 4 = 25 - 10x + x^2 + 1 + 2y + y^2 \\
\Leftrightarrow \quad & -2x + 1 - 4y + 4 = -10x + 25 + 2y + 1 \\
\Leftrightarrow \quad & 8x - 6y - 21 = 0
\end{aligned}$$

The required equation is $8x - 6y - 21 = 0$. Later on we will describe this equation as a line. Specifically, the perpendicular bisector of the segment $\overline{AB}$.

Problem 2.1.3

If the points $A = (-4, 3)$ and $B = (1, 5)$ are two vertices of a parallelogram, and $M = (2, 1)$ is the midpoint of its diagonals,

a. find the other two vertices.

b. find the length of the adjacent sides to the vertex A.

Solution

a. Let $C = (c_1, c_2)$ and $G = (g_1, g_2)$ be the other two vertices.

Since $M = (2, 1)$ is the midpoint of the diagonal $\overline{BC}$:

$$2 = \frac{c_1 + 1}{2}, \; 1 = \frac{c_2 + 5}{2}$$

$$\Rightarrow \quad c_1 = 3, \; c_2 = -3$$

$$\Rightarrow \quad \boldsymbol{C = (3, -3)}$$

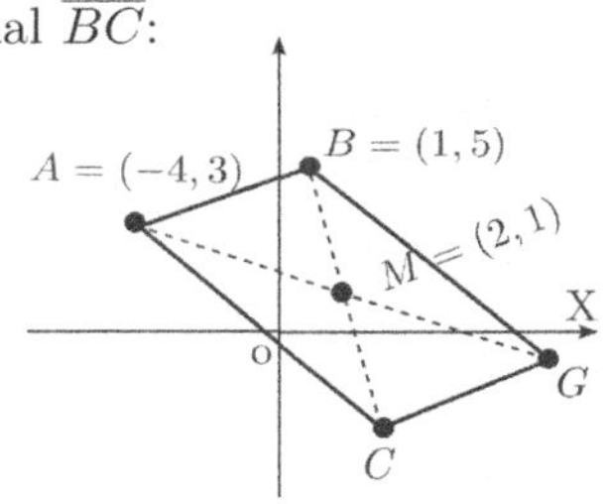

Since $M = (2, 1)$ is the midpoint of the diagonal $\overline{AG}$:

$$2 = \frac{-4 + g_1}{2}, \; 1 = \frac{3 + g_2}{2} \Rightarrow g_1 = 8, \; g_2 = -1$$

$$\Rightarrow \boldsymbol{G = (8, -1)}$$

b. $d(A, B) = \sqrt{(1 - (-4))^2 + (5 - 3)^2} = \sqrt{5^2 + 2^2} = \sqrt{29}$

$d(A, C) = \sqrt{(3 - (-4))^2 + (-3 - 3)^2} = \sqrt{7^2 + (-6)^2} = \sqrt{85}$

Problem 2.1.4

Prove that the segments joining the midpoints of opposite sides of a quadrilateral share a common midpoint.

Solution

Let's take a random quadrilateral. Since the distance between points does not vary with translations and reflections, we can place one vertex on the origin, and one side on the positive X-axis, as shown in the figure.

Let $A = (a_1, a_2), B = (b_1, b_2)$ and $C = (c, 0)$ be the other vertices.

If M, N, R and S are the midpoints of the sides of the quadrilateral, using the midpoint formula, we have:

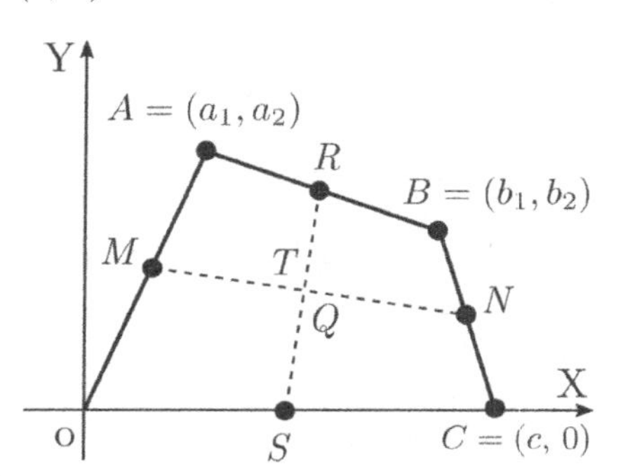

$$M = \left(\frac{a_1}{2}, \frac{a_2}{2}\right), N = \left(\frac{c + b_1}{2}, \frac{b_2}{2}\right),$$

$$S = \left(\frac{c}{2}, 0\right), R = \left(\frac{a_1 + b_2}{2}, \frac{a_2 + b_2}{2}\right)$$

Now, if $T = (t_1, t_2)$ is the midpoint of $\overline{NM}$, then:

$$t_1 = \frac{1}{2}\left[\frac{a_1}{2} + \frac{c + b_1}{2}\right] = \frac{a_1 + c + b_1}{4}, \quad t_2 = \frac{1}{2}\left[\frac{a_2}{2} + \frac{b_2}{2}\right] = \frac{a_2 + b_2}{4}$$

Hence,

$$T = \left(\frac{a_1 + c + b_1}{4}, \frac{a_2 + b_2}{4}\right)$$

On the other hand, if $Q = (q_1, q_2)$ is the midpoint of $\overline{SR}$, then:

$$q_1 = \frac{1}{2}\left[\frac{c}{2} + \frac{a_1 + b_1}{2}\right] = \frac{c + a_1 + b_1}{4}, \quad q_2 = \frac{1}{2}\left[0 + \frac{a_2 + b_2}{2}\right] = \frac{a_2 + b_2}{4}$$

Hence,

$$Q = \left(\frac{c + a_1 + b_1}{4}, \frac{a_2 + b_2}{4}\right)$$

We can see that $T = Q$, meaning that both midpoints coincide.

EXERCISES 2.1

In exercises 1 through 3, calculate the distance between points P and Q, and determine the midpoint of segment $\overline{PQ}$.

1. $P = (0, 0)$, $Q = (1, 2)$

2. $P = (1, 3)$, $Q = (3, 5)$

3. $P = (-1, 1)$, $Q = (1, \sqrt{2})$

4. Prove that the points $A = (-2, 4)$, $B = (-1, 3)$ and $C = (2, -1)$ are collinear.

5. If $A = (-3, -5)$, $M = (0, 2)$ and M is the midpoint of the segment $\overline{AB}$, find B.

6. If $B = (8, -12)$, $M = (7/2, 3)$ and M is the midpoint of the segment $\overline{AB}$, find A.

7. Prove that $A = (2, -3)$, $B = (4, 2)$ and $C = (-1, 4)$ are the vertices of an isosceles triangle.

8. Prove that $A = (4, 1)$, $B = (2, 2)$ and $C = (-1, -4)$ are the vertices of a right triangle.

9. Prove that $A = (1, 2)$, $B = (4, 8)$, $C = (5, 5)$ and $D = (2, -1)$ are the vertices of a parallelogram.

10. Prove that $A = (0, 2)$, $B = (1, 1)$, $C = (2, 3)$ and $D = (-1, 0)$ are the vertices of a rhombus.

11. Prove that $A = (1, 1)$, $B = (11, 3)$, $C = (10, 8)$ and $D = (0, 6)$ are the vertices of a rectangle.

12. Prove that $A = (-4, 1)$, $B = (1, 3)$, $C = (3, -2)$ and $D = (-2, -4)$ are the vertices of a square.

13. Find the points $P = (x, 2)$ such that their distance to the point $(-1, -2)$ is 5 units.

14. Find the points $P = (1, y)$ such that their distance to the point $(-4, 1)$ is 13 units.

15. Find an equation in terms of the two variables, x and y, satisfied by the coordinates of all points $P = (x, y)$ that are equidistant from the points $A = (6, 1)$ and $B = (-4, -3)$.

16. Find an equation in terms of the two variables, x and y, satisfied by the coordinates of all points $P = (x, y)$ with a distance of 3 units from the origin.

17. The midpoints of the sides of a triangle are $M = (2, -1)$, $N = (-1, 4)$ and $Q = (-2, 2)$. Find the vertices.

18. Two adjacent vertices of a parallelogram are $A = (2, 3)$ and $B = (4, -1)$. If the the point $M = (1, -3)$ bisects the diagonals, find the other two vertices.

19. The vertices of a quadrilateral are $A = (-2, 14)$, $B = (3, -4)$, $C = (6, -2)$ and $D = (6, 6)$. Find the intersection point of the diagonals.

SECCION 2.2

EQUATION GRAPHS. SYMMETRY AND TRANSLATIONS

Definition The **graph** of a two-variable equation $F(x, y) = 0$ is the set:

$$G = \{(x, y) \in \mathbb{R}^2 / F(x, y) = 0\}$$

Two equations are **equivalent** if they share the same solutions; thus, the equations $y = \frac{x}{2}$ and $2y = x$ are equivalent. Equivalent equations also share the same graph.

In general, sketching the graph of an equation is not a simple task. It requires good understanding of derivatives, a topic covered in the course of Differential Calculus. Yet, if the equation is not too complex, its graph could be sketched by plotting some key points.

Among these points, are the ones where the graph intersects the axes. The abscissas of the points where the graph cuts the X-axis are called **abscissas at the origin**. These can be found replacing $y = 0$ in the equation. Similarly, the ordinates of the points where the graph cuts the Y-axis are called **ordinates at the origin**; they can be found by replacing $x = 0$ in the equation.

Example 2.2.1 Sketch the graph of the equation: $y = x$

Solution

Intersection with the x-axis:

$$y = 0 \Rightarrow x = 0$$

Hence, the graph intersects the x-axis at the point $(0, 0)$.

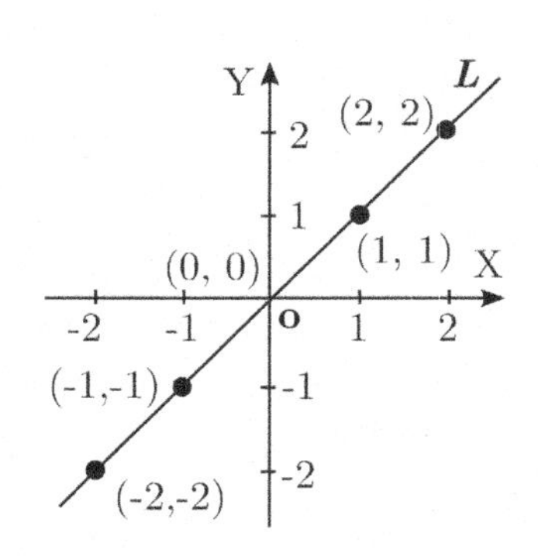

Intersection with the y-axis:

$$x = 0 \Rightarrow y = 0$$

Hence, the graph intersects the y-axis at the point $(0, 0)$.

The following table provides additional points.

x	-2	-1	0	1	2	3
y	-2	-1	0	1	2	3

The graph of $y = x$ is the line L, called the **main diagonal** or the **principal diagonal** of the plane.

Example 2.2.2 Sketch the graph of the equation: $y = x^2$

Solution

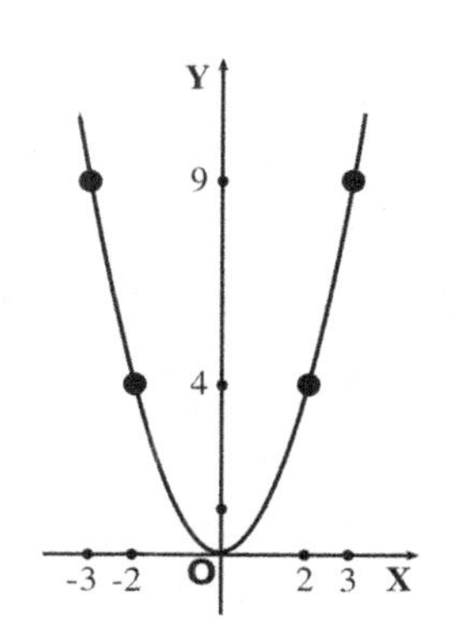

Intersection with the x-axis:

$$y = 0 \Rightarrow x^2 = 0 \Rightarrow x = 0$$

Hence, the graph intersects the x-axis at the point $(0, 0)$.

Intersection with the y-axis:

$$x = 0 \Rightarrow y = 0^2 = 0$$

Hence, the graph intersects the Y-axis at the point $(0, 0)$.

The following table provides additional points.

x	-3	-2	0	1	2	3
y	9	4	0	1	4	9

This curve is called a **parabola** with vertex at the origin. In Chapter 3, we will analyze this curve in more depth.

Example 2.2.3 Sketch the graph of the equation: $x^2 + 4y^2 = 4$.

Solution

We must create a table that provides some points where the coordinates satisfy this equation. First, let's find the intersections with the axes.

Intersection with the X-axis:

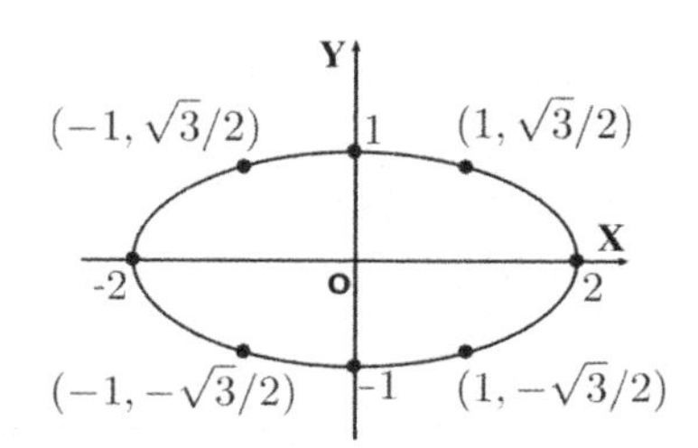

$$y = 0 \Rightarrow x^2 + 4(0)^2 = 4$$

$$\Rightarrow x = 2 \quad \text{or} \quad x = -2$$

Hence, the graph cuts the X-axis at the points: $(2, 0)$ and $(-2, 0)$.

Intersection with the y-axis:

$$x = 0 \Rightarrow (0)^2 + 4y^2 = 4$$
$$\Rightarrow y = 1 \quad \text{or} \quad y = -1$$

Hence, the graph cuts the X-axis at the points $(0, 1)$ and $(0, -1)$.

To obtain other points, we must give some values to x and y. Then, we clear the corresponding values of x or y in the resulting equation. The following table provides some of these points.

x	-2	-1	0	1	2
y	0	$\pm\sqrt{3}/2$	± 1	$\pm\sqrt{3}/2$	0

This curve is called a **ellipse**. We will also meet her again in chapter 3.

SYMMETRIES AND REFLECTIONS

Given two points, $\boldsymbol{A}$ and $\boldsymbol{B}$, we can state that both are **symmetric** with respect to the line $\boldsymbol{L}$ if L is the perpendicular bisector of the segment $\overline{\boldsymbol{AB}}$. In this case, the line L is the **line of symmetry** or **axis of symmetry**.

In the figure, $\boldsymbol{M}$ is the midpoint of the segment $\overline{\boldsymbol{AB}}$.

If we consider line L as a mirror, then, the point B is the reflection of the point A on the mirror.

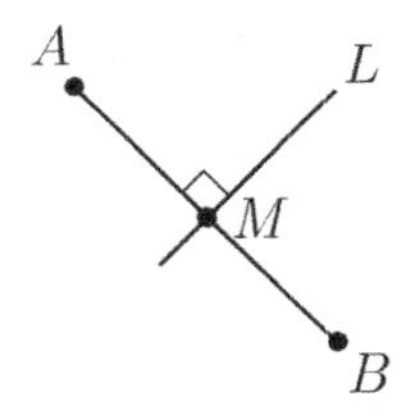

Two points $\boldsymbol{A}$ and $\boldsymbol{B}$ are **symmetric with respect to a point O** if O is the midpoint of the segment $\overline{AB}$, that is, O is the **center of symmetry**.

Definition **Symmetry.**

a. A graph is symmetric with respect to a line, known as the line of symmetry, if there exists another point on the graph for every given point such that they are symmetric with respect to the line.

b. A graph is symmetric with respect to a point, known as the center of symmetry, if there exists another point on the graph for every given point such that they are symmetric with respect to the original point.

Theorem 2.2.1

An equation of the **circle** with center $\boldsymbol{C = (h, k)}$ and radius $\boldsymbol{r}$ is:

$$\boldsymbol{(x-h)^2 + (y-k)^2 = r^2}$$

Particularly, if the center is the origin $\boldsymbol{(0, 0)}$, and r is the radius, then:

$$\boldsymbol{x^2 + y^2 = r^2}$$

Proof

$P = (x, y)$ is at the circle if and only if:

$$d(P, C) = r \Leftrightarrow \sqrt{(x-h)^2 + (y-h)^2} = r \Leftrightarrow (x-h)^2 + (y-k)^2 = r^2$$

Example 2.2.6

Find an equation of the circle with center $C = (2,\ 1)$ and radius 3.

Solution

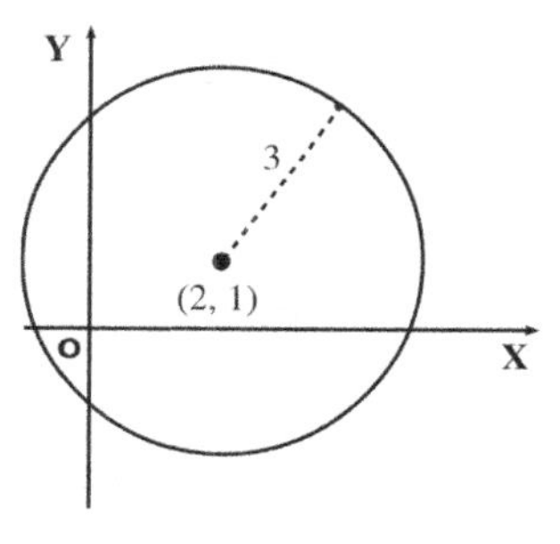

According to Theorem 2.2.1, the **standard form** of the equation of this circle is:

$$(x-2)^2 + (y-1)^2 = 3^2$$

Squaring terms and simplifying the equation, we get the **general form** of the equation of this circle. That is:

$$x^2 + y^2 - 4x - 2y - 4 = 0$$

TRANSLATION

If you take a closer look at the above figure, you will notice that the circle $(x-h)^2 + (y-k)^2 = r^2$, with center (h, k), can be obtained by performing a translation of the circle $x^2 + y^2 = r^2$, centered at the origin $(0, 0)$.

We can carry out the translation of the origin $(0, 0)$ to the point (h, k) as follows:

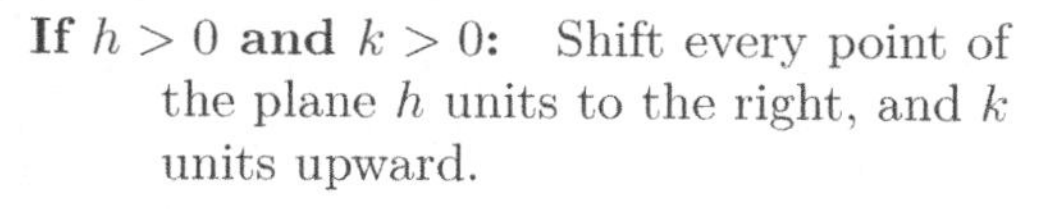

If $h > 0$ and $k > 0$: Shift every point of the plane h units to the right, and k units upward.

If $h < 0$ and $k < 0$: Shift every point of the plane $|\ h\ |$ units to the left, and $|\ k\ |$ units downward.

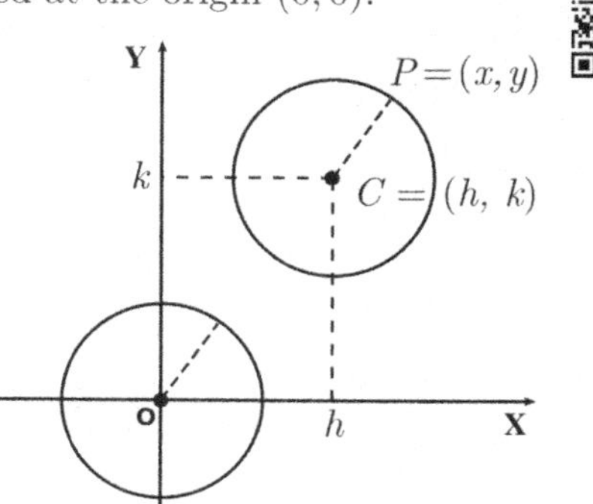

The above observation is synthesized in what is known as the *Translation Criterion*.

TRANSLATION CRITERION

The graph of the equation $\boldsymbol{F(x-h,\, y-k)=0}$ is obtained from the graph of the equation $\boldsymbol{F(x,\, y)=0}$ by the translation that takes the **origin** to the point $\boldsymbol{(h,\, k)}$.

Example 2.2.7 Graph the equation:

$$x^2 - 2x + 4y^2 + 16y + 13 = 0$$

Solution

Completing squares:

$$\begin{aligned}
& x^2 - 2x + 4y^2 + 16y + 13 = 0 \\
\Leftrightarrow\ & (x^2 - 2x + \quad) + (4y^2 + 16y + \quad) = -13 \\
\Leftrightarrow\ & (x^2 - 2x + \quad) + 4(y^2 + 4y + \quad) = -13 \\
\Leftrightarrow\ & (x^2 - 2x + 1) + 4(y^2 + 4y + 4) = -13 + 1 + 16 \\
\Leftrightarrow\ & (x-1)^2 + 4(y+2)^2 = 4 \\
\Leftrightarrow\ & (x-1)^2 + 4(y-(-2))^2 = 4
\end{aligned}$$

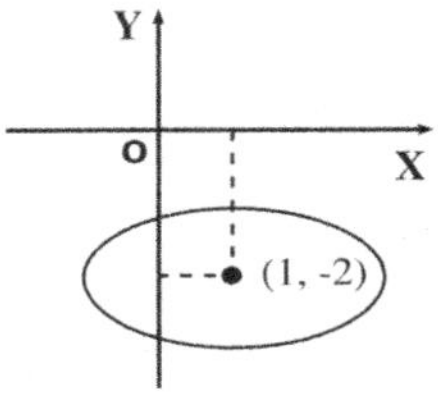

Hence, the graph of the equation $x^2 - 2x + 4y^2 + 16y + 13 = 0$ is obtained from the graph of the equation $x^2 + 4y^2 = 4$ (drawn in the example 2.2.2) by translating the origin to the point $(h, k) = (1, -2)$.

SOLVED PROBLEMS 2.2

Problem 2.2.1

Find the equation of the circle with a diameter equal to segment $\overline{AB}$, where $A = (-2, 1)$ and $B = (4, 7)$.

Solution

The center of the circle is the midpoint of $\overline{AB}$. Hence the center is:

$$M = \left(\frac{-2+4}{2}, \frac{1+7}{2}\right) = (1,\, 4)$$

The radius of the circle is the distance between M and the endpoint B of $\overline{AB}$. So:

$$r = d(M, B) = \sqrt{(4-1)^2 + (7-4)^2} = \sqrt{18}$$

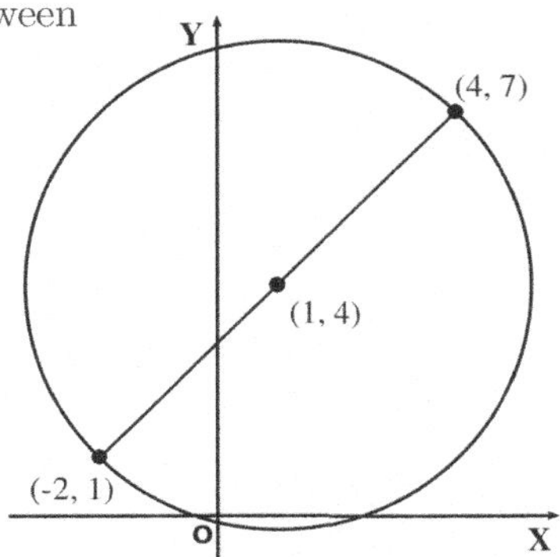

Hence, an equation of the circle is:

$$(x-1)^2 + (y-4)^2 = 18$$

or

$$x^2 + y^2 - 2x - 8y - 1 = 0$$

Problem 2.2.2

Find an equation of the circle that passes through the points $Q = (2, -2)$ and $S = (6, -4)$, and have radius $\sqrt{10}$.

Solution

Let $C = (h, k)$ be the center of the circle. Since Q and S are points of the circle, we have that:

$$d(C, Q) = r \quad \text{and} \quad d(C, S) = r$$

$$\Rightarrow \quad d(C, Q)^2 = r^2 \quad \text{and} \quad d(C, S)^2 = r^2$$

$\Rightarrow$

$$(h-2)^2 + (k+2)^2 = 10$$

and

$$(h-6)^2 + (k+4)^2 = 10$$

$\Rightarrow$

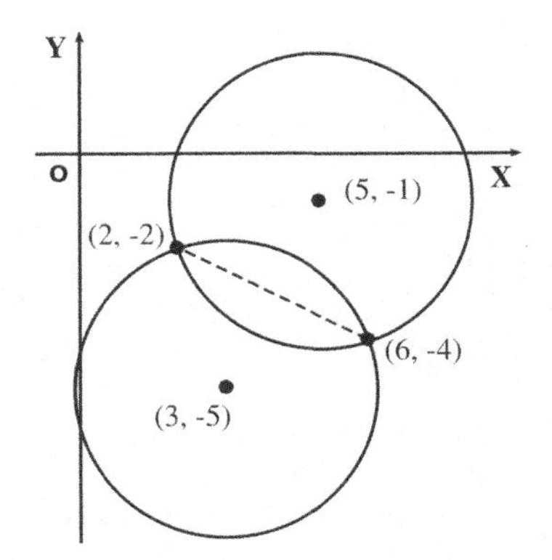

$$h^2 + k^2 - 4h + 4k - 2 = 0 \quad \textbf{(a)}$$

and

$$h^2 + k^2 - 12h + 8k + 42 = 0 \quad \textbf{(b)}$$

Subtracting equation (a) from equation (b):

$$-8h + 4k + 44 = 0 \Rightarrow -2h + k + 11 = 0 \Rightarrow k = 2h - 11$$

Replacing this value of k in (a):

$$\begin{aligned} h^2 + (2h-11)^2 - 4h + 4(2h-11) - 2 = 0 \quad &\Rightarrow \quad 5h^2 - 40h + 75 = 0 \\ \Rightarrow \quad h^2 - 8h + 15 = 0 \quad &\Rightarrow \quad (h-5)(h-3) = 0 \\ &\Rightarrow \quad h = 5 \quad \text{or} \quad h = 3 \end{aligned}$$

If $h = 5$, then $k = 2(5) - 11 = -1$ and $C = (5, -1)$.

If $h = 3$, then $k = 2(3) - 11 = -5$ and $C = (3, -5)$.

We have two solutions, one for each C center found, these are:

$$(x-5)^2 + (y+1)^2 = 10 \qquad \text{and} \qquad (x-3)^2 + (y+5)^2 = 10$$

Problem 2.2.3

Graph the following equations using the translation and inversion criteria:

a. $xy^2 = 4a^2(2a - x)$ **b.** $x = -y^2$ **c.** $x - 3 = -(y-2)^2$

Solution

a. $xy^2 = 4a^2(2a - x)$ is obtained from the equation of the Witch of Agnesi, example 2.2.4 (Part a):

$$yx^2 = 4a^2(2a - y)$$

This is fulfilled by swapping the variables x and y. Hence, the graph of $xy^2 = 4a^2(2a - x)$ is the reflection of the graph of the Witch of Agnesi over the main diagonal.

b. We obtained the graph of $x = y^2$ in the example 2.2.5. We also have that $x = -y^2 \Rightarrow -x = y^2$. This equation can be obtained from $x = y^2$ by swapping x and y. Hence, the graph of $x = -y^2$ or $-x = y^2$ is obtained by reflecting the graph of $x = y^2$ over the Y-axis.

c. The graph of $x - 3 = -(y-2)^2$ is obtained from the graph of $x = -y^2$ by translating the origin to the point (3, 2).

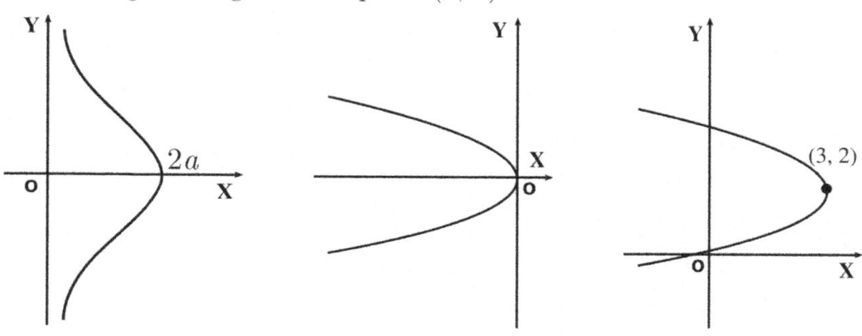

a. $xy^2 = 4a^2(2a - x)$ **b.** $x = -y^2$ **c.** $x - 3 = -(y-2)^2$

EXERCISES 2.2

In exercises 1 through 7, use the test of symmetry to determine if the graph of the equation is symmetric with respect to the X-axis, Y-axis, or the origin.

1. $y = x^2$ **2.** $xy = 1$ **3.** $\frac{x^2}{4} + \frac{y^2}{9} = 1$ **4.** $\frac{x^2}{4} - \frac{y^2}{9} = 1$

5. $y^2(2 - x) = x^3$ **6.**$x^2 + y^2 + x = \sqrt{x^2 + y^2}$ **7.** $(x^2 + y^2)^2 = x^2 - y^2$

In the exercises 8 through 16, find an equation of the circle satisfying the given conditions.

8. Center $(2, -1)$; $r = 5$

9. Center $(-3, 2)$; $r = \sqrt{5}$

10. Center in the origin, pass through $(-3, 4)$

11. Center $(1, -1)$, pass through $(6, 4)$

12. Center $(1, -3)$, is tangent to the X-axis.

13. Center $(-4, 1)$, is tangent to the Y-axes.

14. A diameter with endpoints: $(2, 4)$ and $(4, -2)$

15. Radius $r = 1$ pass through: $(1, 1)$ and $(1, -1)$

16. Passing through the points $(0, 0)$, $(0, 8)$ and $(6, 0)$

In exercises 17 through 22, prove that the equation corresponds to a circle by finding its center and radius.

17. $x^2 + y^2 - 2x - 3 = 0$

18. $x^2 + y^2 + 4y - 4 = 0$

19. $x^2 + y^2 + y = 0$

20. $x^2 + y^2 - 2x + 4y - 4 = 0$

21. $2x^2 + 2y^2 - x + y - 1 = 0$

22. $16x^2 + 16y^2 - 48x - 16y - 41 = 0$

In the exercises 23, 24 and 25 graph the equations applying the translation criterion to the semi-cubical parabola (ex. 2.2.7-b).

23. $(y - 1)^2 = (x + 1)^3$ **24.** $(x - 1)^2 = (y + 1)^3$ **25.** $(y + 1)^2 = (x - 1)^3$

In the exercises 26 through 28, graph the equation applying the translation and inversion criteria to the graph of the Agnesi Witch (example 2.2.7-a).

26. $(x - 3)^2(y - 2) = 4(4 - y)$

27. $(y - 3)^2(x - 2) = 4(4 - x)$

28. $(x + 3)^2(y + 2) = 4(-y)$

SECCION 2.3

LINES AND LINEAR EQUATIONS

A **linear equation in two variables**, x and y, is an equation of the form:

$$\boldsymbol{Ax + By + C = 0}, \text{ where } \boldsymbol{A \neq 0} \text{ or } \boldsymbol{B \neq 0}$$

The graph of a linear equation in two variables is always a line. Conversely, any equation that represents a line is a linear equation in two variables. Let's explore the different forms this equation can take.

THE SLOPE OF A LINE

Assume we are moving along a line L from the point $P_1 = (x_1, y_1)$ to the point $P_2 = (x_2, y_2)$. The vertical change $y_2 - y_1$ is called the **rise**; and the horizontal change $x_2 - x_1$ is called the **run**.

Observe that:

- L is a vertical line $\Leftrightarrow$ the run is:

$$x_2 - x_1 = 0$$

- L is a horizontal line $\Leftrightarrow$ if the rise is:

$$y_2 - y_1 = 0$$

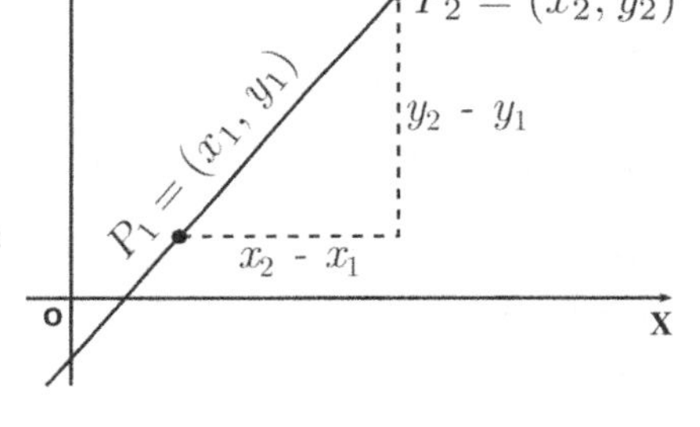

This leads to the following definition.

Definition

The **slope** of a non vertical line L passing through the points $P_1 = (x_1, y_1)$ and $P_2 = (x_2, y_2)$ is given by the formula:

$$m = \frac{\boldsymbol{y_2 - y_1}}{\boldsymbol{x_2 - x_1}} = \frac{\text{Rise}}{\text{Run}}$$

Remark

- The slope of a vertical line is not defined. This occurs when $x_2 - x_1 = 0$.
- We also have that:

$$m = \frac{y_1 - y_2}{x_1 - x_2} \qquad \text{since,} \qquad \frac{y_1 - y_2}{x_1 - x_2} = \frac{y_2 - y_1}{x_2 - x_1}$$

However: $m \neq \dfrac{y_2 - y_1}{x_1 - x_2} \quad \wedge \quad m \neq \dfrac{y_1 - y_2}{x_2 - x_1}$

- The slope of a line, denoted by m, remains constant regardless of the specific pair of points chosen to calculate it. In other words, if we have another pair points of L, $P_1' = (x_1', y_1')$ and $P_2' = (x_2', y_2')$, then, using a similar triangles argument, we have:

$$m = \frac{y_2 - y_1}{x_2 - x_1} = \frac{y_2' - y_1'}{x_2' - x_1'}$$

- The slope m of a line gives the number of units that the line goes up ($m > 0$) or down ($m < 0$) for each horizontal unit moving to the right.

The line is horizontal if $m = 0$.

The line is oblique if $m \neq 0$.

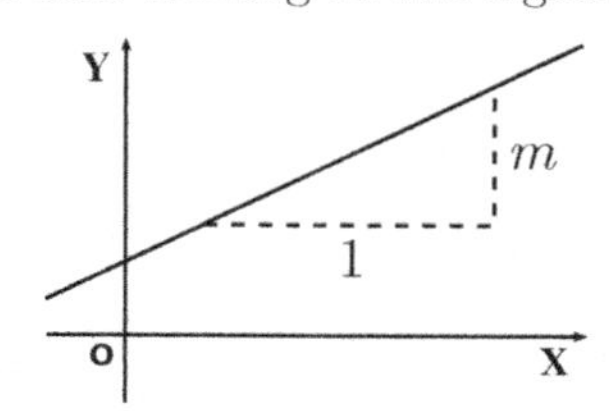

Example 2.3.1

Find the slope of the line passing through the points $P_1 = (1, -2)$ and $P_2 = (3, 4)$.

Solution

$$m = \frac{4 - (-2)}{3 - 1} = \frac{6}{2} = 3, \quad \text{or} \quad m = \frac{-2 - 4}{1 - 3} = \frac{-6}{-2} = 3$$

Theorem 2.3.1 **Point-slope form of the equation of the line.**

The equation of the line with slope $\boldsymbol{m}$ that passes through the point $\boldsymbol{P_0 = (x_0, y_0)}$ is given by:

$$\boldsymbol{y - y_0 = m(x - x_0)}$$

Proof

Let $P = (x, y)$ be another point of the line.

By the definition of slope, we have:

$$\frac{y - y_0}{x - x_0} = m \Rightarrow y - y_0 = m(x - x_0)$$

Example 2.3.2

Find a equation of the line L passing through the points $(-2, 5)$ and $(1, -1)$.

Solution

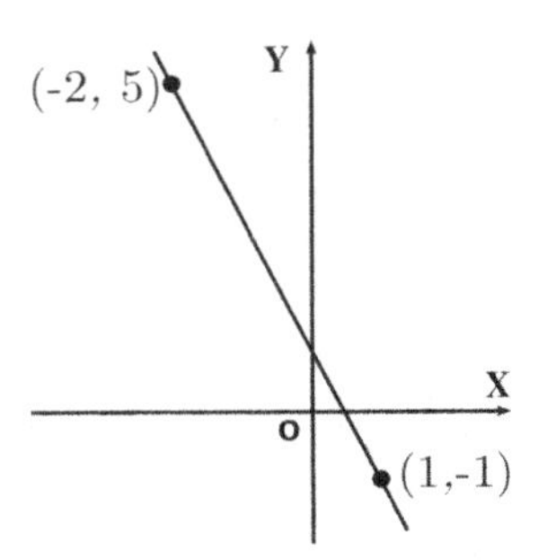

Firstly, let's find the slope of the line L:

$$m = \frac{-1-5}{1-(-2)} = \frac{-6}{3} = -2$$

Now, we must find the point-slope form of the equation of the line.

We can take, as P_0, any of the two given points, $(-2, 5)$ or $(1, -1)$. Thus, if $P_0 = (1, -1)$, then:

$$y - (-1) = -2(x-1) \Rightarrow y + 1 = -2x + 2 \Rightarrow y + 2x - 1 = 0$$

If we take the point $P_0 = (0, b)$ of the point-slope equation, in which the line intersects the Y-axis, then:

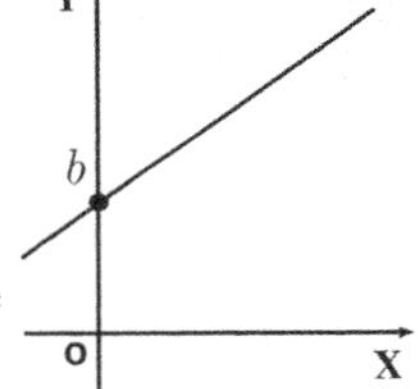

$$y - b = m(x - 0) \Rightarrow y = mx + b$$

This equation is called the **Slope-Intercept** form of the equation of the line.

Theorem 2.3.2 **Slope-Intercept form.**

An equation of the line with slope $\boldsymbol{m}$, passing through $\boldsymbol{(0, b)}$, is given by:

$$\boldsymbol{y = mx + b}$$

VERTICAL AND HORIZONTAL LINES

None of the above line equations describe vertical lines because they do not have a slope. Let us see why.

Assume that a given **vertical line $\boldsymbol{L_1}$** intersects the X-axis at the point $(a, 0)$.

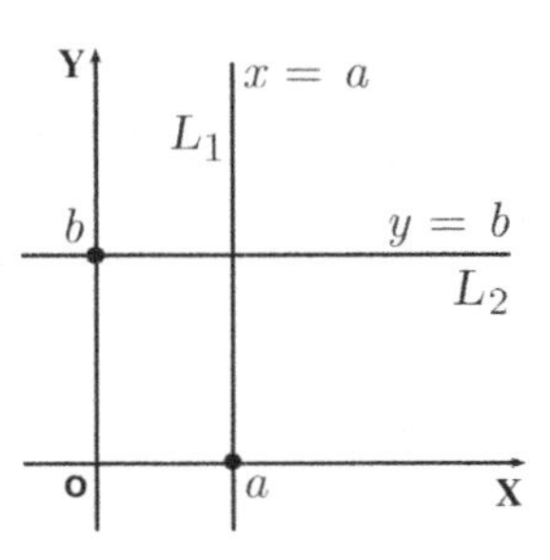

A point (x, y) is in the line L_1 if and only if its abscissa is a. That is, $x = a$. Hence, an equation of this vertical line is $\boldsymbol{x = a}$.

Now, assume that a given **horizontal line $\boldsymbol{L_2}$** intersects the Y-axis at the point $(0, b)$.

The slope of a horizontal line L_2 is $m = 0$. Hence, if we replace $m = 0$ in the slope-intercept form of the equation of the line, we get $\boldsymbol{y = b}$.

The next theorem is a summary of the previous statement.

Theorem 2.3.3 **Equation of a line.**

1. An equation of the vertical line that intersects the X-axis at the point $(a, 0)$ is the following:
$$\boldsymbol{x = a}$$

2. An equation of the horizontal line that intersects the Y-axis at the point $(0, b)$ is the following:
$$\boldsymbol{y = b}$$

Example 2.3.3 Find an equation of the line that:

1. is vertical and passes through the point (-2, 3).

2. is horizontal and passes through the point (-2, 3).

Solution

1. $x = -2$ **2.** $y = 3$

LINEAR EQUATION

A **linear equation in two variables**, x and y, is an equation of the form:

$$\boldsymbol{Ax + By + C = 0}, \text{ where } \boldsymbol{A \neq 0} \text{ or } \boldsymbol{B \neq 0}$$

We know that all the equations corresponding to oblique, horizontal and vertical lines are linear equations. Now we will demonstrate that the converse statement is also true. That is, the graph of a linear equation is a line. In fact, the name "linear equation" derives from this result.

Theorem 2.3.4 The graph of a linear equation:

$$\boldsymbol{Ax + By + C = 0}, \quad \boldsymbol{A \neq 0} \text{ or } \boldsymbol{B \neq 0}, \text{ is a } \textbf{line}. \text{ Moreover:}$$

1. If $A \neq 0$ and $B \neq 0$, the line is **oblique**.

2. If $A = 0$ and $B \neq 0$, the line is **horizontal**.

3. If $A \neq 0$ and $B = 0$, the line is **vertical**.

Proof

Case 1. If $A \neq 0$ and $B \neq 0$, then, isolating y:

$$y = -\frac{A}{B}x - \frac{C}{B}$$

The graph of this equation is a line. Since the slope is $m = -\frac{A}{B} \neq 0$, the line is oblique.

Case 2. If $A = 0$ and $Ax + By + C = 0$, then:

$$By + C = 0 \Rightarrow y = -\frac{C}{B}$$

Hence, the graph is a horizontal line.

Case 3. If $B = 0$ and $Ax + By + C = 0$, then:

$$Ax + C = 0 \Rightarrow x = -\frac{C}{A}$$

Hence, the graph is a vertical line.

Convention

To simplify, we can say "*the line* $Ax + By + C = 0$" instead of "*the line that corresponds to the graph of the equation* $Ax + By + C = 0$".

Example 2.3.4

Given the line $L : 2x - 3y + 12 = 0$, find the slope, ordinate at the origin and the abscissa at the origin of L. Plot the graph.

Solution

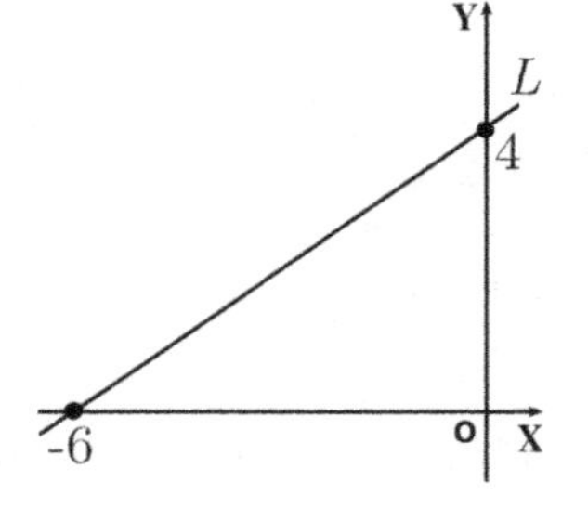

Isolating y: $\quad y = \frac{2}{3}x + 4$

Then, the slope is: $\quad m = \frac{2}{3}$

Replacing $x = 0$ in $2x - 3y + 12 = 0$, we get $\boldsymbol{y = 4}$. Hence, the ordinate at the origin is 4.

Replacing $y = 0$ in $2x - 3y + 12 = 0$, we get $x = -6$. Hence, the abscissa at the origin is -6.

When drawing the graph of a line, it is sufficient to know just two of its points. In this case we already have the pair of points (0, 4) and (-6, 0), obtained from the ordinate and the abscissa at the origin. The graph is plotted by drawing the line joining these points.

Example 2.3.5

Let L_1 be the line passing through the points $P_1 = (4, 6)$ and $P_2 = (5, 8)$. Find the point where L_1 intersects the line L_2: $x + y - 7 = 0$.

Solution

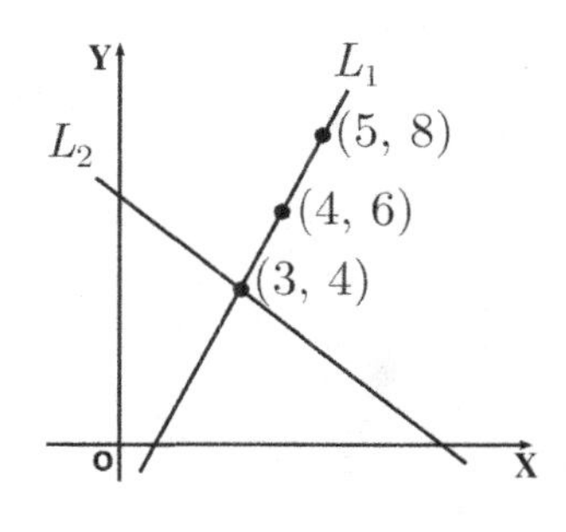

First, we must find the equation of L_1.

Since L_1 passes through $P_1 = (4, 6)$ and $P_2 = (5, 8)$, we have:

$$y - 6 = \frac{8-6}{5-4}(x - 4) \Leftrightarrow y - 6 = 2(x - 4)$$

$$\Leftrightarrow 2x - y - 2 = 0$$

Hence, $L_1 : \ 2x - y - 2 = 0$

The coordinates of the intersection point of L_1 and L_2 must also satisfy the equations of L_1 and L_2. That means we have to solve the system of equations:

$$L_1 : \ 2x - y - 2 = 0$$
$$L_2 : \ x + y - 7 = 0$$

The solution is: $x = 3$ and $y = 4$. Hence, the point of intersection is (3, 4).

PARALLEL LINES

The lines L_1 and L_2 are **parallel** if they do not intersect or if they coincide in every point. That is, L_1 and L_2 are parallel $\Leftrightarrow L_1 \cap L_2 = \varnothing$ or $L_1 = L_2$.

The following theorem translates parallelism in terms of slopes.

Theorem 2.3.5 Let L_1 and L_2 be two lines in a plane.

If L_1 and L_2 are non vertical, with slopes m_1 and m_2 respectively, then:

$$\boldsymbol{L_1 \text{ and } L_2 \text{ are parallel} \Leftrightarrow m_1 = m_2}$$

Proof

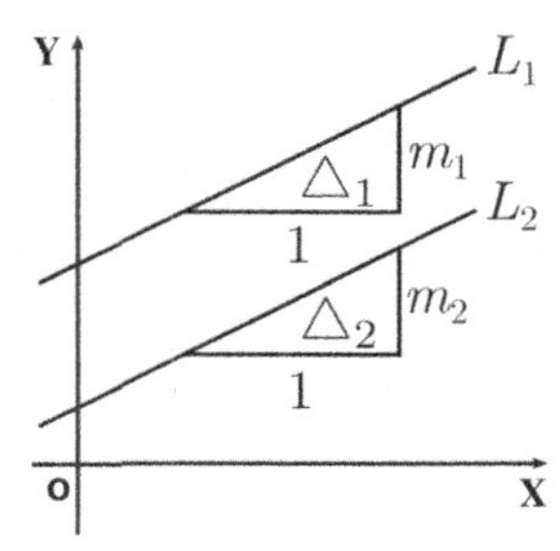

Consider the right triangles $\triangle_1$ and $\triangle_2$ of the figure. We have that:

L_1 are L_2 parallel

$\Leftrightarrow \triangle_1$ and $\triangle_2$ are congruent

$\Leftrightarrow m_1 = m_2$

Example 2.3.6

Find an equation of the line L_1, passing through $P_1 = (-1, 1)$, and parallel to the line L_2: $2x + 3y - 8 = 0$.

Solution

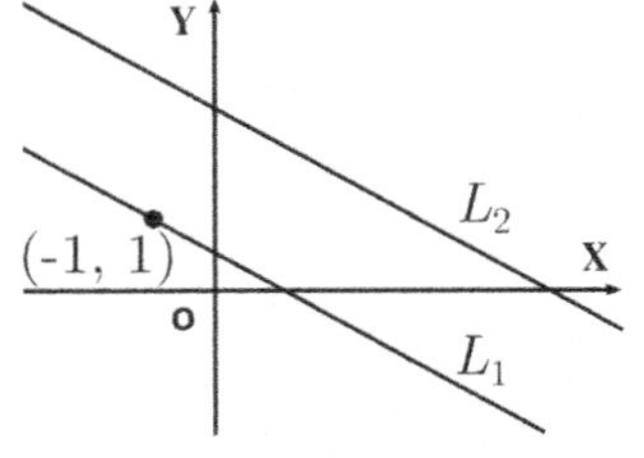

We have that:

$$2x + 3y - 8 = 0 \Leftrightarrow y = -\frac{2}{3}x + \frac{8}{3}$$

Hence, the slope of L_2 is $m = -\frac{2}{3}$

Since L_1 and L_2 are parallel, then, according to the theorem 2.3.5, the slope of L_1 is $m = -\frac{2}{3}$. Moreover, since L_1 passes through $P_1 = (-1, 1)$, we have that:

$$L_1 : \ y - 1 = -\frac{2}{3}(x + 1) \Leftrightarrow L_1 : \ 2x + 3y - 1 = 0$$

PERPENDICULAR LINES

Two lines are **perpendicular** if both intersect each other at a right angle.

The next theorem translates perpendicularity in terms of slopes.

Theorem 2.3.6 Let L_1 and L_2 be two non vertical lines in a plane. If the slopes of L_1 and L_2 are m_1 and m_2 respectively. Then:

$$\mathbf{L_1 \text{ and } L_2 \text{ are perpendicular} \Leftrightarrow m_1 m_2 = -1}$$

Proof

See solved problem 2.3.9.

Example 2.3.7 **Find:**

a. an equation of the line L_1 that passes through $P_1 = \left(\frac{15}{8}, 7\right)$, and is perpendicular to the line $L_2 : 3x - 4y - 12 = 0$.

b. the intersection point of L_1 and L_2.

Solution

a. Let m_1 and m_2 be the slopes of L_1 and L_2, respectively.

By the previous theorem, we have that:

$$m_1 = -\frac{1}{m_2}$$

But:

$$L_2\colon 3x - 4y - 12 = 0 \Leftrightarrow L_2\colon y = \frac{3}{4}x - 3$$

Hence, $m_2 = \frac{3}{4}$, therefore, $m_1 = -\frac{1}{3/4} = -\frac{4}{3}$

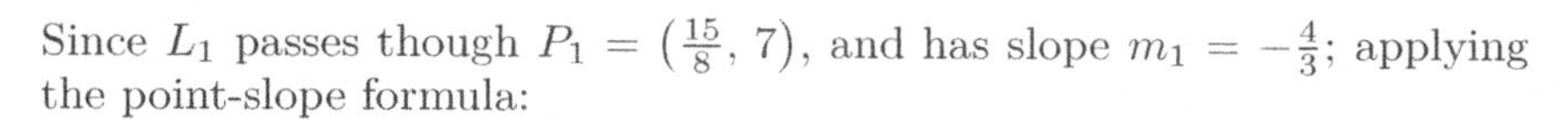

Since L_1 passes though $P_1 = \left(\frac{15}{8}, 7\right)$, and has slope $m_1 = -\frac{4}{3}$; applying the point-slope formula:

$$L_1\colon y - 7 = -\frac{4}{3}\left(x - \frac{15}{8}\right) \Leftrightarrow L_1\colon 8x + 6y - 57 = 0$$

b. Let's solve the system determined by the equations of L_1 and L_2:

$$\begin{aligned} L_1 &: 8x + 6y - 57 = 0 \\ L_2 &: 3x - 4y - 12 = 0 \end{aligned}$$

The solution is: $x = 6$ and $y = \frac{3}{2}$. Hence, the intersection point is $\left(6, \frac{3}{2}\right)$.

DISTANCE BETWEEN A POINT AND A LINE

The **distance** from a point P to a line L is the distance from P to the point Q, where Q is the intersection of L with the perpendicular line to L that passes through P. That is:

$$d(P, L) = d(P, Q)$$

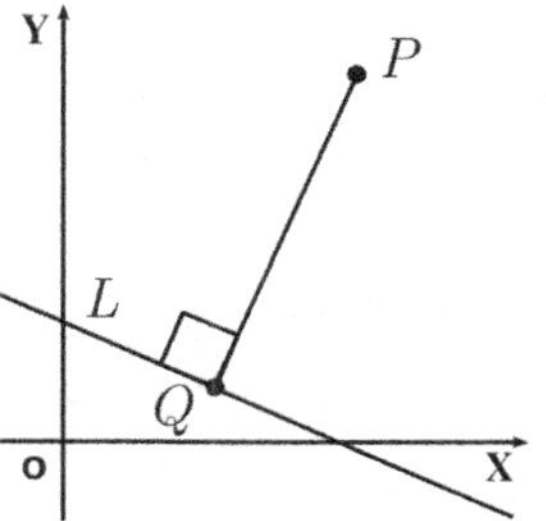

The next theorem presents a simple formula for calculating the distance between a point and a line. The proof is given in the solved problem 2.3.10.

Theorem 2.3.7

The distance from a point $P = (x_0, y_0)$ to the line $L:\ Ax + By + C = 0$ is given by the formula:

$$\boldsymbol{d(P, L) = \frac{|Ax_0 + By_0 + C|}{\sqrt{A^2 + B^2}}}$$

Example 2.3.8 Find the distance from the point $P = (-2, 3)$ to the line:

$$L:\ 3x - 4y - 2 = 0$$

Solution

$$d(P, L) = \frac{|Ax_0 + By_0 + C|}{\sqrt{A^2 + B^2}} = \frac{|3(-2) + (-4)(3) - 2|}{\sqrt{(3)^2 + (-4)^2}} = \frac{20}{5} = 4$$

Example 2.3.9 Find the distance between the parallel lines:

$$L_1:\ 2y - x - 8 = 0 \quad \text{and} \quad L_2:\ 2y - x + 2 = 0$$

Solution

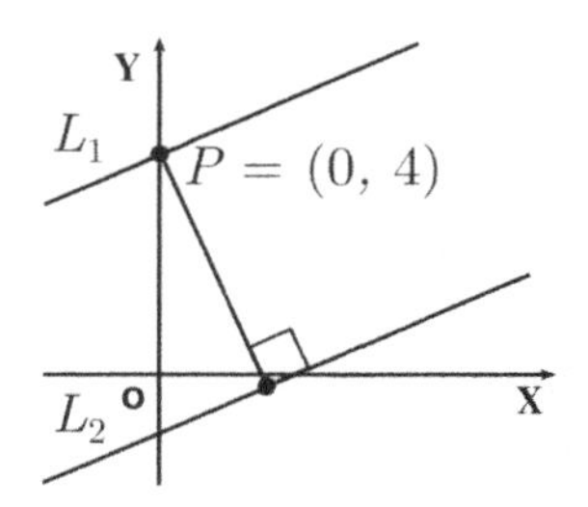

Clearly, the distance between two parallel lines is the distance from any point on one line to the other. In this manner, let's find a point of L_1. For instance, we have the point P where L_1 intersects the Y-axis:

If $x = 0$, then $2y - 8 = 0$, therefore $y = 4$.

Hence $P = (0, 4)$. Now, we have:

$$d(L_1, L_2) = d(P, L_2) = \frac{|(2)(0) + (-1)(4) + (2)|}{\sqrt{(2)^2 + (-1)^2}} = \frac{2}{\sqrt{5}} = \frac{2\sqrt{5}}{5}$$

SOLVED PROBLEMS 2.3

Problem 2.3.1

Using slopes, prove that the points $P_1 = (-3, -3)$, $P_2 = (3, 1)$ and $P_3 = (6, 3)$ are collinear (lie on the same line).

Solution

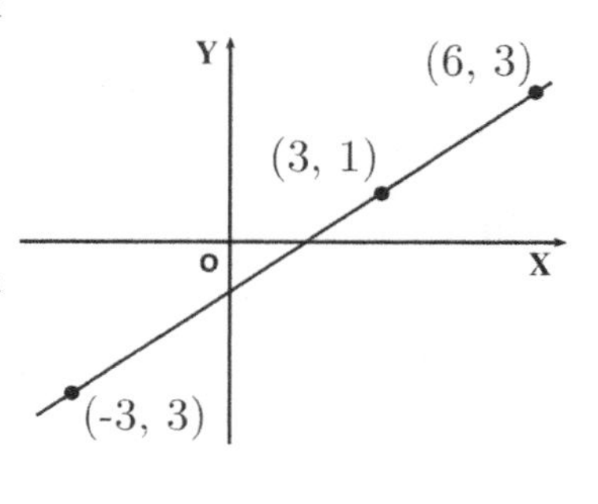

If m_1 is the slope of the line passing through $P_1 = (-3, -3)$ and $P_2 = (3, 1)$, then:

$$m_1 = \frac{1 - (-3)}{3 - (-3)} = \frac{4}{6} = \frac{2}{3}$$

If m_2 is the slope of the line passing through $P_1 = (-3, -3)$ and $P_3 = (6, 3)$, then:

$$m_2 = \frac{3 - (-3)}{6 - (-3)} = \frac{6}{9} = \frac{2}{3}$$

Clearly, if $m_1 = m_2$, the two lines are parallel. Given that these two lines pass through the point P_1, we can certify that both lines coincide; therefore, the three given points are collinear.

Problem 2.3.2 Considering the line L: $y = 5$, find a equation of the line:

a. L_1 passing through the point $P = (-4, 2)$, and parallel to L.

b. L_2 passing through the point $P = (-4, 2)$, and perpendicular to L.

Solution

a. The line $L : y = 5$ is horizontal.

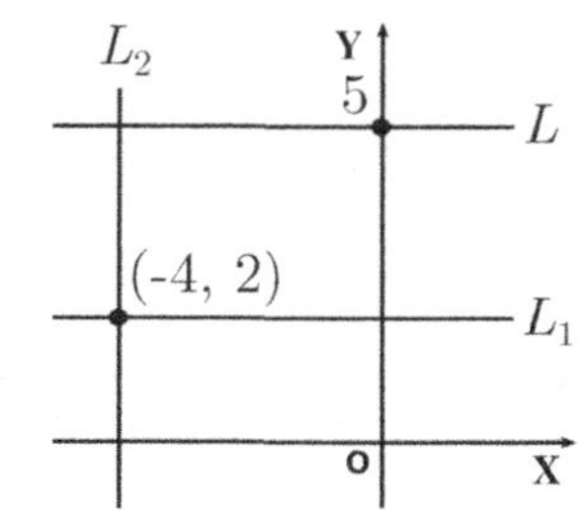

L_1 is parallel to L, then is also horizontal.

Furthermore, since L_1 passes through the point $P = (-4,\ 2)$, an equation for this line is:

$$L_1\colon\ y = 2$$

b. The line L_2 is perpendicular to a horizontal line, therefore, L_2 is vertical.

Furthermore, since L_2 passes through $P = (-4,\ 2)$, an equation for this line is:

$$L_2\colon\ x = -4$$

Problem 2.3.3 Prove that the following lines are parallel:

$$L_1 : 8x + 3y - 5 = 0 \quad \text{and} \quad L_2 : 6y + 16x = 7$$

Solution

The slopes of L_1 and L_2 are, respectively:

$$m_1 = -\frac{8}{3} \qquad \wedge \qquad m_2 = -\frac{16}{6} = -\frac{8}{3}$$

Since $m_1 = m_2 = -\frac{8}{3}$, by the theorem 2.3.5, L_1 and L_2 are parallel.

Problem 2.3.4 Prove that the next lines are perpendicular:

$$L_1\colon\ 3x - \sqrt{2}y - 5 = 0, \qquad \text{and} \qquad L_2\colon\ \sqrt{2}x + 3y - 6 = 0$$

Solution

Let's find the slopes of the lines. Isolating y on each equation, we have:

$$L_1 : y = \frac{3}{\sqrt{2}}x - 5, \quad L_2 : y = -\frac{\sqrt{2}}{3}x + 2$$

The slopes of L_1 and L_2 are, respectively:

$$m_1 = \frac{3}{\sqrt{2}} \quad \wedge \quad m_2 = -\frac{\sqrt{2}}{3}$$

We have that:

$$m_1 m_2 = \frac{3}{\sqrt{2}}\left(-\frac{\sqrt{2}}{3}\right) = -1$$

Hence, according to the theorem 2.3.6, L_1 and L_2 are perpendicular.

Problem 2.3.5

Find the equation of the line that is perpendicular to $L : 3y - 4x - 15 = 0$ and forms a triangle of area 6 with the coordinate axes.

Solution

The slope of the line L: $3y - 4x - 15 = 0$ is:

$$m = \frac{4}{3}$$

Hence, the slope of the line we are looking for is:

$$m_1 = -\frac{1}{m} = -\frac{1}{\frac{4}{3}} = -\frac{3}{4}$$

Accordingly, this line has an equation of the form:

$$y = -\frac{3}{4}x + b \tag{1}$$

Let $(a, 0)$ be the point where this line intersects the X-axis. Replacing the coordinate of this point in the previous equation:

$$0 = -\frac{3}{4}a + b \Rightarrow a = \frac{4}{3}b \tag{2}$$

The area of the triangle formed by the line and the axes is:

$$\frac{|\,a\,||\,b\,|}{2} = 6 \Leftrightarrow |\,ab\,| = 12$$

Replacing (2) in the above equation:

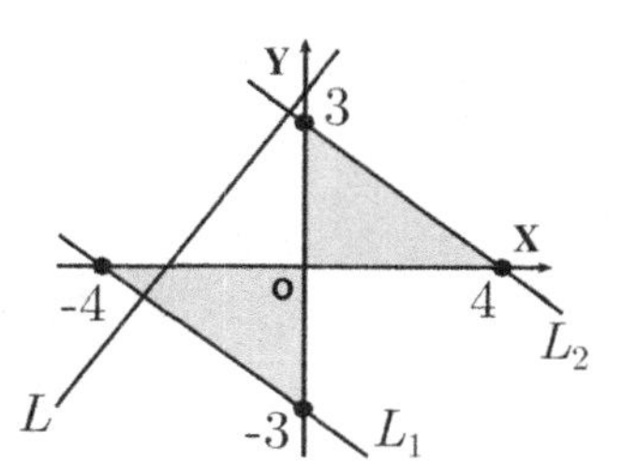

$$|\,ab\,| = 12 \Leftrightarrow \left|\frac{4}{3}bb\right| = 12 \Leftrightarrow b^2 = 9$$
$$\Leftrightarrow b = \pm 3$$

Replacing $b = 3$ and $b = -3$ in equation (1), we get two solutions:

$$L_1 : \; y = -\frac{3}{4}x + 3 \quad \text{or} \quad L_2 : \; y = -\frac{3}{4}x - 3$$

Problem 2.3.6

Find an equation of the perpendicular bisector of $\overline{AB}$, where $A = (1,\,2)$ and $B = (5, -1)$. *Call to mind that the perpendicular bisector of a segment is the perpendicular line that passes through the midpoint of the segment.*

Solution

The slope of the line passing through $A = (1, 2)$ and $B = (5, -1)$ is:

$$m' = \frac{-1-2}{5-1} = \frac{-3}{4}$$

The slope of the perpendicular bisector is:

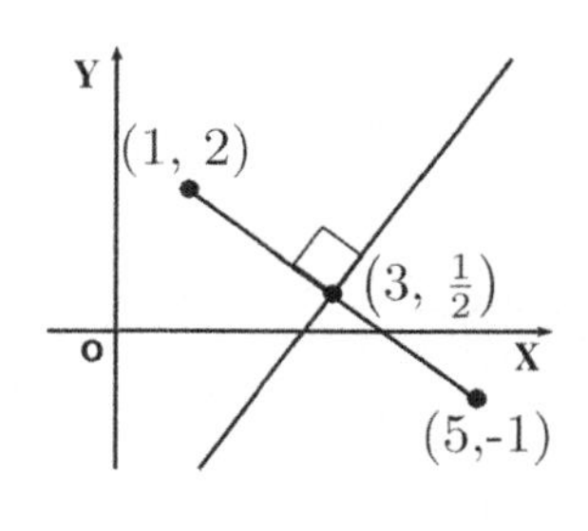

$$m = -\frac{1}{m'} = -\frac{1}{-\frac{3}{4}} = \frac{4}{3}$$

On the other hand, the midpoint $\overline{AB}$ is:

$$M = \left(\frac{1+5}{2}, \frac{2+(-1)}{2}\right) = \left(3, \frac{1}{2}\right)$$

Hence, a point-slope equation of the perpendicular bisector is:

$$y - \frac{1}{2} = \frac{4}{3}(x-3) \Leftrightarrow 8x - 6y - 21 = 0$$

Problem 2.3.7

Given a circle with center $C = (1, -1)$, and its tangent line $L : 5x - 12y + 9 = 0$, find an equation of this circle.

Solution

The radius of this circle is equal to the distance from its center $C = (1, -1)$ to the tangent line L. This is:

$$r = d(C, L) = \frac{|5(1) - 12(-1) + 9|}{\sqrt{(5)^2 + (-12)^2}}$$

$$= \frac{26}{\sqrt{169}} = 2$$

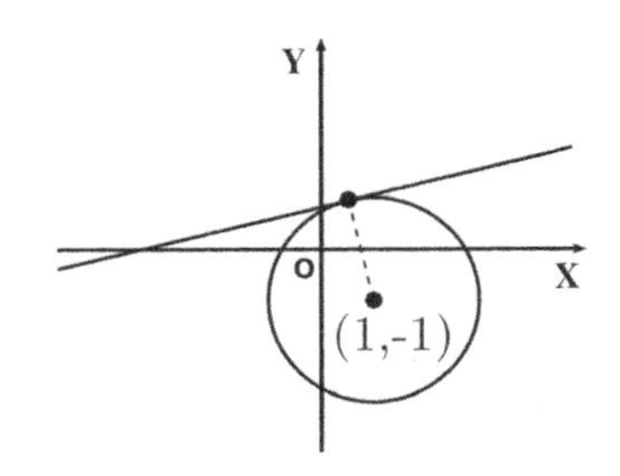

Hence, an equation of the circle is:

$$(x - 1)^2 + (y + 1)^2 = 2^2 \qquad \text{or} \qquad x^2 + y^2 - 2x + 2y - 2 = 0$$

Problem 2.3.8

Find an equation of the circle passing through the point $Q = (3, 6)$, given that the line L: $3x + y + 1 = 0$ is tangent to this circle at the point $P = (-1, 2)$.

Solution

First of all, we need to find the center C of the circle.

C is the intersection of the lines L_1 and L_2, where L_1 is the line passing through the point $P = (-1, 2)$ Moreover, L_1 is perpendicular to the line L.

L_2 is the perpendicular bisector of the segment $\overline{PQ}$, that is, the perpendicular line to $\overline{PQ}$, which passes through its midpoint M.

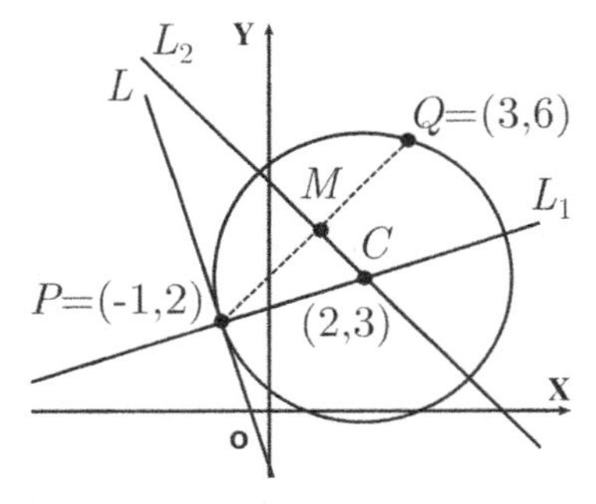

We proceed in five steps.

1. Find an equation of the line L_1 that passes through the point $P = (-1, 2)$ and is perpendicular to L.

   The slope of L is $m = -3$. Hence, the slope of L_1 is $m_1 = \frac{1}{3}$.

   In addition:

$$L_1 : y - 2 = \frac{1}{3}(x + 1) \Leftrightarrow L_1 : x - 3y + 7 = 0$$

2. Find an equation of the line L_2, the perpendicular bisector of $\overline{PQ}$.

The slope of the segment $\overline{PQ}$ is:

$$m' = \frac{6-2}{3-(-1)} = 1$$

The slope of L_2 is:

$$m_2 = \frac{-1}{m'} = \frac{-1}{1} = -1$$

The midpoint of $\overline{PQ}$ is:

$$M = \left(\frac{3+(-1)}{2}, \frac{6+2}{2}\right) = (1,\, 4)$$

Hence:

$$L_2\colon\ y - 4 = -1(x-1) \Leftrightarrow L_2\colon\ x + y - 5 = 0$$

3. Find the center C of the circle. Since C is the intersection of the lines L_1 and L_2, we shall find the result of the system given by the equations of both lines:

$$\begin{cases} x - 3y + 7 = 0 \\ x + y - 5 = 0 \end{cases} \quad \Rightarrow C = (2,3)$$

4. Find the radio of the circle:

$$r = d(C,P) = \sqrt{(-1-2)^2 + (2-3)^2} = \sqrt{10}$$

5. Finally, the equation of the circle is:

$$(x-2)^2 + (y-3)^2 = 10 \quad \text{or} \quad x^2 + y^2 - 4x - 6y + 3 = 0$$

Problem 2.3.9 **Prove the theorem 2.3.6**

If L_1 and L_2 are two non vertical lines with slopes m_1 and m_2, respectively, prove that:

$$\boldsymbol{L_1 \text{ and } L_2 \text{ are perpendicular} \Leftrightarrow m_1 m_2 = -1}$$

Solution

We can assume that the intersection point of the lines is the origin.

The slope-intercept equations of these lines are:

$$L_1 : y = m_1 x \quad \text{and} \quad L_2 : y = m_2 x$$

Let $P = (x_1,\, m_1x_1) \neq (0,0)$ be a point of L_1, and $Q = (x_2,\, m_2x_2) \neq (0,0)$ be a point of L_2.

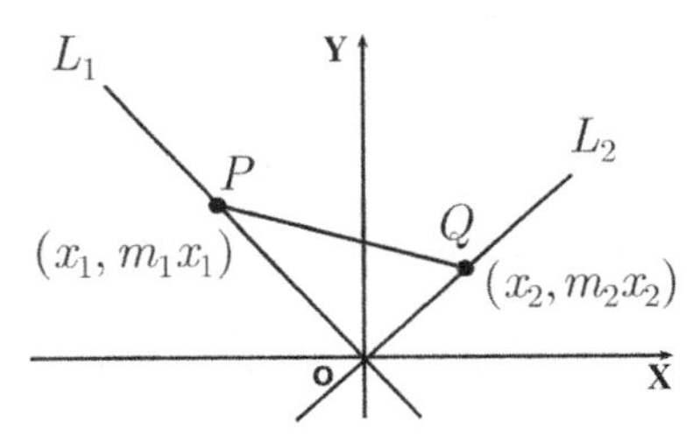

Since:

$x_1 \neq 0 \wedge x_2 \neq 0$, we have $x_1x_2 \neq 0$

Now, according to the Pythagoras theorem:

$$\begin{aligned} L_1 \text{ and } L_2 \text{ are perpendicular} &\Leftrightarrow \triangle POQ \text{ is a right triangle} \\ &\Leftrightarrow d(P,Q)^2 = d(O,P)^2 + d(O,Q)^2 \end{aligned}$$

But:

$$\begin{aligned} d(P,\, Q)^2 &= (x_2 - x_1)^2 + (m_2x_2 - m_1x_1)^2 \\ &= {x_2}^2 - 2x_2x_1 + {x_1}^2 + (m_2x_2)^2 - 2m_2m_1x_2x_1 + (m_1x_1)^2 \end{aligned}$$

$$d(O,\, P)^2 = {x_1}^2 + (m_1x_1)^2 \quad \text{and} \quad d(O,\, Q)^2 = {x_2}^2 + (m_2x_2)^2$$

Hence, L_1 and L_2 are perpendicular if and only if:

$$\begin{aligned} {x_2}^2 - 2x_2x_1 + {x_1}^2 + (m_2x_2)^2 - 2m_2m_1x_2x_1 + (m_1x_1)^2 \\ = {x_1}^2 + (m_1x_1)^2 + {x_2}^2 + (m_2x_2)^2 \end{aligned}$$

$$\begin{aligned} &\Leftrightarrow \quad -2x_2x_1 - 2m_2m_1x_2x_1 = 0 \quad &&\Leftrightarrow \quad -2x_2x_1(1 + m_2m_1) = 0 \\ &\Leftrightarrow \quad 1 + m_2m_1 = 0 \quad &&\Leftrightarrow \quad m_2m_1 = -1 \end{aligned}$$

Problem 2.3.10 **Prove the theorem 2.3.7**

Prove that the distance from $P_0 = (x_0,\, y_0)$ to the line $L : Ax + By + C = 0$ is given by:

$$d(P, L) = \frac{|Ax_0 + By_0 + C|}{\sqrt{A^2 + B^2}}$$

Solution

Let L_1 be the line that passes through the point $P = (x_0, y_0)$, and is also perpendicular to L.

The slope of L is:

$$m = -\frac{A}{B},$$

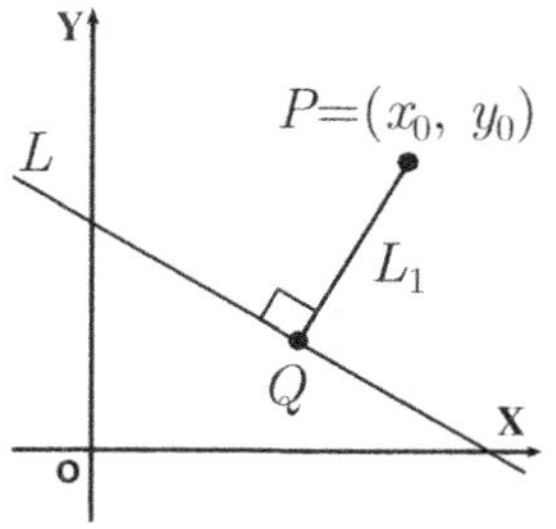

hence, the slope of L_1 is: $m_1 = \frac{B}{A}$

The slope-point equation of L_1 is:

$$y - y_0 = \frac{B}{A}(x - x_0)$$

$$\Leftrightarrow Ay - Bx + (Bx_0 - Ay_0) = 0$$

Let's find the coordinates of Q, the intersection of L and L_1. In doing so, we must find the solution for the system:

$$Ax + By + C = 0 \quad (1)$$

$$Ay - Bx + (Bx_0 - Ay_0) = 0 \quad (2)$$

We found that:

$$Q = \left(\frac{B^2x_0 - ABy_0 - AC}{A^2 + B^2}, \frac{A^2y_0 - ABx_0 - BC}{A^2 + B^2} \right)$$

Now:

$$d(P, L)^2 = d(P, Q)^2 = \left(\frac{B^2x_0 - ABy_0 - AC}{A^2 + B^2} - x_0 \right)^2 + \left(\frac{A^2y_0 - ABx_0 - BC}{A^2 + B^2} - y_0 \right)^2$$

$$= \left(\frac{-A}{A^2 + B^2} \right)^2 (Ax_0 + By_0 + C)^2 + \left(\frac{-B}{A^2 + B^2} \right)^2 (Ax_0 + By_0 + C)^2$$

$$= \frac{A^2 + B^2}{(A^2 + B^2)^2}(Ax_0 + By_0 + C)^2 = \frac{1}{A^2 + B^2}(Ax_0 + By_0 + C)^2$$

Taking square root of both sides:

$$d(P, L) = \frac{|Ax_0 + By_0 + C|}{\sqrt{A^2 + B^2}}$$

Problem 2.3.11

Given a non-vertical line $L: y - y_0 = m(x - x_0)$, with slope $m \neq 0$, prove that the slope of L equals the tangent of the angle $\boldsymbol{\alpha}$, the angle generated by the intersection of L with the X-axis. In other words, prove that:

$$\boldsymbol{m = \tan\alpha}$$

Solution

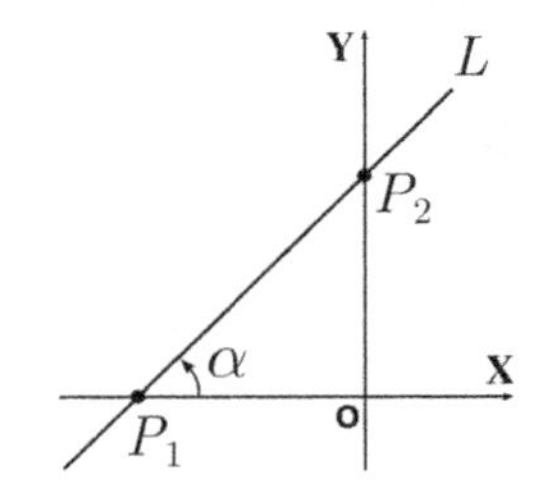

We are free to assume that:

- $m > 0$
- L intersects the X-axis at $P_1 = (x_1,\, 0)$
- L intersects the Y-axis at $P_2 = (0,\, y_2)$
- $x_1 < 0$ and $y_2 > 0$

According to the trigonometric ratios, we have, in the triangle $\triangle P_1 \mathbf{o} P_2$:

$$\tan\alpha = \frac{\text{opposite side}}{\text{adjacent side}}$$

Moreover:

$$\begin{aligned} \text{opposite side} &= y_2 \qquad &(\text{since } y_2 > 0)\\ \text{adjacent side} &= -x_1 \qquad &(\text{since } x_1 < 0) \end{aligned}$$

Replacing these values in the tangent formula of trigonometric ratios:

$$\tan\alpha = \frac{y_2}{-x_1} = -\frac{y_2}{x_1} \qquad (1)$$

Now we back up in the definition of slope for L. Considering both points $P_1 = (x_1,\, 0)$ and $P_2 = (0,\, y_2)$, let's calculate m with the slope formula:

$$\begin{aligned} m &= \frac{y_2 - y_1}{x_2 - x_1} = \frac{y_2 - 0}{0 - x_1}\\ &= \frac{y_2}{-x_1} = -\frac{y_2}{x_1} \qquad (2) \end{aligned}$$

From (1) and (2), we conclude that:

$$\boldsymbol{m = \tan\alpha}$$

Notice that if L is horizontal($m = 0$), then $\alpha = 0$. Similarly, if L is vertical, then $\alpha = \frac{\pi}{2}$, and $\tan\left(\frac{\pi}{2}\right)$ does not exist, therefore, m does not exist either.

EXERCISES 2.3

1. Using slopes, prove that the points $A = (2, 1)$, $B = (-4, -2)$, $C = (1, 1/2)$ are collinear.

In the exercises 2 through 9, find an equation of the line that satisfies the given conditions. Express the equation with this form $y = mx + b$.

2. Pass through (1, 3); has slope 5.

3. Pass through the origin; has slope 5.

4. Pass through (1, 1) and (2, 3).

5. x-Intercept 5; y-Intercept 2.

6. Pass through (1, 3), and is parallel to the line $5y + 3x - 6 = 0$.

7. Pass through (4, 3), and is perpendicular to the line $5x + y - 2 = 0$.

8. Parallel to $2y + 4x - 5 = 0$, and pass through the intersection of the lines:
$$5x + y = 4 \quad \text{and} \quad 2x + 5y - 3 = 0$$

9. Pass through (8,-6), and intersects the axes at equal distances from the origin.

10. Given the line L: $2y - 4x - 7 = 0$:

    a. find the line passing through $P = (1, 1)$, and perpendicular to L.

    b. find the distance from the point $P = (1, 1)$ to L.

11. Using slopes, prove that the points $A = (3, 1)$, $B = (6, 0)$ and $C = (4, 4)$ are the vertices of a right triangle. Find the area of this triangle.

12. Determine which lines are parallel and which are perpendicular.

    a. $L_1 : 2x + 5y - 6 = 0$ **b.** $L_2 : 4x + 3y - 6 = 0$

    c. $L_3 : -5x + 2y - 8 = 0$ **d.** $L_4 : 5x + y - 3 = 0$

    e. $L_5 : 4x + 3y - 9 = 0$ **f.** $L_6 : -x + 5y - 20 = 0$

13. Find the perpendicular bisector of the segment joining the given points:

a. $(1, 0)$ and $(2, -3)$ **b.** $(-1, 2)$ and $(3, 10)$

c. $(-2, 3)$ and $(-2, -1)$

14. The endpoints of one of the diagonals of a rhombus are $(2, -1)$ and $(14, 3)$. Find an equation of the line that contains the other diagonal. *Hint: the diagonals of a rhombus are perpendicular.*

15. Find the distance from the origin to the line $4x + 3y - 15 = 0$.

16. Find the distance from the point (0,-3) to the line $5x - 12y - 10 = 0$.

17. Find the distance from the point (1,-2) to the line $x - 3y = 5$.

18. Find the distance between the parallel lines $3x - 4y = 0$, $3x - 4y = 10$.

19. Find the distance between the parallel lines $3x - y + 1 = 0$, $3x - y + 9 = 0$.

20. Find the distance from the point $Q = (6, -3)$ to the line passing through $P = (-4, 1)$ and parallel to the line $4x + 3y = 0$.

21. Determine the value of C in the equation of the line L: $4x + 3y + C = 0$. It is known that the distance from the point $Q = (5, 9)$ to the line L is 4 times the distance between the point $P = (-3, 3)$ and the line L.

22. Find the lines that are parallel to line $5x + 12y - 12 = 0$ and are 4 units away from it.

23. Find the equation of the tangent line to the circle $x^2 + y^2 - 4x + 6y - 12 = 0$ at the point (-1, 1).

24. Find the equations of the two lines passing through the point $P = (2, -8)$, and are also tangent to the circle $x^2 + y^2 = 34$.

25. In the above exercise, find the points where the tangent lines make contact with the circle.

26. Find the equation of two lines parallel to $2x - 2y + 5 = 0$, which are also tangent to the circle $x^2 + y^2 = 9$.

27. Find the equation of the tangent line to the circle $x^2 + y^2 + 2x + 4y - 20 = 0$ at the point (2, 2).

28. Find the equation of the circle with center $C = (1, -1)$ that is also tangent to the line $5x - 12y + 22 = 0$.

29. Find the equation of the circle passing through the point $Q = (4, 0)$, that is also tangent to the line $3x - 4y + 20 = 0$ at the point $P = (-12/5,\ 16/5)$.

30. Find the equation of the circle passing through the points (3, 1) and (-1, 3), with center in the line $3x - y - 2 = 0$.

31. Both parallel lines, $2x + y - 5 = 0$ and $2x + y + 15 = 0$, are tangent to a circle. If one point of tangency is $B = (2, 1)$, find an equation of the circle.

32. Find an equation of the line passing through the point $P = (8, 6)$, which also produces a triangle of area 12 with the coordinate axes.

33. Determine the values of k and n in the equations of the lines:

$$L_1 : kx - 2y - 3 = 0, \quad \text{and} \quad L_2 : 6x - 4y - n = 0,$$

a. if L_1 intersects L_2 in a single point.

b. if L_1 and L_2 are perpendicular.

c. if L_1 and L_2 are parallel and not coincident.

d. if L_1 and L_2 are coincident.

34. Determine for what values of k and n the lines:

$$kx + 8y + n = 0 \quad \text{and} \quad 2x + ky - 1 = 0,$$

a. are parallel and not coincident.

b. are coincident.

c. are perpendicular.

35. The center of a square is $C = (1, -1)$, and one of its sides is on the line $x - 2y = -12$. Find the equations of the lines containing the other sides.

36. Prove that the points $A = (1, 4)$, $B = (5, 1)$, $C = (8, 5)$ and $D = (4, 8)$ are the vertices of a rhombus (a quadrilateral whose sides have equal length). Verify that the diagonals are perpendicular.

37. Let a and b be the x-intersection and the y-intersection of a line. If $a \neq 0$ and $b \neq 0$, prove that an equation for this line is $\frac{x}{a} + \frac{y}{b} = 1$.

38. Roberto is playing pool in a championship.

He must hit, without spin, the *eight* ball with the *white* ball using two cushions of the table, as shown in the figure.

If the white ball is on the point $P = (2, 6)$, and the red ball on $Q = (3, 2)$, find the points A and B of the cushions of the table where the ball must hit to be successful.

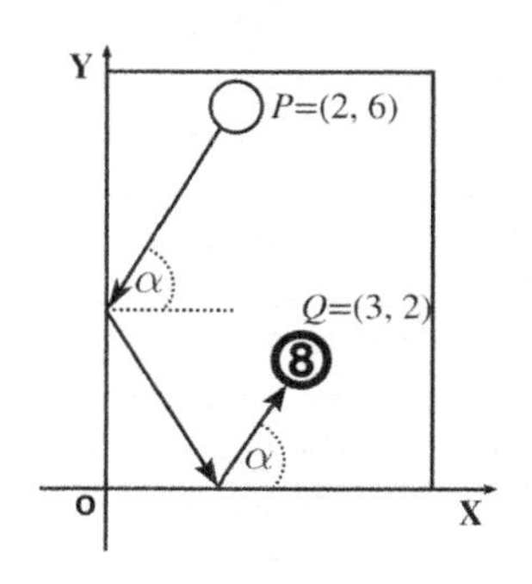

Did you know this?

Before Descartes, Geometry and Algebra were isolated fields. Geometry had been carried from Mesopotamia to Greece by Greek scholars in the 6th century B.C. while algebra appeared in the Middle East shortly after 250 A.D.

In 300 B.C. Euclid published his work, ***The Elements****, giving rise to* ***Euclidean Geometry****, later improved by such figures as* ***Apollonius****.*

Ancient Greece fell into crisis after its adhesion to Rome in 146 B.C. putting an end to Greek cultural dominance. This situation led to a stagnation in the field of Geometry for several centuries.

The Greek migration driven by the crisis resulted in an unexpected cultural expansion of Greece into Persia, leading to the spread of Greek mathematics in the Middle East. In 250 A.D., the Greek mathematician ***Diophantus*** *published his work* ***Arithmetica****, which introduced first- and second-degree equations.*

In 628 A.D. the Indian mathematician, ***Brahmagupta****, published his work,* ***Doctrine of Brahma Correctly Established****, introducing novel methods for solving equations.*

Modern Algebra as we know it emerged during the Islamic Golden Age thanks to the caliph, ***Al-Mamun****, who established the academy and library,* ***The House of Wisdom*** *in Baghdad, where the best scientific books from all over the world were translated into Arabic. In this scenario,* ***Al-Khwarismi*** *published his masterpiece,* ***Compendium of Calculus by Reintegration and Comparison*** *(year 813) where Algebra gets its name, since "al-ŷabr" means "reintegration" in Arabic. The translations of this work reached the western world, generating great impact in the scientific community of Europe.*

Descartes ***Analytic Geometry*** *allowed the unification of both currents, Geometry and Algebra, in the Cartesian plane. The equations revealed by the mathematicians of the East could be represented graphically in this plane; but what is even more surprising is that the* ***Conic Sections****, curves discovered many centuries earlier by the wise men of Ancient Greece, could also get an algebraic representation.*

Thanks to this unification, initiated by Descartes and Fermat, Geometry received a new impetus, allowing modern scientists to continue the unfinished work of the Ancient Greek scholars.

3

THE CONICS

Apollonius of Perga
(262 - 190 A.C.)

APOLLONIUS OF PERGA, also known as "*The Great Geometer*", was born in the small Greek city of Perga in southern Asia Minor, which is now known as Murtina in Turkey. In the New Testament of the Bible, Acts 13 states that Paul, the Apostle, visited this town during his first missionary journey, approximately 300 years after Apollonius wrote his famous work **The Conics**. This is a small proof of how far ahead of his time the scholar was, given the prominent role of this work in the development of Geometry for many centuries.

Another outstanding work by Apollonius is **On the Burning Mirrors**, where he describes the reflection properties of a parabolic mirror. He proved that light rays parallel to the axis, striking the interior surface, will reflect to hit the focus of the parabola or, in this case, of the parabolic mirror. Legends suggest that *Archimedes* used this concept to defend his home town from the Roman army.

In 215 B.C, the Roman navy, leaded by the General Marcus Claudius Marcellus, attacked Syracuse, a Greek city located in the Sicily Island, Italy.

Thanks to various war machines invented by the scholar, the Greeks managed to hold off the far superior Roman army for three years. One of these weapons was the **Archimedes Death Ray**, a parabolic mirror that focused the sun rays on a single spot to set wooden ships on fire.

Apollonius, Euclid and Archimedes are considered the most outstanding mathematicians of the Ancient Greece.

SECCION 3.1

INTRODUCTION

The conics play an outstanding role in the study of Calculus. These curves have been studied by numerous mathematicians for more than 2300 years, and are distinguished by their wide range of applications, such as the study of planetary motion, architecture, telescope and antenna design, etc.

A visual representation of a conic requires an understanding of the origin of the **Double Right Circular Cone**.

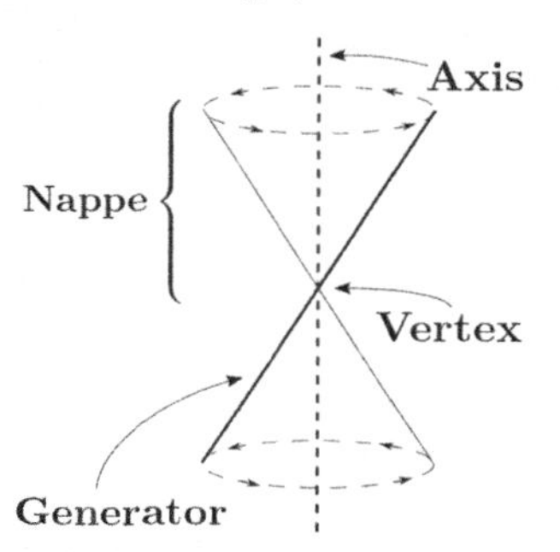

The Double Right Circular Cone is generated with the revolution of a straight line (generator) on an axis, not being parallel or perpendicular with each other. This action generates two cones (nappes) joined by a common **vertex**.

There are three Conics: **parabola**, **ellipse** and **hyperbola**. These curves are given the name of **Conic Sections**, or simply Conics, because they result from intersecting a Right Circular Cone with a plane, as when cutting a slice of bread with a knife. Conics can be **degenerate** or **non-degenerate**, depending on the position of the plane when intersecting the cone. In the early sections of this chapter we will study non-degenerate conics; while degenerate conics will be discussed in the last section of this chapter.

If the plane is perpendicular to the axis of the cone, a circle is produced; if the plane is not perpendicular to the axis, and intersects only one nappe, a parabola or an ellipse is produced. If the plane is not perpendicular to the axis, and intersects both nappes of the cone, a hyperbola is produced.

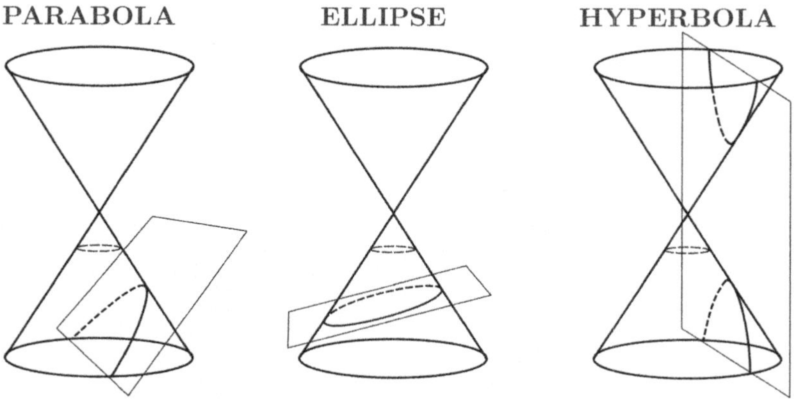

Each of these magnificent curves deserve its own section.

SECCION 3.2

THE PARABOLA

Definition

From the perspective of Analytic Geometry, a **parabola** is the set of all points in a plane that are equidistant from a fixed point $\boldsymbol{F}$, called the **focus**, and a fixed line $\boldsymbol{D}$, called the **directrix**.

- The fixed point F is the **focus**.
- The fixed line D is the **directrix**.
- The line passing through the focus, being perpendicular to the directrix, is the **axis** or **axis of symmetry** of the parabola.

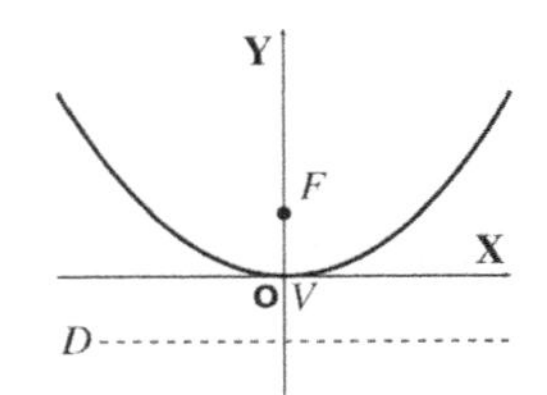

- The point V on the axis, half-way from F to D, is called the **vertex**.

STANDARD FORM OF THE EQUATION OF A PARABOLA

To obtain the equation of a parabola in the simplest possible way, we must place the vertex of the parabola at the origin, and its axis on one of the coordinate axis. The directrix will coincide with the other coordinate axis.

Case 1. Parabola with vertex at the origin, and vertical axis.

Let $F = (0, p)$ be the focus. The directrix is:

$$\boldsymbol{D : y = -p}$$

Let $P = (x, y)$ be any point. We have:

$$d(P, F) = \sqrt{x^2 + (y - p)^2} \quad \text{and} \quad d(P, D) = \mid y + p \mid$$

Now, by definition, $P = (x, y)$ is in the parabola if:

$$\begin{aligned} d(P, F) = d(P, D) &\Leftrightarrow \sqrt{x^2 + (y - p)^2} = \mid y + p \mid \\ &\Leftrightarrow x^2 + (y - p)^2 = (y + p)^2 \\ &\Leftrightarrow x^2 = 4py \qquad (1) \end{aligned}$$

If $p > 0$: the parabola opens upward.

If $p < 0$: the parabola opens downward.

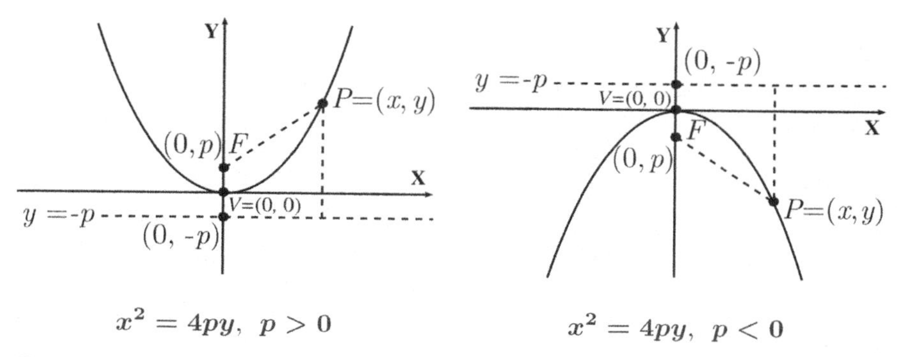

$\boldsymbol{x^2 = 4py,\ p > 0}$ $\boldsymbol{x^2 = 4py,\ p < 0}$

Case 2. Parabola with vertex at the origin, and horizontal axis.

Let $F = (p, 0)$ be the focus. The directrix is $P = (x, y)$.

Let $P = (x, y)$ be any point of the parabola. We have:

$$d(P, F) = \sqrt{(x-p)^2 + y^2} \quad \text{and} \quad d(P, D) = \mid x + p \mid$$

Now, since P is in the parabola, by definition:

$$\begin{aligned} d(P, F) = d(P, D) &\Leftrightarrow \sqrt{(x-p)^2 + y^2} = \mid x + p \mid \\ &\Leftrightarrow (x-p)^2 + y^2 = (x+p)^2 \\ &\Leftrightarrow y^2 = 4px \end{aligned} \qquad (2)$$

If $\boldsymbol{p > 0}$: the parabola opens to the right.

If $\boldsymbol{p < 0}$: the parabola opens to the left.

When y is replaced by $-y$, the equation remains unchanged, so the graph is symmetric about the X-axis.

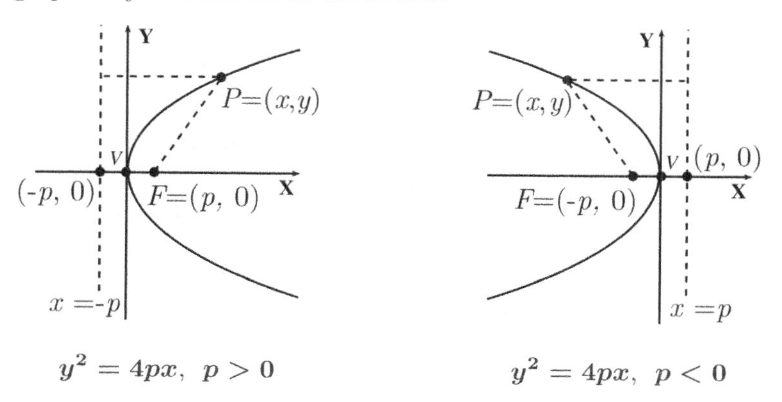

$\boldsymbol{y^2 = 4px,\ p > 0}$ $\boldsymbol{y^2 = 4px,\ p < 0}$

We summarize the previous results in the next theorem.

Theorem 3.2.1 **Standard form of the equation of the parabola.**

1. The **Standard form** of the equation of a parabola with vertex at the origin, and vertical axis is:

$$\boxed{x^2 = 4py}$$

The **focus** is $F = (0, p)$ and the **directrix**, $y = -p$. If $p > 0$, the parabola opens upwards. If $p < 0$, it opens downwards.

2. The **standard form** of the equation of a parabola with vertex at the origin and horizontal axis is:

$$\boxed{y^2 = 4px}$$

The **focus** is $F = (p, 0)$ and the directrix, $x = -p$. If $p > 0$, the parabola opens to the right. If $p < 0$, it opens to the left.

Example 3.2.1 Find the focus and directrix of the parabola:

$$x^2 = -16y$$

Solution

We have:

$$x^2 = -16y \Rightarrow 4p = -16 \Rightarrow p = -4$$

Hence, the focus is $F = (0, -4)$, and the directrix, $y = 4$.

Definition

The **Latus Rectum** of a parabola is the segment that runs through the focus and is perpendicular to the axis, having its endpoints on the parabola. The length of the Latus Rectum is called the **Focal Diameter** of the parabola.

If L is the focal diameter, then:

$$L = 4 \mid p \mid$$

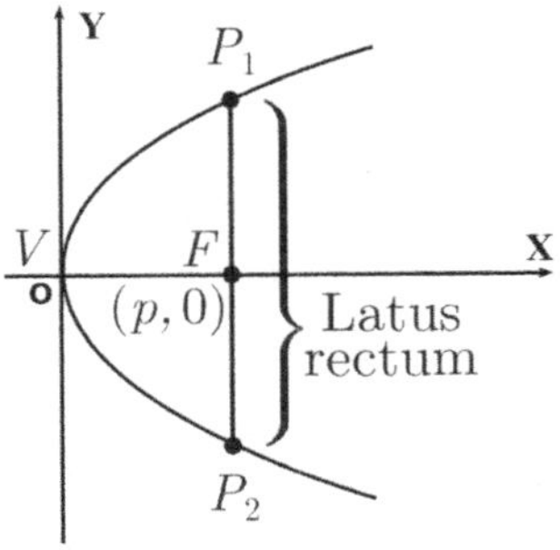

Y
P_1
V
O
F
$(p, 0)$
X
Latus rectum
P_2

Indeed, consider the parabola $y^2 = 4px$. If y_1 is the ordinate of the point P_1, then:

$$P_1 = (p, y_1)$$

Since P_1 is at the parabola, we have:

$$(y_1)^2 = 4p(p) = 4p^2 \Rightarrow y_1 = \sqrt{4p^2} = 2 \mid p \mid$$

Hence, the length of the latus rectum is:

$$2y_1 = 4 \mid p \mid$$

Example 3.2.2

A parabola passing through the point $(-1, 2\sqrt{2})$ has its vertex at the origin and an axis that coincides with the X-axis.

a. Find the standard form of the equation of the parabola.

b. Find the focus and the directrix.

c. Find the focal diameter.

Solution

a. We are looking for an equation of the form:

$$y^2 = 4px$$

Since $(-1, 2\sqrt{2})$ is at the parabola, we have:

$$\left(2\sqrt{2}\right)^2 = 4p(-1) \Rightarrow 8 = -4p \Rightarrow p = -2$$

The standard form of the equation of the parabola is $y^2 = -8x$.

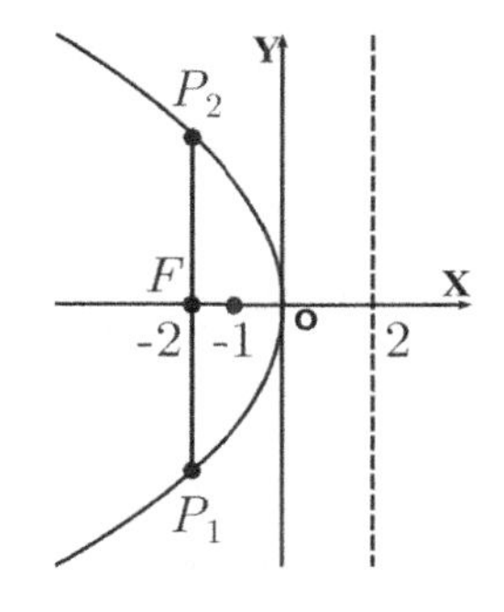

b. $F = (p, 0) = (-2, 0)$. Directrix: $x = 2$.

c. The focal diameter is the segment: $\overline{P_1P_2}$. Its length is:

$$L = 4 \mid p \mid = 4 \mid -2 \mid = 8$$

STANDARD FORM OF THE EQUATION OF A SHIFTED PARABOLA

If the vertices of the parabolas of theorem 3.2.1 are shifted from the origin to the point (h, k), keeping the axis parallel to one of the coordinate axes, the following results are obtained:

1. The standard form of the equation of the parabola with vertex $\boldsymbol{(h, k)}$, and axis parallel to the Y-axis is:

$$\boldsymbol{(x - h)^2 = 4p(y - k)}$$

The **focus** is $\boldsymbol{F = (h, (p + k))}$ and the directrix, $\boldsymbol{y = -p + k}$.

If $\boldsymbol{p > 0}$: the parabola opens **upward**.

If $\boldsymbol{p < 0}$: the parabola opens **downward**.

2. The standard form of the equation of the parabola with vertex (h, k), and axis parallel to the X-axis is:

$$(y-k)^2 = 4p(x-h)$$

The **focus** is $F = ((p+h), k)$, and the directrix, $x = -p + h$.

If $p > 0$: the parabola opens to the **right**.

If $p < 0$: the parabola opens to the **left**.

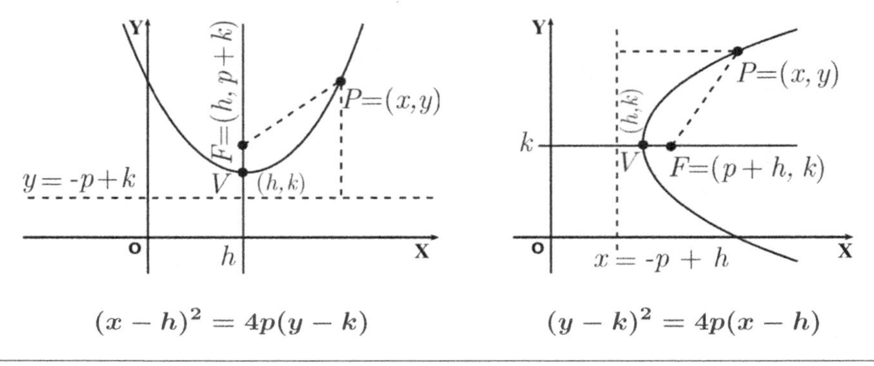

$(x-h)^2 = 4p(y-k)$ $\qquad$ $(y-k)^2 = 4p(x-h)$

Example 3.2.3 Find the standard form of the equation of the parabola with focus $F = (2, -2)$, and directrix $x = 8$.

Solution

We are looking for a equation of the form:

$$(y-k)^2 = 4p(x-h)$$

We must find the values of h and k. In this case, we know that:

$$F = ((p+h), k)$$

and the directrix is: $x = -p + h$

Hence:

$$F = ((p+h), k)) = (2, -2) \quad \text{and} \quad x = -p + h = 8$$
$$\Rightarrow p + h = 2,\ k = -2,\ -p + h = 8$$
$$\Rightarrow p = -3,\ h = 5,\ k = -2$$

Therefore, the equation of the parabola is:

$$(y-(-2))^2 = 4(-3)(x-5), \text{ that is: } (y+2)^2 = -12(x-5)$$

Example 3.2.4 Prove that the following equation is a parabola:

$$3x^2 - 12x + 4y + 8 = 0$$

Find the vertex, axis, focus and directrix.

Solution

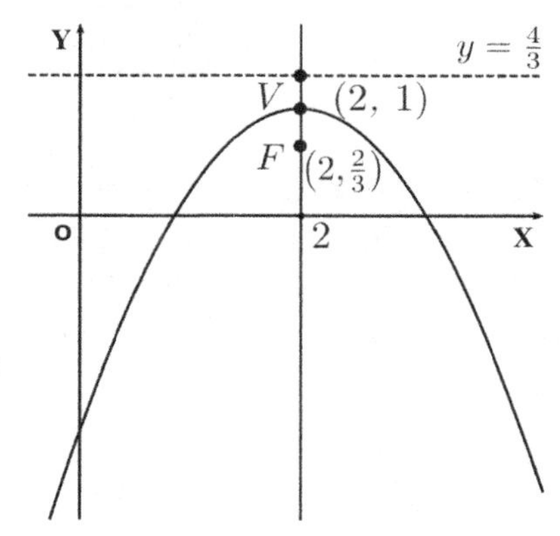

Completing the square:

$$\begin{aligned}
&3x^2 - 12x + 4y + 8 = 0 \\
&\Leftrightarrow 3x^2 - 12x = -4y - 8 \\
&\Leftrightarrow 3(x^2 - 4x \qquad) = -4y - 8 \\
&\Leftrightarrow 3(x^2 - 4x + 4) = -4y - 8 + 12 \\
&\Leftrightarrow 3(x - 2)^2 = -4(y - 1) \\
&\Leftrightarrow (x - 2)^2 = -\frac{4}{3}(y - 1)
\end{aligned}$$

The above equation is the standard form of the equation of the shifted parabola with vertex $V = (h, k) = (2, 1)$, and axis $x = 2$

Besides,

$$4p = -\frac{4}{3} \Rightarrow p = -\frac{1}{3}$$

Hence:

$$F = (h, (p + k)) = \left(2, \left(-\frac{1}{3} + 1\right)\right) = \left(2, -\frac{2}{3}\right)$$

The directrix is:

$$y = -p + k = -\left(-\frac{1}{3}\right) + 1 \Rightarrow y = \frac{4}{3}$$

REFLECTION PROPERTY OF THE PARABOLA

The parabola has very important applications in physics, astronomy, engineering, and many other areas. Most of these applications are based on the **reflection property** of the parabola, which states that:

Light rays from a source placed at the focus will be reflected on the parabola, being oriented in a direction parallel to the axis of symmetry

Conversely, light rays approaching the parabola parallel to the axis will be reflected and converge at the focus.

This property will be proved in the solved problem 3.2.7.

Rays leaving the focus ***Rays reaching to the focus***

If a parabola is rotated about its axis of symmetry, the surface formed is called a **circular paraboloid** or a **paraboloid of revolution**.

A parabolic mirror is a type of mirror with a surface that forms a paraboloid of revolution. Such mirrors are used in the design of automobile headlights, telescopes, radars, displays, satellite dishes, and more.

Example 3.2.5

An engineer is designing a flashlight that incorporates a parabolic mirror as a light reflector. The mirror must have a depth of 4 cm and a diameter of 12 cm for the rim.

a. Find the equation of the parabola used to shape the mirror.

b. Find the distance between the vertex and the point where the light source should be placed (the focus).

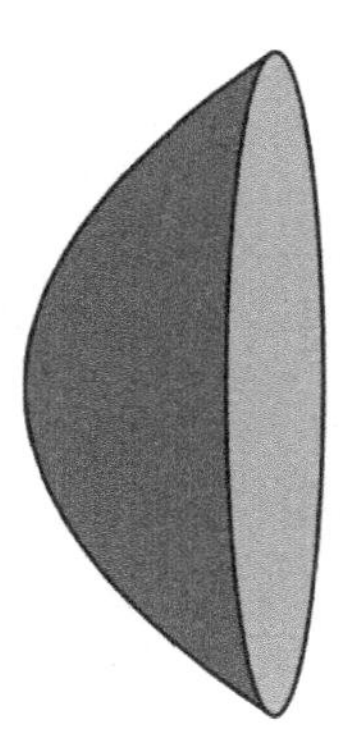

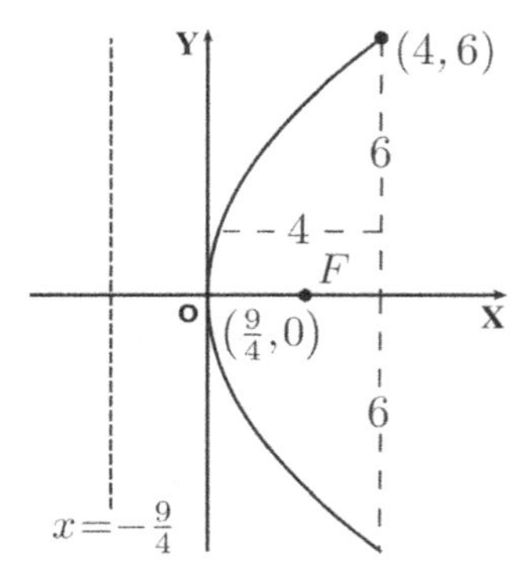

Solution

a. Let's place the parabola with its vertex at the origin, and opening to the right. The equation of the parabola has the form $y^2 = 4px$. We must find the value of p.

The point (4, 6) is at the parabola, so:

$$6^2 = 4p(4) \Rightarrow 36 = 16p \Rightarrow p = \frac{9}{4}$$

Hence, the equation of the parabola is $y^2 = 4\left(\frac{9}{4}\right)x$. That is, $y^2 = 9x$

b. The focus is $F = (p, 0) = \left(\frac{9}{4}, 0\right)$. Hence, the light source should be placed at $\frac{9}{4} = 2.25\ cm.$ from the vertex.

Did you know this?

In 1990, NASA put into orbit the ***Hubble*** *Space Telescope, fulfilling the dream of astronomers to have an observatory beyond the atmosphere. It has a parabolic mirror 2.4 m. in diameter, rotates at an average altitude of 575 km. above the Earth's surface, and circles the Earth every 96 minutes.*

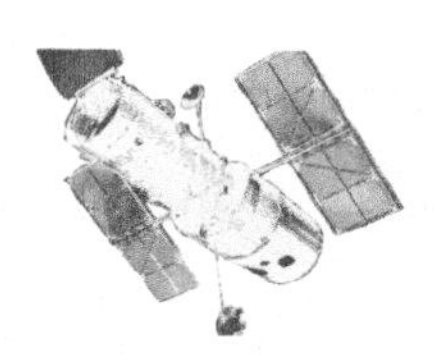

This telescope was named after the American astronomer ***Edwin Powell Hubble*** *(1889-1953), who published astonishing findings on the expansion of the universe in 1929, giving rise to the Big Bang theory. This telescope was superseded by* ***James Webb*** *Space Telescope in 2021.*

SOLVED PROBLEMS 3.2

Problem 3.2.1

A given parabola opens to the right. If the endpoints of its Latus Rectum are (6, −4) and (6, 8), find an equation of the parabola.

Solution

The focus is the midpoint of the latus rectum; that is $F = (6, 2)$. The length of the latus rectum is $L = 8 - (-4) = 12$.

We know that $L = 4|p|$

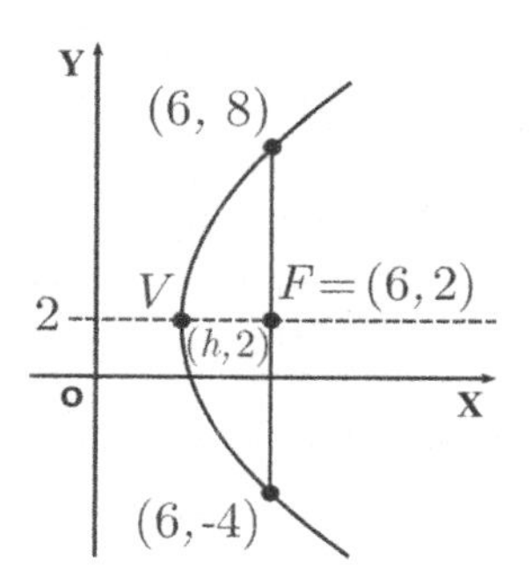

Since the parabola opens to the right, then:

$$p > 0$$

Therefore, $4p = 12 \Rightarrow p = 3$

If $V = (h, 2)$ is the vertex, we must have that:

$$h + p = 6 \Rightarrow h + 3 = 6 \Rightarrow h = 3$$

Thereby, an equation of the parabola is:

$$(y-2)^2 = 12(x-3)$$

Problem 3.2.2

A water tank has the form of a revolution paraboloid. The height of the tank is 9 m. and its cover has a diameter of 12 m. If the level of the water is 4 m. below the cover, find the diameter of the surface of the water.

Solution

We must place the origin of the coordinates at the base of the tank, as shown in the figure. The equation of the parabola is $x^2 = 4py$.

Since the point (6, 9) is at the parabola:

$$(6)^2 = 4p(9) \Rightarrow p = 1$$

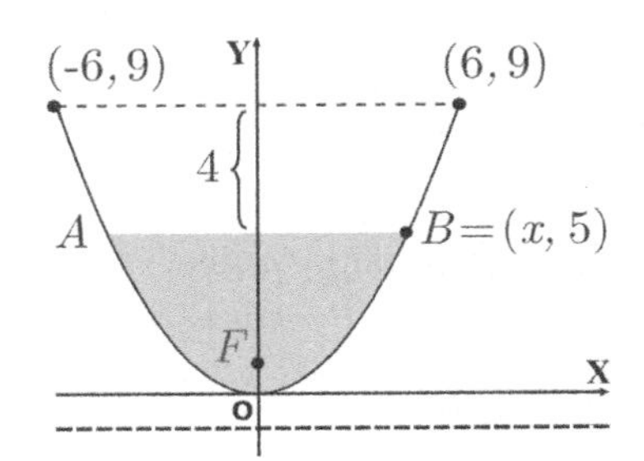

Then, the equation of the parabola is

$$x^2 = 4y$$

Since $B = (x, 5)$ is also a point of the parabola, we have:

$$x^2 = 4(5) \Rightarrow x = \sqrt{4 \times 5} = 2\sqrt{5}$$

Now, the diameter of the water surface is $2\left(2\sqrt{5}\right) = 4\sqrt{5}$

Problem 3.2.3

The towers of a suspension bridge are 400 m. apart, and rise 90 m. above the road. The cable between the towers has the shape of a parabola. Its lowest point is 10 m. above the road.

a. Find a equation of the parabola determined by the cable.

b. Find the height of the cable at 50 m. from the right tower.

Solution

a. We must place the X-axis on the road; the parabola with its vertex at the point (0, 10); and the Y-axis on the axis of the parabola.

The equation of the parabola has the form:

$$x^2 = 4p(y-10)$$

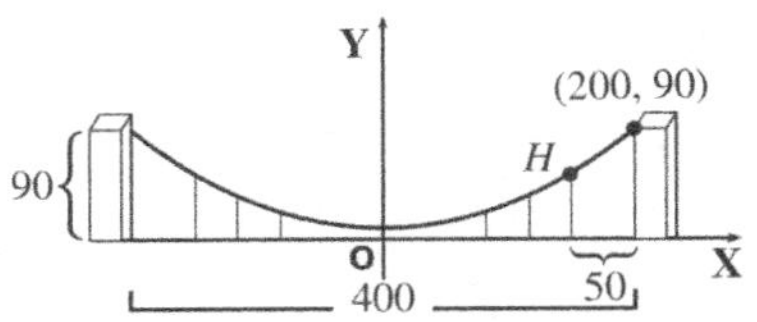

The point (200, 90) lies on the parabola. Hence:

$$(200)^2 = 4p(90 - 10) \Rightarrow 40,000 = 320p \Rightarrow p = 125$$

The equation we seek is $x^2 = 4(125)(y - 10)$. That is:

$$x^2 = 500(y - 10).$$

b. If H be the point of the parabola that lies 50 m. away from the right tower, then its abscissa is:

$$x = 200 - 50 = 150$$

If $H = (150, y)$, then the ordinate y is the height of the cable we are looking for. Since $H = (150, y)$ is at the parabola, we have:

$$(150)^2 = 500(y - 10) \Rightarrow 22,500 = 500y - 5,000 \Rightarrow y = 55$$

Hence, at a distance of 50 meters from the right tower, the height of the cable is 55 meters.

Problem 3.2.4 Prove that the following assertion is correct:

The vertex of a parabola is the closest point to the focus.

Solution

Let's consider the parabola $y^2 = 4px$, with $p > 0$. In other words, an open-right parabola with vertex at the origin and an axis that coincides with the X-axis.

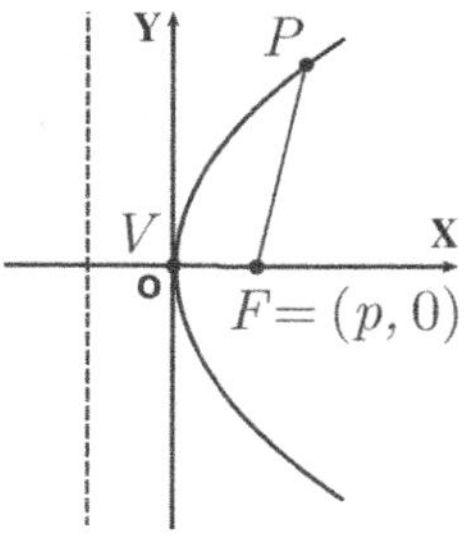

Y P V X O $F = (p, 0)$

The focus is $F = (p, 0)$.

Any point of the parabola is of the form:

$$P = \left(x,\ \sqrt{4px}\right)$$

The distance from P to the focus is:

$$d(P, F) = \sqrt{(x - p)^2 + \left(\sqrt{4px} - 0\right)^2} = \sqrt{x^2 - 2px + p^2 + 4px}$$

$$= \sqrt{x^2 + 2px + p^2} = \sqrt{(x + p)^2} = \mid x + p \mid = x + p$$

This distance is minimal when $x = 0$. Hence, the point of the parabola closest to the focus is:

$$P = \left(0,\ \sqrt{4p(0)}\right) = (0, 0) = V$$

Furthermore, this minimum distance is p.

Problem 3.2.5 The orbit of a comet.

The orbit of a comet is a parabola with the sun at one of its focus. When the comet is at a distance of $20\sqrt{2}$ millions of $Km.$ from the sun, the line passing through the sun and the comet forms an angle of $45°$ with the axis of the parabola. Find the minimum distance between the comet and the sun.

Solution

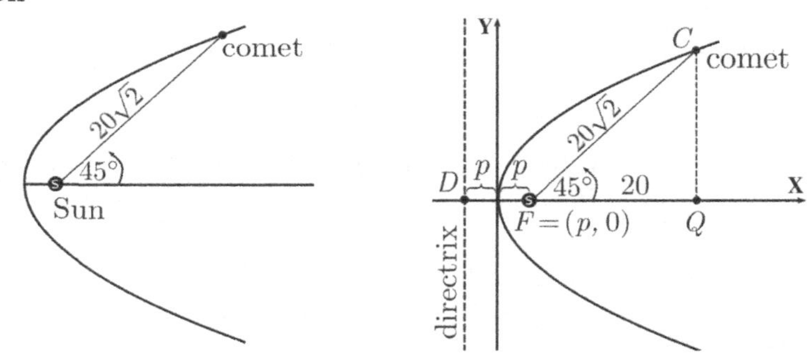

We must place the parabola with its vertex at the origin, opening to the right. Thus, the focus is on the X-axis and $F = (p, 0)$. The directrix is $x = -p$.

Let C be the point of the parabola where the comet is located when its distance from the sun is $20\sqrt{2}$ million kilometers. Take the segment $\overline{QC}$ that is perpendicular to the axis. The length of this segment is:

$$d(F, Q) = 20\sqrt{2}\cos(45°) = 20\sqrt{2}\frac{\sqrt{2}}{2} = 20$$

According to the definition of parabola:

$$d(C, \text{ Directrix}) = d(C, F)$$

But:

$$d(C, \text{ Directrix}) = d(D, Q) = d(D, F) + d(F, Q) = 2p + 20$$

Besides, $d(C, F) = 20\sqrt{2}$

Hence,

$$2p + 20 = 20\sqrt{2} \Rightarrow p = 10\left(\sqrt{2} - 1\right)$$

According to solved problem 3.2.4, the minimum distance from the comet to the sun is:

$$d(V, F) = p = 10\left(\sqrt{2} - 1\right) \text{ million kilometers.}$$

The result we get in the following problem can be easily obtained after we learn derivatives in the next course (Differential Calculus). However, this result is critical at this point to prove the reflection property of a parabola. That's why we will restrict ourselves to algebraic methods for solving the problem, even though this limitation makes the process a bit longer.

Problem 3.2.6 **Slope of the tangent line to a parabola**

Prove that the slope of the tangent line to a parabola $y^2 = 4px$, at any point $P = (x_1, y_1)$, is:

$$m = \frac{2p}{y_1}$$

Solution

The equation of the tangent line to the parabola $y^2 = 4px$, at the point $P = (x_1, y_1)$, is $y = m(x - x_1) + y_1$, where m is the slope to be found.

We must find the intersection of the tangent line with the parabola. In this regard, we can replace y in the equation of the parabola with the value of y given in the equation of the tangent. That is:

$$(m(x - x_1) + y_1)^2 = 4px$$

Squaring and factorizing,

$$m^2x^2 + \left(2mx_1 - 2m^2x_1 - 4p\right)x + \left({y_1}^2 + m^2{x_1}^2 - 2mx_1y_1\right) = 0$$

Since the tangent line intersects the parabola in a single point, the previous second-degree equation must have only one solution. This can only be possible if both roots are identical, i.e., its discriminant $b^2 - 4ac$ equals zero. That is:

$$\left(2mx_1 - 2m^2x_1 - 4p\right)^2 - 4m^2\left({y_1}^2 + m^2{x_1}^2 - 2mx_1y_1\right) = 0$$

Performing the operations and simplifying:

$$x_1m^2 - y_1m + p = 0$$

Therefore,

$$m = \frac{y_1 \pm \sqrt{{y_1}^2 - 4px_1}}{2x_1} \qquad (1)$$

But, $P = (x_1, y_1)$ is a point of the parabola, then:

$${y_1}^2 = 4px_1 \qquad (2)$$

We have that:

$$x_1 = \frac{{y_1}^2}{4p} \tag{3}$$

Now, replacing (2) in (1):

$$m = \frac{y_1 \pm \sqrt{(4px_1) - 4px_1}}{2x_1} = \frac{y_1 \pm (0)}{2x_1}$$

$$\Rightarrow m = \frac{y_1}{2x_1} \tag{4}$$

Al last, replacing (3) in (4):

$$m = \frac{y_1}{2\left(\frac{{y_1}^2}{4p}\right)} = \frac{2p}{y_1}$$

Problem 3.2.7 **Prove the reflection property of the parabola.**

Let $P = (x_1, y_1)$ be a point of a given parabola, and $\overline{N}$ be the *normal line* (perpendicular to the tangent line) of the parabola at point P. $\boldsymbol{\alpha}$ is the angle between $\overline{N}$ and the segment that joins P and the focus ($\overline{PF}$). $\boldsymbol{\beta}$ is the angle between $\overline{N}$ and the line $\overline{L}$ passing through P, which is also parallel to the axis of the parabola. The next proposition must be satisfied:

$$\boldsymbol{\alpha = \beta}$$

Proof

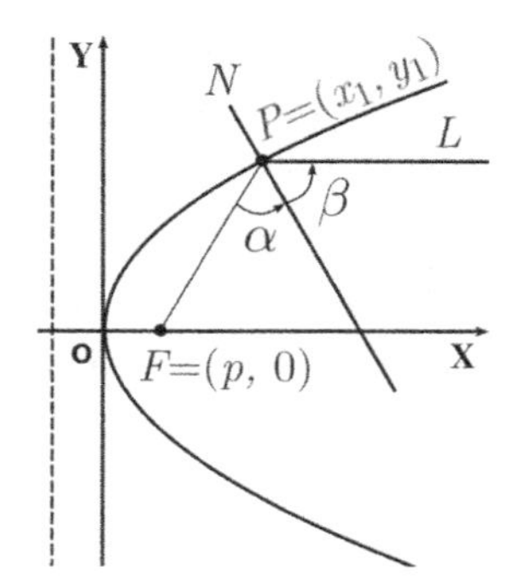

We are free to take a parabola with vertex at the origin, which opens to the right, and whose axis coincides with the X-axis.

The equation of this parabola has the form:

$$y^2 = 4px$$

According to the previous solved problem, the slope of the tangent line to the parabola at point $P = (x_1, y_1)$ is $m = \frac{2p}{y_1}$.

The slope of the line segment $\overline{FP}$ is:

$$m_1 = \frac{y_1}{x_1 - p} \tag{1}$$

Since $\overline{N}$ is perpendicular to the tangent line, its slope is:

$$m_2 = -\frac{1}{m} = -\frac{y_1}{2p} \qquad (2)$$

Since $\overline{L}$ is parallel to the X-axis, its slope equals zero.

If we extend the segment $\overline{FP}$, we see that θ is the supplementary angle of $\alpha + \beta$, that is:

$$\theta = \pi - (\alpha + \beta)$$

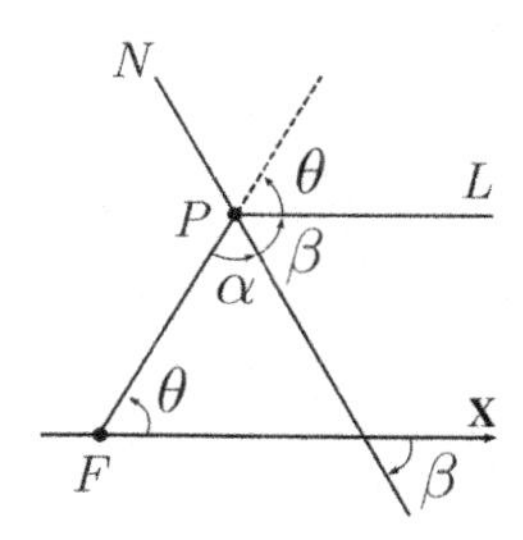

Besides, θ and β are congruent to the acute angles formed at the intersections of the X-axis with the lines $\overline{FP}$ and $\overline{N}$, respectively.

According to the solved problem 2.3.11, we have that the tangents of θ and $-\beta$ equal the slopes of the straight lines $\overline{FP}$ and $\overline{N}$, respectively, that is:

$$\tan\theta = m_1 \qquad (3)$$

$$\tan(-\beta) = m_2 \Rightarrow -\tan\beta = m_2 \qquad \text{(trigonometric formula 10)}$$

Then:

$$\tan\beta = -m_2 \qquad (4)$$

Now:

$$\begin{aligned}
\tan\alpha &= \tan(\pi - (\theta+\beta)) && \text{(supplementary angle)}\\
&= \tan\left((-(\theta+\beta)) + \pi\right) = \tan\left(-(\theta+\beta)\right) && \text{(trigonometric form. 22)}\\
&= -\tan(\theta+\beta) && \text{(trigonometric form. 10)}\\
&= -\left[\frac{\tan\theta + \tan\beta}{1 - \tan\theta\tan\beta}\right] && \text{(trigonometric form. 25)}
\end{aligned}$$

$$= \frac{-\tan\theta - \tan\beta}{1 - \tan\theta\tan\beta} \qquad (5)$$

Replacing (3) and (4) in (5):

$$\tan\alpha = \frac{-(m_1) - (-m_2)}{1 - (m_1)(-m_2)} = \frac{m_2 - m_1}{1 + m_1 m_2} \qquad (6)$$

Replacing (1) and (2) in (6):

$$\tan\alpha = \frac{m_2 - m_1}{1 + m_1 m_2} = \frac{\left(-\dfrac{y_1}{2p}\right) - \left(\dfrac{y_1}{x_1 - p}\right)}{1 + \left(\dfrac{y_1}{x_1 - p}\right)\left(-\dfrac{y_1}{2p}\right)} = \frac{-x_1 y_1 - p y_1}{2px_1 - 2p^2 - {y_1}^2}$$

Since $P_1 = (x_1, y_1)$ is at the parabola, we have that ${y_1}^2 = 4px_1$. Replacing this equality in the above expression, we have:

$$\tan\alpha = \frac{-x_1y_1 - py_1}{2px_1 - 2p^2 - 4px_1} = \frac{-y_1(x_1+p)}{-2p(x_1+p)} = \frac{y_1}{2p} \qquad (7)$$

Now, we proceed to calculate the tangent of β replacing (2) in (4):

$$\tan\beta = -\left(-\frac{y_1}{2p}\right) = \frac{y_1}{2p} \qquad (8)$$

Finally, from (7) and (8), we get the expected result: $\boldsymbol{\alpha = \beta}$.

Did you know this?

*In Physics, the result of the above problem is defined by the **Law of Reflection** as follows:*

If a ray of light L_1 strikes a mirror, its reflection follows the path of the straight line L_2. If α is the angle formed by L_1 and the normal line N, and β is the angle formed by N and L_2, then $\boldsymbol{\alpha = \beta}$.

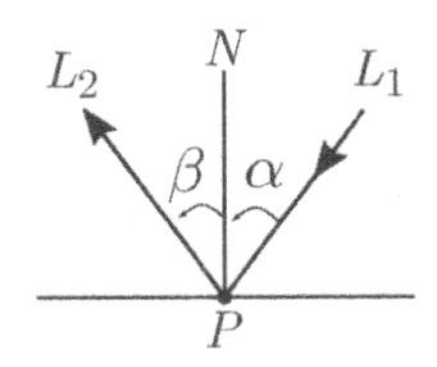

EXERCISES 3.2

In the exercises 1 through 5, find the focus, the directrix and the length of the latus rectum (focal diameter) of the parabola, *L*.

1. $x^2 = 4y$ **2.** $3x^2 + 4y = 0$ **3.** $y^2 - 6x = 0$

4.$y^2 + 20x = 0$ **5.** $4y^2 + x = 0$

In the exercises 6 through 10, find the vertex, axis, focus, directrix and the length of the latus rectum of the parabola, *L*.

6. $x^2 - 4x - 8y = -12$ **7.** $y^2 + 10y = x - 26$ **8.** $y^2 - 4y = 2x + 4$

9. $4x^2+4x+4y+1 = 0$ **10.** $9x^2 + 24x + 72y + 88 = 0$

In the exercises 11 through 23, find an equation of the parabola with the given properties

11. Focus $(-6, 0)$, directrix: $x = 6$. **12.** Focus $(0, 4)$, directrix: $y = -4$.

13. Focus $(2, 5)$,
directrix: $y = -1$

14. Focus $\left(-\frac{7}{8}, -2\right)$,
directrix: $x = -\frac{9}{8}$.

15. Vertex $(-2, 2)$,
directrix: $x = 2$.

16. Vertex $(-2, 2)$,
directrix: $y = -2$.

17. Vertex $(3, 1)$, Focus: $(3, 5)$

18. Vertex $(0, 0)$, axis: $x = 0$,
passes through $(3, -2)$

19. Vertex $(1, 2)$, axis: parallel to X-axis, passes through $(5, 8)$.

20. Vertex $(1, -2)$, axis: parallel to Y-axis, length of latus rectum: 6.

21. directrix: $x = -2$, axis: $y = 1$, length of latus rectum: 8.

22. Endpoints of the latus rectum: $(1, 1)$ and $(7, 1)$. It opens upwards.

23. Vertex $(0,\ 0)$, $0)$, endpoints of latus rectum: $(-4, k)$ and $(4,\ k)$. It opens downwards.

24. A ball is thrown horizontally from the edge of the rooftop of a 64 meter high building.

The trajectory of the ball is a parabola with its vertex at the edge of the roof, having an axis coincident with the wall adjacent to this edge. The ball passes through a point that is 20 meters away from the wall when its height is 16 meters.

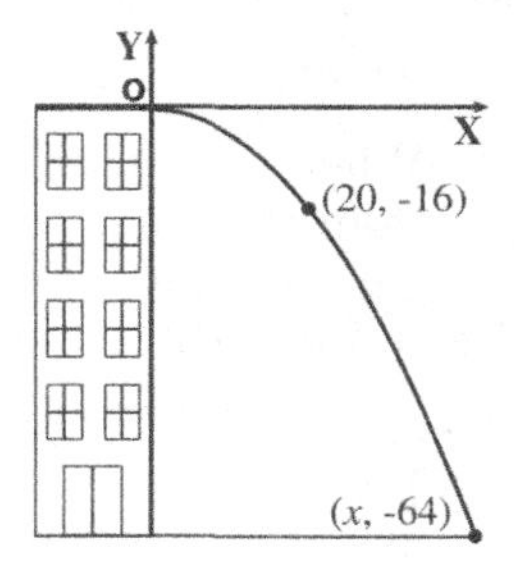

a. Find a equation of the ball trajectory using the coordinate system, where the origin lies on the vertex and the Y-axis coincides with the axis of the parabola.

b. Find the distance between the wall and the point where the ball hits the floor.

25. A lighthouse has a parabolic mirror of 2 $cm.$ of a depth, and a rim with a diameter of 12 $cm.$ At what distance from the vertex is placed the light source if the reflected rays are parallel to the axis of the parabola?

26. A satellite dish of a parabolic antenna has a rim of 1 $m.$ of diameter, and a receptor that lies on its center. Find the depth of the dish.

27. The towers of a suspension bridge are 150 $m.$ apart, and rise 23 $m.$ above the road. The cable between the towers has the shape of a parabola, of which the lowest point is 8 $m.$ above the road.

a. Find an equation of the parabola determined by the cable.

b. Find the height of the cable at 15 m. from the tower.

28. A bridge is held over a concrete parabolic arch.

This arch has a length of 200 feet at water level, and a height of 50 feet at its center.

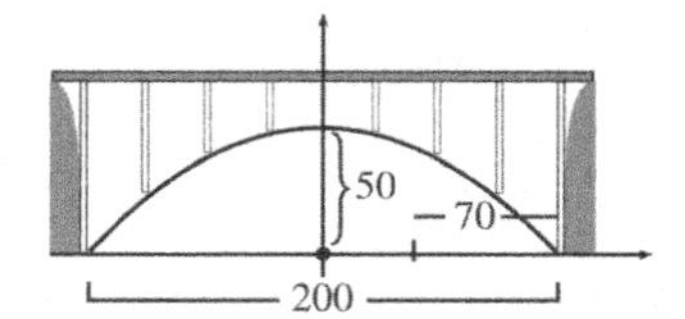

a. Find an equation of the parabola using the coordinate system given in the figure.

b. Find the height at water level of the arc at 70 feet from its right end.

29. A comet has a parabolic orbit with the sun on its focus. When the comet is at a distance of 60 millions of Km. away from the sun, the line passing through the sun and the comet forms a $60°$ angle with the axis of the parabola. Find shortest distance between the comet and the sun.

30. A satellite was placed in parabolic orbit with focus at the center of the moon.

When the satellite is 5,814 km. away from the lunar surface, the axis of the parabola and the straight line passing through the satellite and the center of the moon form a 60-degree angle. The shortest distance between the satellite and the lunar surface is 150 km.

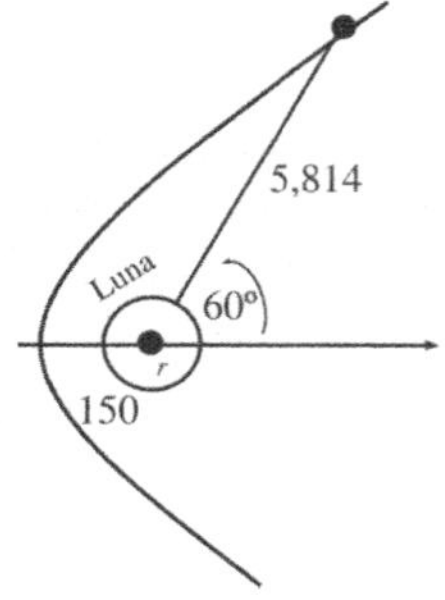

Find the radio of the moon.

Hint: $p = 150 + r$ *and solved problem 3.2.5.*

31. Find the standard form of the equation of a parabola with its axis parallel to the X-axis, and passing through the points (3, 1), (4, 3) and (12, 7).

Hint: The three points satisfy the equation $(y - h)^2 = 4p(x - k)$.

32. Find the standard form of the equation of a parabola whose axis is parallel to the Y-axis, passing through the points (1,0), (-1,6) and (2,3).

33. Prove that the equation of the tangent line to the parabola $y^2 = 4px$ at any point $P = (x_1, y_1)$ is $y_1y = 2p(x + x_1)$.

Hint: See the solved problem 3.2.6.

SECCION 3.3

THE ELLIPSE

Definition

As seen in section 3.1, according to Greek Geometry, an **ellipse** occurs when the plane intersects only one of the nappes of the Right Circular Cone. In Analytic Geometry, an ellipse is the set of all points in the plane such that the sum of their distances from two fixed points, $\boldsymbol{F_1}$ and $\boldsymbol{F_2}$, is constant.

These two fixed points are called the **foci** (plural of focus). The midpoint of the line segment whose ends are F_1 and F_2 is the **center of the ellipse**.

STANDARD FORM OF THE EQUATION OF AN ELLIPSE

Let's place center of the ellipse at the origin and the foci on the X-axis, having $F_1 = (-c, 0)$ and $F_2 = (c, 0)$ as coordinates.

If $2a$ is the constant of the definition, then:

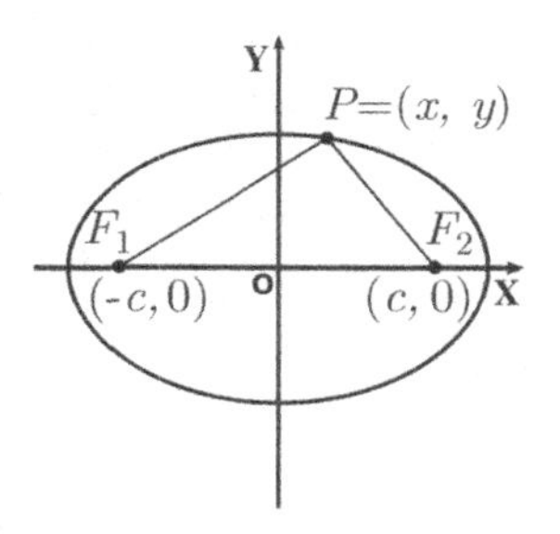

$P = (x, y)$ is in the ellipse

$$\Leftrightarrow d(P, F_1) + d(P, F_2) = 2a$$

$$\Leftrightarrow \sqrt{(x+c)^2 + y^2} + \sqrt{(x-c)^2 + y^2} = 2a$$

$$\Leftrightarrow \sqrt{(x-c)^2 + y^2} = 2a - \sqrt{(x+c)^2 + y^2}$$

$$\Leftrightarrow x^2 - 2cx + c^2 + y^2 = 4a^2 - 4a\sqrt{(x+c)^2 + y^2} + x^2 + 2cx + c^2 + y^2$$

$$\Leftrightarrow a\sqrt{(x+c)^2 + y^2} = a^2 + cx$$

$$\Leftrightarrow a^2(x^2 + 2cx + c^2 + y^2) = a^4 + 2a^2cx + c^2x^2$$

$$\Leftrightarrow (a^2 - c^2)x^2 + a^2y^2 = a^2(a^2 - c^2) \qquad (1)$$

Dividing by $a^2\left(a^2 - c^2\right)$:

$$\frac{x^2}{a^2} + \frac{y^2}{a^2 - c^2} = 1 \qquad (2)$$

Elementary geometry tells us that the sum of the lengths of any two sides in a triangle is always greater than the length of the third side.

If we apply this result to the triangle in the above figure, we get:

$$\begin{aligned} d(F_1, P) + d(P, F_2) &> d(F_1, F_2) \\ \Rightarrow 2a &> 2c \\ \Rightarrow a &> c \\ \Rightarrow a^2 - c^2 &> 0 \end{aligned}$$

Let $b = \sqrt{a^2 - c^2}$, then $b^2 = a^2 - c^2$. Replacing this equation in (1), we get:

$$\frac{x^2}{a^2} + \frac{y^2}{b^2} = 1$$

The line passing through the foci intersects the ellipse in the points:

$$V_1 = (-a, 0) \quad \text{and} \quad V_2 = (a, 0)$$

These points are called **vertices** of the ellipse.

The segment $\overline{V_1V_2}$ is called **major axis**, and its length is $2a$. The line passing through the center that is perpendicular to the major axis cuts the ellipse in the points:

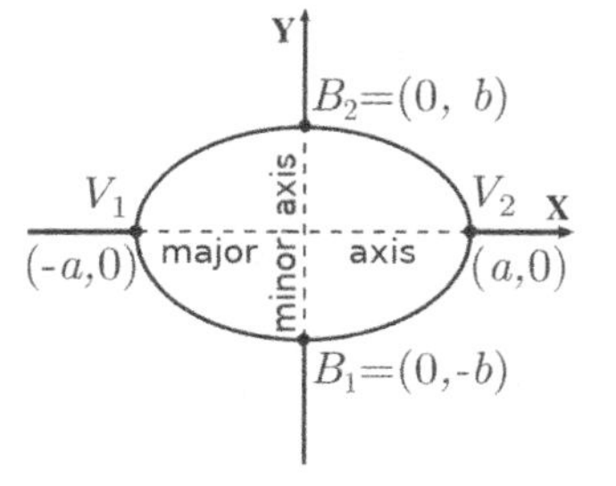

$$B_1 = (0, -b) \quad \text{and} \quad B_2 = (0, b)$$

The segment $\overline{B_1B_2}$ is called the **minor axis**, and its length is $2b$.

If $c = 0$, then the two foci coincide and are equal to the origin of the coordinates. Moreover, in this case we have that:

$$b = \sqrt{a^2 - c^2} = \sqrt{a^2 - (0)^2} = a,$$

this way, the ellipse becomes a **circle** of radius $r = a = b$.

If the foci are on the Y-axis, then:

$$F_1 = (0, -c) \quad \text{and} \quad F_2 = (0, c)$$

Using similar reasoning as above, we can obtain the equation for this ellipse:

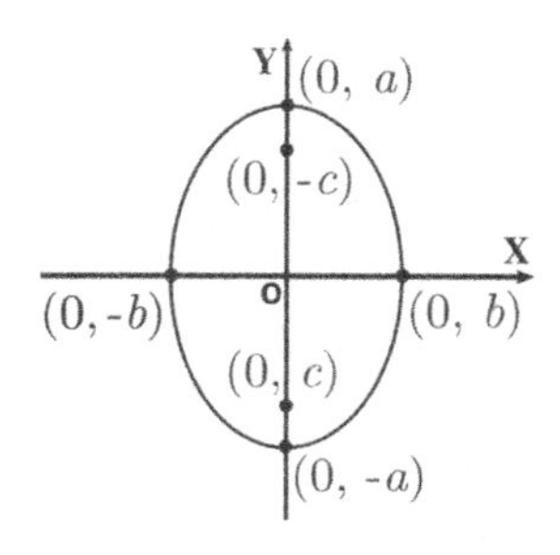

$$\frac{x^2}{b^2} + \frac{y^2}{a^2} = 1,$$

where, as before: $b^2 = a^2 - c^2$.

The next theorem summarizes the above results.

Theorem 3.3.1 **Standard form of the equation of an ellipse.**

1. The **standard** form of the equation of an ellipse with **center at the origin**, major axis on the X-axis, and constant $\boldsymbol{2a}$, is:

$$\frac{x^2}{a^2} + \frac{y^2}{b^2} = 1, \text{ where } a \geq b > 0 \text{ and } b^2 = a^2 - c^2$$

The foci are: $F_1 = (-c, 0)$ and $F_2 = (c, 0)$

2. The **standard** form of the equation of an ellipse with **center at the origin**, major axis on the Y-axis, and constant $\boldsymbol{2a}$, is

$$\frac{x^2}{b^2} + \frac{y^2}{a^2} = 1, \text{ where } a \geq b > 0 \text{ and } b^2 = a^2 - c^2$$

The foci are: $F_1 = (0, -c)$ and $F_2 = (0, c)$

Remark

To find the coordinate axis where the foci are located, we simply identify the variable with the larger denominator in the ellipse equation.

Example 3.3.1 Prove that the graph of the following equation is an ellipse:

$$9x^2 + 16y^2 = 144$$

Find the foci, vertices, length of the major and minor axis.

Solution

Let's transform this equation into the standard form of the equation of an ellipse. For this purpose, we must divide the given equation by 144:

$$\frac{9x^2}{144} + \frac{16y^2}{144} = \frac{144}{144} \Leftrightarrow \frac{x^2}{16} + \frac{y^2}{9} = 1$$

$$\Leftrightarrow \frac{x^2}{4^2} + \frac{y^2}{3^2} = 1$$

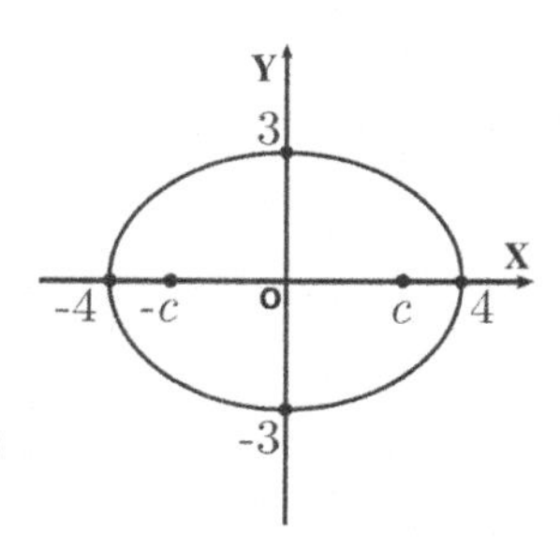

Theorem 3.3.1 (part 1) says that this expression is the standard form of the equation of an ellipse.

Furthermore, according to the previous remark, the foci are on the X-axis, meaning that $a = 4$ and $b = 3$. We also have that:

$$c = \sqrt{a^2 - b^2} = \sqrt{4^2 - 3^2} = \sqrt{16 - 9} = \sqrt{7}$$

Hence:

- Foci: $F_1 = (-\sqrt{7}, 0)$ y $F_2 = (\sqrt{7}, 0)$
- Vertices: $V_1 = (-4, 0)$ y $V_2 = (4, 0)$
- Length of the major axis $= 2a = 2(4) = 8$
- Length of the minor axis $= 2b = 2(3) = 6$

Definition The **eccentricity** of the ellipse is the ratio:

$$e = \frac{c}{a} = \frac{\sqrt{a^2 - b^2}}{a}$$

Since $0 < c < a$, then $0 < e = \frac{c}{a} < 1$. If e is close to 1, them c is close to a, meaning that the ellipse is elongated. If e is close to 0, then the ellipse is closer to become a circle.

Example 3.3.2

If an ellipse have its center in the origin, an eccentricity of $e = \frac{4}{5}$, and one of its focus is (0, 4), find:

a. the other focus.

b. the standard form of the equation of the ellipse.

Solution

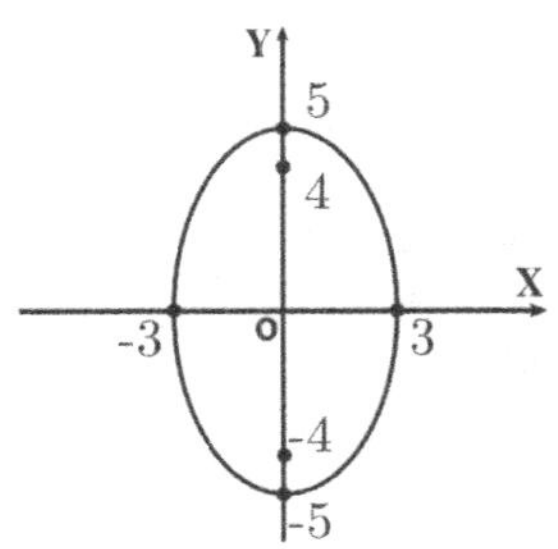

a. The other focus is $(0, -4)$.

b. We have that $c = 4$.

Then:

$$e = \frac{c}{a} \Rightarrow \frac{4}{5} = \frac{4}{a} \Rightarrow a = 5$$

On the other hand:

$$b = \sqrt{a^2 - c^2} = \sqrt{5^2 - 4^2} = \sqrt{9} = 3$$

The standard form of the equation for this ellipse is:

$$\frac{x^2}{3^2} + \frac{y^2}{5^2} = 1, \quad \text{or} \quad \frac{x^2}{9} + \frac{y^2}{25} = 1$$

Example 3.3.3

The center of an ellipse is in the origin and the foci are on the X-axis. The distances between one of the foci and the vertices are 25 and 1, respectively.

a. Find the eccentricity of the ellipse.

b. Find the standard form of the equation for this ellipse.

Solution

a. Let be:

The indicated focus: $F_2 = (c, 0)$.

The vertices:

$V_1 = (-a, 0)$ and $V_2 = (a, 0)$

We have:

$$d(V_1, F_2) = d(V_1, \text{O}) + d(\text{O}, F_2) = a + c = 25$$
$$d(F_2, V_2) = d(\text{O}, V_2) - d(\text{O}, F_2) = a - c = 1$$

Solving the system:

$$\begin{cases} a + c = 25 \\ a - c = 1 \end{cases} \quad \text{we get: } a = 13,\ c = 12$$

Hence, $e = \dfrac{c}{a} = \dfrac{12}{13}$

b. $b^2 = a^2 - c^2 = 13^2 - 12^2 = 169 - 144 = 25$

So, the standard form of the equation for this ellipse is: $\dfrac{x^2}{169} + \dfrac{y^2}{25} = 1$

Definition **Latus Rectum of an ellipse:**

A Latus Rectum of an ellipse is the segment that runs through a focus, is perpendicular to the major axis and has endpoints on the ellipse.

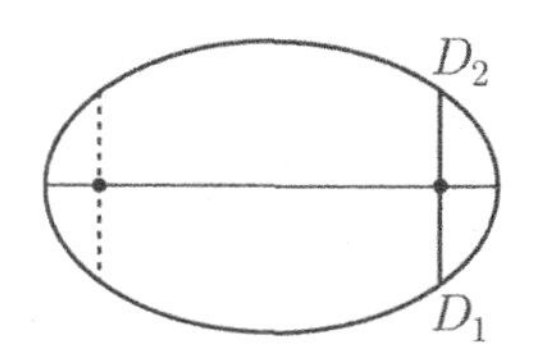

Since an ellipse has two foci, it will have two Latus Rectum. The segment $\overline{D_1D_2}$ is one of them, the other is the dotted segment of the figure.

In solved problem 3.3.3 we will demonstrate that the length of a Latus Rectum of an ellipse is given by the formula:

$$L = \frac{2b^2}{a}$$

Example 3.3.4

The center of an ellipse is at the origin and one focus is $(0, 6)$. If the length of the latus rectum is $\frac{64}{5}$, find the standard form equation for this ellipse.

Solution

We have:

$$c = 6 \quad \text{and} \quad b^2 = a^2 - c^2 \Rightarrow b^2 = a^2 - 36 \qquad (1)$$

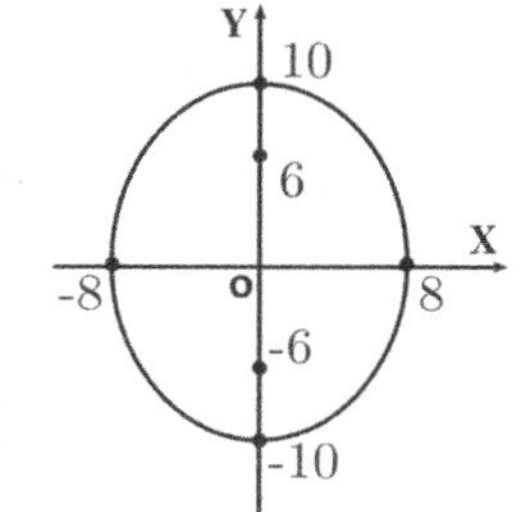

On the other hand:

$$L = \frac{2b^2}{a} \Rightarrow \frac{64}{5} = \frac{2b^2}{a} \Rightarrow b^2 = \frac{32}{5}a \qquad (2)$$

From (1) and (2), we get:

$$a^2 - 36 = \frac{32}{5}a \Rightarrow 5a^2 - 32a - 180 = 0 \Rightarrow a = 10 \quad \text{and} \quad b = 8$$

Then, the standard form equation for the ellipse is:

$$\frac{x^2}{8^2} + \frac{y^2}{10^2} = 1$$

STANDARD FORM OF THE EQUATION OF A SHIFTED ELLIPSE

1. The **standard form** of the equation of an ellipse with **center** (h, k), major axis parallel to the X-axis, and constant $2a$ is:

$$\frac{(x-h)^2}{a^2} + \frac{(y-k)^2}{b^2} = 1, \text{ where } a \geq b > 0 \text{ and } b^2 = a^2 - c^2$$

The foci are $F_1 = ((-c+h), k)$ and $F_2 = ((c+h), k)$.

2. The **standard form** of the equation of an ellipse with **center** (h, k), major axis parallel to the Y-axis, and constant $2a$ is:

$$\frac{(x-h)^2}{b^2} + \frac{(y-k)^2}{a^2} = 1, \text{ where } a \geq b > 0 \text{ and } b^2 = a^2 - c^2$$

The foci are $F_1 = (h, (-c+k))$ and $F_2 = (h, (c+k))$.

Example 3.3.5 Prove that the graph of the following equation is an ellipse:

$$4x^2 + y^2 - 24x - 4y + 24 = 0$$

Find the foci, vertices, length of the axes and eccentricity.

Solution

We seek to transform this equation into one on its standard form. For this purpose, we proceed completing squares:

$$\begin{aligned}
&4x^2 + y^2 - 24x - 4y + 24 = 0 \\
&\quad\Leftrightarrow 4\left(x^2 - 6x + \quad\right) + \left(y^2 - 4y + \quad\right) = -24 \\
&\quad\Leftrightarrow 4\left(x^2 - 6x + 9\right) + \left(y^2 - 4y + 4\right) = -24 + 36 + 4 \\
&\quad\Leftrightarrow 4(x-3)^2 + (y-2)^2 = 16 \\
&\quad\Leftrightarrow \frac{(x-3)^2}{4} + \frac{(y-2)^2}{16} = 1
\end{aligned}$$

The part 2 of the previous proposition says that this is the standard form of the equation of the ellipse with center $(h, k) = (3, 2)$ and major axis parallel to the Y-axis. Besides,

$$a^2 = 16 \Rightarrow a = 4$$

Hence:

$$\begin{aligned}
V_1 &= (3,\ (2-a)) = (3,\ (2-4)) = (3, -2) \\
V_2 &= (3,\ (2+a)) = (3,\ (2+4)) = (3,\ 6)
\end{aligned}$$

On the other hand:

$$\begin{aligned}
b^2 = 4 \Rightarrow c^2 &= a^2 - b^2 = 16 - 4 \\
&\Rightarrow c = \sqrt{12} = 2\sqrt{3}
\end{aligned}$$

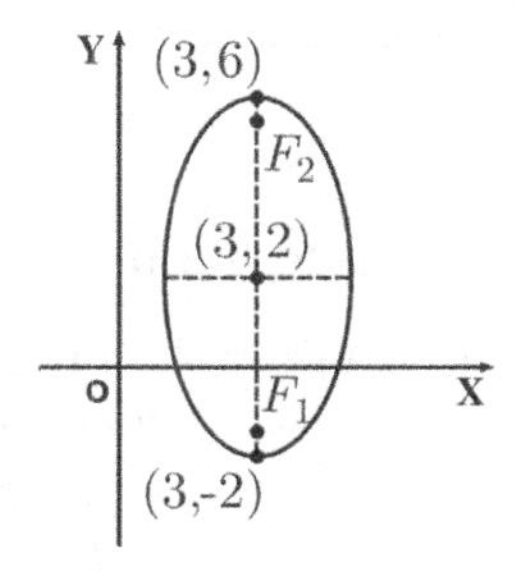

Hence:

$$F_1 = (3,\ (2-c)) = \left(3,\ (2-2\sqrt{3})\right)$$

$$F_2 = (3,\ (2+c)) = \left(3,\ (2+2\sqrt{3})\right)$$

The eccentricity is:

$$e = \frac{c}{a} = \frac{2\sqrt{3}}{4} = \frac{\sqrt{3}}{2}$$

The length of the major axis is:

$$2a = 2(4) = 8$$

The length of the minor axis is:

$$2b = 2(2) = 4$$

REFLECTION PROPERTY OF THE ELLIPSE

Like the parabola, the ellipse also exhibits a curious reflection property. A light ray or a sound wave that originates at one focus is reflected on the ellipse until it reaches the other focus. This will be proven in the solved problem 3.3.4.

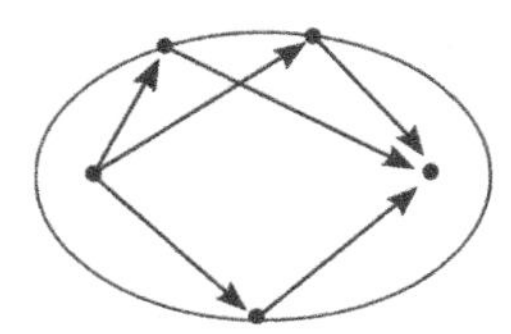

Did you know this?

There exist several elliptical domes. Among the most famous we have the Capitol's Statuary Hall in Washington D.C, the Mormon Tabernacle in Salt Lake City and the Saint Paul's Cathedral in London.

The last one was designed by mathematician and architect ***Christopher Wren*** *(1632-1723).*

Mormon Tabernacle

In these domes a sound at one focus will reflect off the dome and reach the other focus, thanks to the reflection property of the ellipse.

These domes are called ***whispering rooms*** *because a whispered sound at one focus can be easily heard at the other focus, despite the distance.*

Example 3.3.6

The dome of the Mormon Tabernacle is 250 feet long, 150 feet wide and 80 feet height. Its longitudinal sections are semi-ellipses. In order to get a high quality recording of a sermon, the preacher must be located at one focus, and the recording equipment at the other focus. Find the position of the foci.

Solution

It's worth mentioning that the width of the dome was only provided to give some idea of the structure's geometry. This information is not necessary to find the solution of the problem.

We have that:

$$2a = 250 \Rightarrow a = 125$$

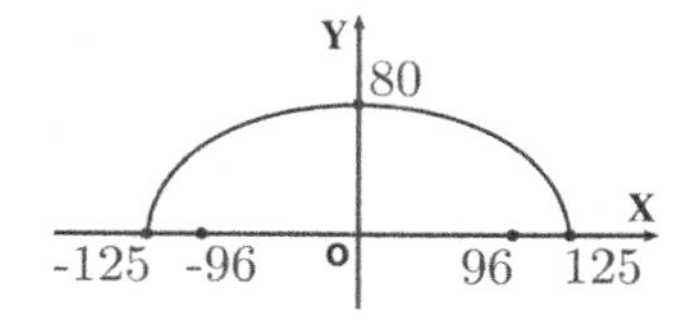

On the other hand, $b = 80$. Hence:

$$c = \sqrt{a^2 - b^2} = \sqrt{(125)^2 - (80)^2}$$

$$= \sqrt{9.225} \approx 96$$

The preacher must locate at 96 feet from the center. The equipment must also be located at 96 feet from the center, but on the opposite side.

THE ELLIPSE IN ASTRONOMY

In 1609, the German astronomer **Johannes Kepler** (1571-1630) published his work **Astronomia Nova** (New Astronomy), where he presented two of his three laws of planetary motion. The third law was published in 1618.

Kepler formulated these laws studying the observations of the Danish astronomer **Tycho Brahe** (1546-1601). Kepler developed his laws empirically, however, they were proved by Newton using the laws of gravity, about 30 years after Kepler died. Here is the first one.

Kepler's first law - Law of Orbits

The Planets move around the Sun following an elliptical pathway, where the Sun locates at one of the foci.

1. Mercury 2. Venus
3. Earth 4. Mars
5. Jupiter 6. Saturn

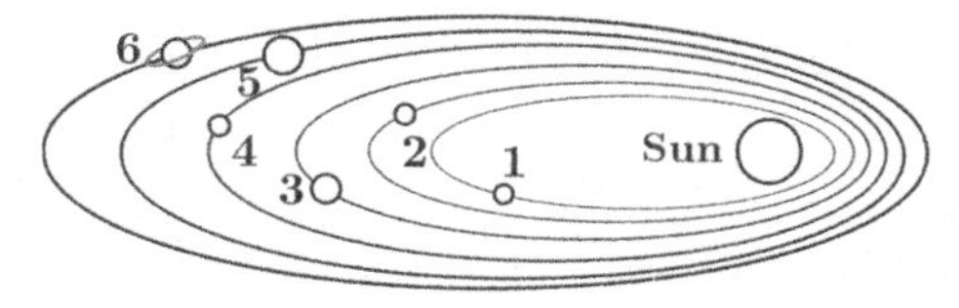

The Kepler laws also rule the motion of comets.

Example 3.3.7 The orbit of the Halley Comet is an ellipse.

The sun locates at one focus, the length of the major axis is $5.34 \times 10^9 Km.$ and the length of the minor axis is $1.36 \times 10^9 Km.$

a. Find an equation of the orbit.

b. Find the eccentricity of the orbit.

c. Find the minimum distance between the comet and the sun.

Solution

a. We take a coordinate system with origin at the center of the orbit and the sun on the positive side of the X-axis.

We have:

$2a = 5.34 \times 10^9 \Rightarrow a = 26.7 \times 10^8$

$2b = 1.36 \times 10^9 \Rightarrow b = 6.8 \times 10^8$

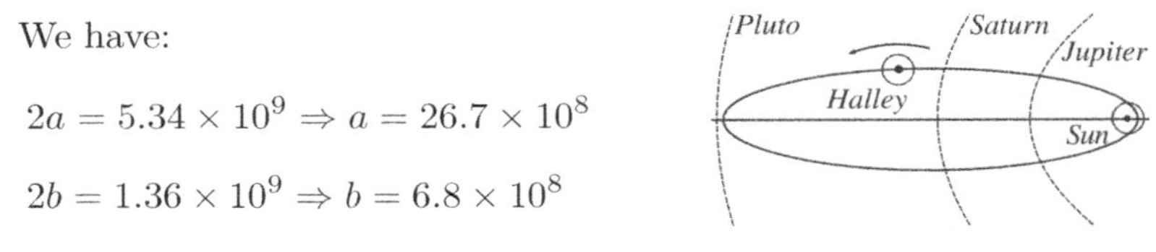

Hence, the equation of the orbit of Halley's Comet is:

$$\frac{x^2}{(26.7)^2 \times 10^{16}} + \frac{y^2}{(6.8)^2 \times 10^{16}} = 1$$

$$\text{or:} \quad \frac{x^2}{712.89 \times 10^{16}} + \frac{y^2}{46.24 \times 10^{16}} = 1$$

b. Let $F = (c, 0)$ be the focus of the ellipse where the sun is located.

We have:

$$c = \sqrt{a^2 - b^2} = \sqrt{(26.7)^2 \times 10^{16} - (6.8)^2 \times 10^{16}} = 25.819 \times 10^8$$

Hence, the eccentricity is:

$$e = \frac{c}{a} = \frac{25.819 \times 10^8}{26.7 \times 10^8} \approx 0.967$$

c. We have that:

$$\text{minimum distance} = a - c$$

$$\Rightarrow \text{minimum distance} = \left(26.7 \times 10^8\right) - \left(25.819 \times 10^8\right) = 88.1 \times 10^6$$

Hence, the minimum distance from the comet to the sun is $88.1 \times 10^6\ km$.

Did you know this?

Halley's comet *is the most famous comet in our solar system. There are historical documents indicating that this comet was seen in 240 B.C. however, it was not recognized as a comet until 1758, when it was given the name Halley, in honor of the English astronomer* ***Edmond Halley*** *(1656-1742), friend of Isaac Newton.*

Halley spotted this comet in 1682 and claimed that it was the same as the one seen in 1531 and 1607. Furthermore, he predicted that it will appear again in the year 1758.

His prediction came true, unfortunately, Halley passed away 16 years earlier. This event was one of the most convincing achievements of the ***Gravitational Theory*** *of Newton.*

The last sighting of this comet was in 1986, and its next appearance will be in the year 2061.

SOLVED PROBLEMS 3.3

Problem 3.3.1

A semi-elliptical archway over a one-way road has a height of 11 feet, and a width of 36 feet. A 12-feet wide and 10-feet high truck is driving through the middle of the road. Will the trunk be able to cross the tunnel without touching the archway?

Solution

The equation of the ellipse is:

$$\frac{x^2}{18^2} + \frac{y^2}{11^2} = 1$$

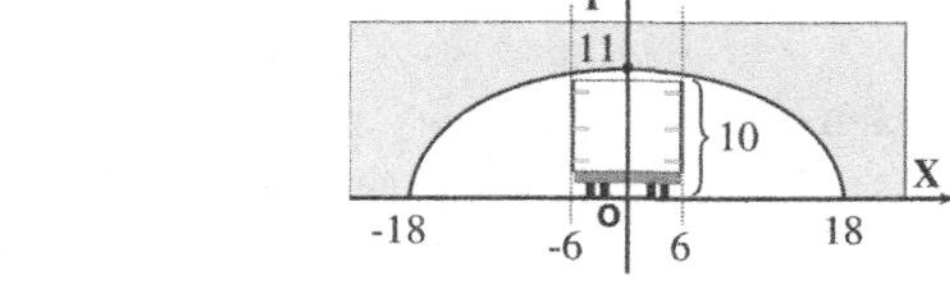

If $x = 6$, then:

$$\frac{y^2}{11^2} = 1 - \frac{6^2}{18^2} = \frac{11^2}{18^2}\left(18^2 - 6^2\right)$$

$$\Rightarrow y = \frac{11}{18}\sqrt{288} = \frac{11}{18}(12)\sqrt{2} \approx 10.37$$

Since $10 < 10.37$, we claim that the truck will cross the tunnel without trouble.

Problem 3.3.2

A satellite has an elliptical orbit, where the center of the earth is located at one focus. The maximum and minimum distances between the satellite and the earth surface are 11,620 and 1,620 Km, respectively. If the radius of the earth is 6,380 Km. find:

a. the eccentricity of the orbit.

b. the standard equation of the orbit using the coordinate system with origin at the center of the orbit, and the center of the earth on the positive side of the X-axis.

Solution

a. Let $2a$ be the length of the major axis of the orbit, r el radius of the earth, and c the coordinate of the center of the earth.

Consider the equation system:

$$\begin{cases} a + c = 11,620 + r \\ a - c = 1,620 + r \end{cases}$$

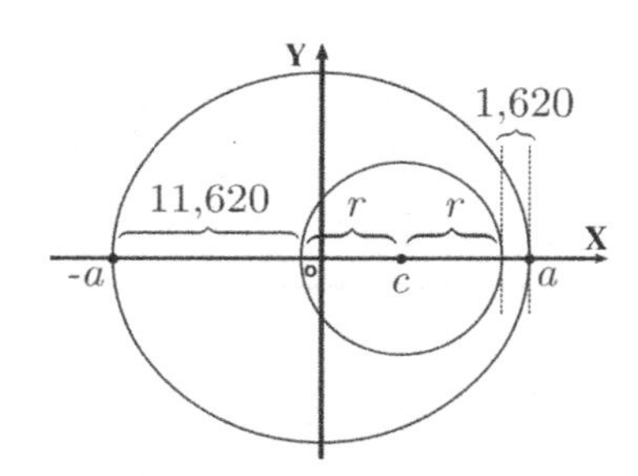

Adding the above equations:

$$2a = (11,620 + 1,620) + 2r = 13,240 + 2r$$

$$\Rightarrow a = 6,620 + r = 6,620 + 6,380 = 13,000$$

Subtracting the second equation of the system from the first one:

$$2c = (11,620 - 1,620) = 10,000 \Rightarrow c = 5,000$$

Hence, the eccentricity of the orbit is:

$$e = \frac{c}{a} = \frac{5,000}{13,000} = \frac{5}{13}$$

b. $b^2 = a^2 - c^2 = (13,000)^2 - (5,000)^2 = (12,000)^2$

Therefore, the standard equation of the orbit is:

$$\frac{x^2}{(13,000)^2} + \frac{y^2}{(12,000)^2} = 1$$

Problem 3.3.3 Length of the latus rectum.

Prove that the length of the latus rectum of an ellipse is given by:

$$L = \frac{2b^2}{a}$$

Solution

We choose a coordinate system with origin at the center of the ellipse. The X-axis will coincide with the major axis. The foci are $F_1 = (0, -c)$ and $F_2 = (0, c)$.

The standard form of the equation is:

$$\frac{x^2}{a^2} + \frac{y^2}{b^2} = 1$$

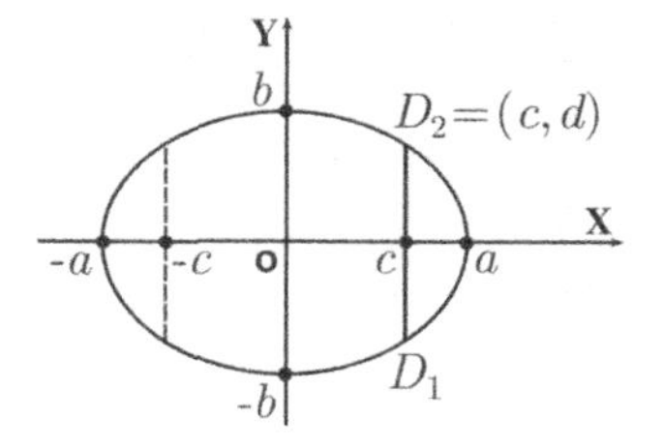

Let $D_2 = (c, d)$ be the endpoint of the latus rectum above the focus $(\boldsymbol{c}, \mathbf{0})$.

Since $D_2 = (c, d)$ is on the ellipse, we have:

$$\frac{c^2}{a^2} + \frac{d^2}{b^2} = 1 \Rightarrow \frac{d^2}{b^2} = 1 - \frac{c^2}{a^2} \Rightarrow d^2 = \frac{b^2}{a^2}\left(a^2 - c^2\right) = \frac{b^2}{a^2}\left(b^2\right)$$

$$\Rightarrow d = \frac{b^2}{a}$$

Hence, the length of the latus rectum is:

$$L = 2d = 2\frac{b^2}{a}$$

Problem 3.3.4 Proof of the reflection property of the ellipse.

Our job will be to demonstrate that the tangent line to an ellipse, at a point $\boldsymbol{P = (x, y)}$, forms two congruent angles, $\boldsymbol{\alpha}$ and $\boldsymbol{\beta}$, with the segments joining P with both foci. That is:

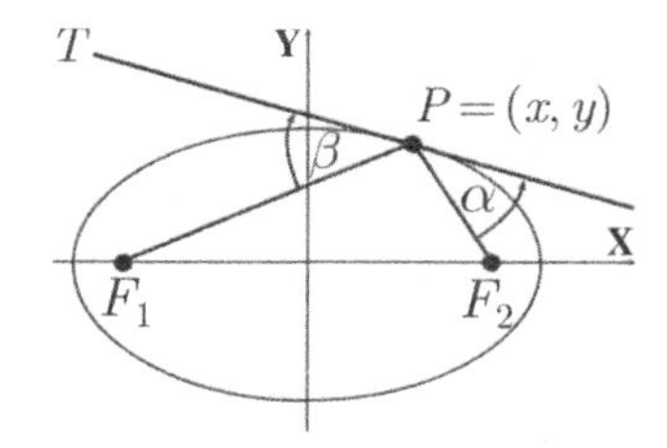

$$\boldsymbol{\alpha = \beta}$$

Solution

According to the problem solved 2.3.11, the slope of the line T equals the tangent of $-\theta$:

$$m_T = \tan(-\theta)$$

$$\Leftrightarrow m_T = -\tan\theta \qquad (1)$$

Now, according to the statement of the exercise 21 (to be demonstrated by the reader), the slope of T at point P is:

$$m_T = -\frac{b^2x}{a^2y} \qquad (2)$$

From (1) and (2) we get:

$$-\tan\theta = -\frac{b^2x}{a^2y}$$

$$\Leftrightarrow \tan\theta = \frac{b^2x}{a^2y} \qquad (3)$$

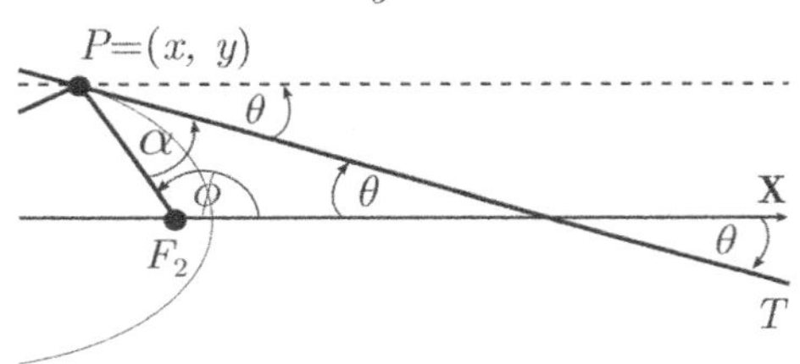

The slope of $\overline{F_2P}$ is:

$$m_{\overline{F_2P}} = \tan\phi$$

But:

$$\phi = \pi - (\alpha + \theta) \qquad \text{(supplementary angles)}$$

$$\begin{aligned} \Rightarrow \tan\phi &= \tan(\pi - (\theta + \alpha)) \\ &= \tan(-(\theta + \alpha)) && \text{(trigonometric formula 22)} \\ &= -\tan(\theta + \alpha) && \text{(trigonometric formula 10)} \end{aligned}$$

Then:

$$m_{\overline{F_2P}} = -\tan(\theta + \alpha) \qquad (4)$$

Besides, by the definition of slope:

$$\begin{aligned} m_{\overline{F_2P}} &= \frac{y - (0)}{x - (c)} && \text{(slope formula)} \\ &= \frac{y}{x - c} && (5) \end{aligned}$$

From (4) and (5) we get:

$$
\begin{aligned}
-\frac{y}{x-c} &= \tan(\theta+\alpha) \\
&= \frac{\tan\theta + \tan\alpha}{1-\tan\theta\tan\alpha} && \text{(trigonometric formula 25)} \\
&= \frac{\left(\frac{b^2x}{a^2y}\right) + \tan\alpha}{1-\left(\frac{b^2x}{a^2y}\right)\tan\alpha} && \text{(from (3))} \\
&= \frac{b^2x + a^2y\ \tan\alpha}{a^2y - b^2x\ \tan\alpha}
\end{aligned}
$$

From which we obtain:

$$
\left(b^2x^2 + a^2y^2\right) + \left(a^2 - b^2\right) xy\ \tan\alpha = a^2cy\ \tan\alpha + b^2cx \qquad (6)
$$

Now, let's work with the expressions $\left(a^2 - b^2\right)$ and $\left(b^2x^2 + a^2y^2\right)$:

$$
a^2 - b^2 = c^2 \qquad \text{(definition of ellipse)}
$$

Since $P = (x,\ y)$ is on the ellipse, if we replace x or y by its corresponding equality in the ellipse equation, we get that:

$$
b^2x^2 + a^2y^2 = a^2b^2
$$

Thus, replacing the last two equivalences in (6):

$$
\begin{aligned}
\left(a^2b^2\right) + \left(c^2\right) xy\ \tan\alpha &= a^2cy\ \tan\alpha + b^2cx \\
\Rightarrow \tan\alpha &= \frac{b^2cx - a^2b^2}{c^2xy - a^2cy} = \frac{b^2\left(cx - a^2\right)}{cy\left(cx - a^2\right)} \\
\Rightarrow \tan\alpha &= \frac{b^2}{cy} \qquad (7)
\end{aligned}
$$

On the other hand, the slope of the line joining the focus $F_1 = (-c,\ 0)$ and the point P, i.e. $\overline{F_1P}$, is:

$$
m_{\overline{F_1P}} = \tan(\beta - \theta) \qquad (8)
$$

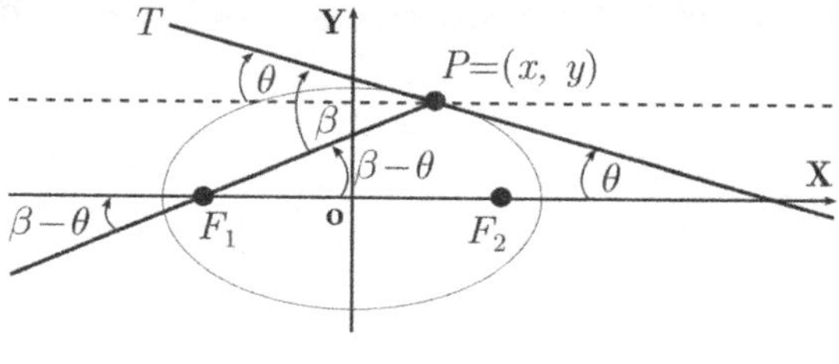

By the definition of slope:

$$m_{\overline{F_1P}} = \frac{y-(0)}{x-(-c)} \qquad \text{(slope formula)}$$

$$= \frac{y}{x+c} \qquad (9)$$

From (8) and (9), we have:

$$\frac{y}{x+c} = \tan(\beta - \theta)$$

$$= \frac{\tan\beta - \tan\theta}{1 + \tan\beta\,\tan\theta} \qquad \text{(trigonometric formula 25)}$$

$$= \frac{\tan\beta - \left(\frac{b^2x}{a^2y}\right)}{1 + \tan\beta\left(\frac{b^2x}{a^2y}\right)} = \frac{a^2y\,\tan\beta - b^2x}{a^2y + b^2x\,\tan\beta} \qquad \text{(from (3))}$$

Following the same procedure as in the previous instance:

$$\tan\beta = \frac{b^2}{cy} \qquad (10)$$

From (7) and (10), we conclude that $\tan\alpha = \tan\beta$; hence $\alpha = \beta$.

EXERCISES 3.3

In the exercises 1 through 12, find the standard equation of the ellipse satisfying the given conditions.

1. Foci: $(\pm 2, 0)$. Vertices: $(\pm 6, 0)$.
2. Foci: $(0, \pm 5)$. Vertices: $(0, \pm 8)$.

3. Focus: $(5, 2)$. Vertices: $(2, 2)$, $(6, 2)$.

4. Focus: $(-4, 0)$. Vertices: (-4, -2), (-4, 8).

5. Vertices: (3, -1), (3, 3). Passing through (2, 1).

6. Vertices: $(\pm 5, 0)$, Length of the minor axis: 6.

7. Vertices: $(-1, \pm 3)$. Length of the minor axis: 4.

8. Vertices: (2, –10), (2, 10). Passing through (6, 3).

9. Focus: $(\pm 2, 0)$. Eccentricity : $e = 2/3$.

10. Vertices: (1, 1), (1, 7). Eccentricity : $e = 1/3$.

11. Focus: $(\pm 3, -1)$. Length of the latus rectum $= 9$.

12. Center: (-2, 2). Vertex: (3, 2). Length of the latus rectum $= 4$.

In the exercises 13 through 15, the graph of the given equation is an ellipse. Find:

a. completing squares, the standard equation.

b. the vertices and the foci.

13. $x^2 + 4y^2 - 6x + 16y = -9$

14. $9x^2 + 4y^2 - 18x + 24y + 9 = 0$

15. $25x^2 + 16y^2 + 100x - 96y = 156$

16. A semi-elliptical archway over a two-way road measures 10 feet in height and 30 feet in width.

A truck with a width of 9 feet and a height of 7.5 feet approaches the archway, driving on one side of the road.

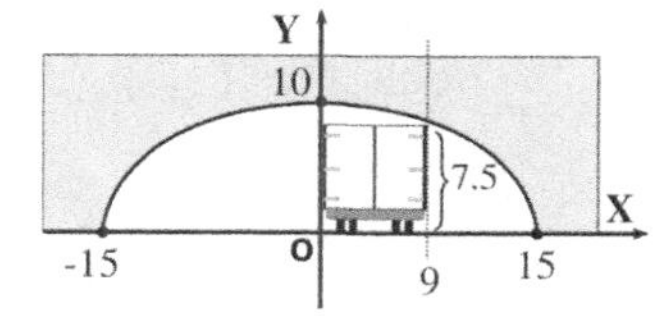

Can the truck cross the tunnel without hitting the archway and without using the other side of the road?

17. The longest section of the Montreal Olympics Stadium is shaped like an ellipse. The length of the major and minor axes are 480 $m.$ and 280 $m.$ respectively. Find the standard equation of this ellipse.

This stadium was built for the 1976 Olympics. The leaning tower seen in the picture is 175 meters long and is the tallest of its kind.

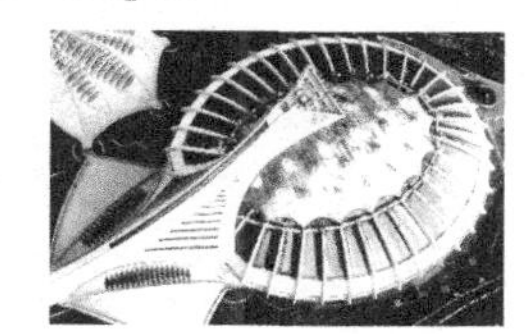

18. Let S be the set of points P of the plane such that the distance from P to the point (2, 0) is a half the distance from P to the line $x = 8$. Find an equation that satisfy all the points of S. Identify this set.

19. Let S be the set of points P of the plane such that the distance from P to the point (0, 4) is $\frac{4}{5}$ the distance between P and the line $y = \frac{25}{4}$. Find equation that satisfy all points of S. Identify this set.

20. A satellite has an elliptical orbit where the center of the moon is at one of the foci. The maximum and minimum distances between the satellite and the moon surface are 4,522 and 522 km, respectively. If the radius of the moon is 1,728 kilometers, find:

- **a.** the eccentricity of the orbit.
- **b.** the standard equation of the orbit using the coordinate system with origin at the center of the orbit, and the center of the moon on the positive side of the X-axis.

21. Let $P = (x_1, y_1)$ be a point of the ellipse $\dfrac{x^2}{a^2} + \dfrac{y^2}{b^2} = 1$;

- **a.** Prove that the slope of the tangent line to the ellipse at the point $P = (x_1, y_1)$ is:

$$m = -\frac{b^2 x_1}{a^2 y_1}$$

First hint: The line T*:* $y = m(x - x_1) + y_1$ *pass through* $P = (x_1, y_1)$*. Second hint:* T *is tangent to the ellipse if* T *intersects the ellipse in a unique point. Follow the steps of the solved problem 3.2.6.*

Third hint: Wait until you learn derivatives.

- **b.** Prove that an equation of the tangent line to an ellipse, T, at the point $P = (x_1, y_1)$, is given by:

$$\frac{x_1 x}{a^2} + \frac{y_1 y}{b^2} = 1$$

SECCION 3.4

THE HYPERBOLA

Definition

In Analytic Geometry, a **Hyperbola** is the set of points on a plane where the difference of their distances from two fixed points is a positive constant. The fixed points are the **foci** of the hyperbola. We also have that:

- the line passing through the foci intersects the hyperbola at two points, $\boldsymbol{V_1}$ and $\boldsymbol{V_2}$, called the **vertices**.
- the line segment $\overline{V_1V_2}$, that joins the vertices, is the **Transverse Axis**.
- the midpoint of the transverse axis is the **center** of the hyperbola.

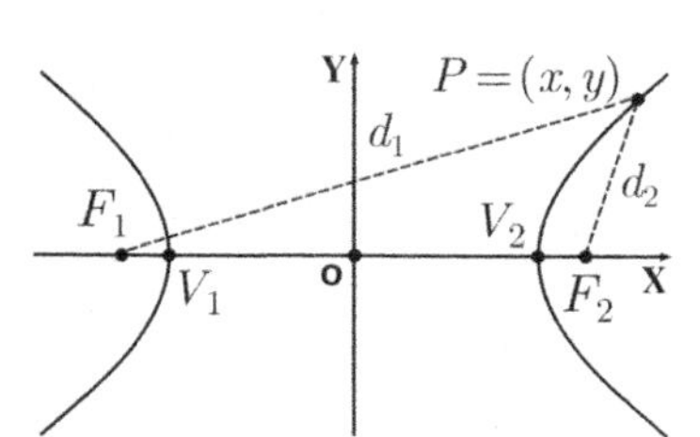

Now, we will find the standard equations of the hyperbola following the same procedure we used for the ellipse.

STANDARD FORM OF THE EQUATION OF A HYPERBOLA

We must place the foci of the hyperbola on the X-axis, with the center at the origin. Let the foci be:

$$\boldsymbol{F_1 = (-c, 0)} \quad \text{and} \quad \boldsymbol{F_2 = (c, 0)}, \text{ where } \boldsymbol{c > 0}$$

If we have that:

- $P = (x, y)$ is a point of the hyperbola
- $\boldsymbol{2a > 0}$ is the positive constant indicated in the definition
- the distances of the definition are $d_1 = d(P, F_1)$ and $d_2 = d(P, F_2)$

then:

$$\boldsymbol{| d_1 - d_2 | = 2a} \tag{1}$$

But:

$$d_1 = \sqrt{(x+c)^2 + y^2} \quad \text{and} \quad d_2 = \sqrt{(x-c)^2 + y^2}$$

Replacing the above expressions in (1):

$$\left| \sqrt{(x+c)^2 + y^2} - \sqrt{(x-c)^2 + y^2} \right| = 2a$$

This is equivalent to:

$$\sqrt{(x+c)^2+y^2}-\sqrt{(x-c)^2+y^2}=2a$$
$$\textbf{or} \quad \sqrt{(x+c)^2+y^2}-\sqrt{(x-c)^2+y^2}=-2a$$

Each one of these two equations can be transformed independently following the same steps, and both will reach the same result. Here, we will only work on the first one, leaving the other as an exercise for the reader.

$$\sqrt{(x+c)^2+y^2}-\sqrt{(x-c)^2+y^2}=2a$$
$$\Rightarrow \sqrt{(x+c)^2+y^2}=2a+\sqrt{(x-c)^2+y^2}$$

Squaring and simplifying:

$$-a\sqrt{(x-c)^2+y^2}=a^2-cx$$

Again, squaring and simplifying :

$$(c^2-a^2)x^2-a^2y^2=a^2(c^2-a^2) \tag{2}$$

We will now prove that, for the case of the hyperbola, we have:

$$\boldsymbol{a<c} \tag{3}$$

From elementary geometry, we know that the difference of the length of any two sides of a triangle is lower than the length of the remaining side.

According to this property, in the triangle $\triangle F_1PF_2$ of the last figure, the difference between the lengths of d_1 and d_2 is lower than the length of the remaining side $d(F_1,F_2)=2c$. Thus:

$$2a=\mid d_1-d_2\mid< d(F_1,F_2)=2c\Rightarrow a<c$$

Now, $a<c\Rightarrow c^2-a^2>0$. Let:

$$\boldsymbol{b^2=c^2-a^2}, \text{ where } \boldsymbol{b>0} \tag{4}$$

Replacing (4) in (3):

$$b^2x^2-a^2y^2=a^2b^2$$

Finally, dividing by a^2b^2:

$$\frac{x^2}{a^2}-\frac{y^2}{b^2}=1$$

If we make $y=0$ in this equation, we obtain $x=\pm a$. Hence, the coordinates of the vertices are:

$$\boldsymbol{V_1=(-a,0)} \quad \text{and} \quad \boldsymbol{V_2=(a,0)}$$

This hyperbola does not intersect the Y-axis. In fact, if $x = 0$, then $y^2 = -b^2$, which does not have real solutions.

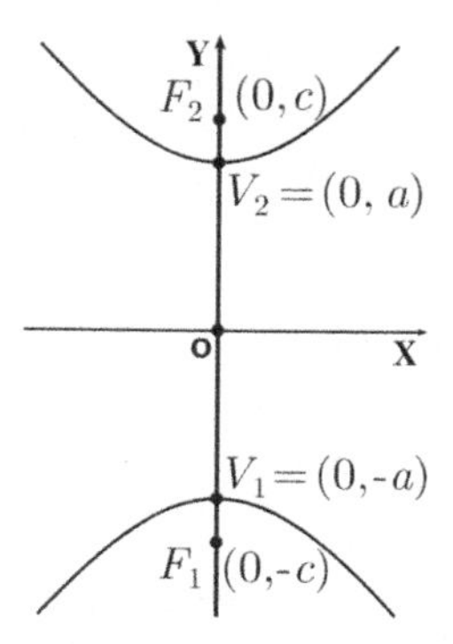

If the center of the hyperbola coincides with the origin, but the foci are on the Y-axis, following the previous arguments, we get that the equation for this hyperbola is:

$$\frac{y^2}{a^2} - \frac{x^2}{b^2} = 1$$

All these results are summarized in the following theorem.

Theorem 3.4.1 **Standard form of the equation of a hyperbola.**

a. The **standard form** of the equation of a hyperbola with center a the **origin**, foci on the X-axis, and constant $\boldsymbol{2a}$, is:

$$\frac{x^2}{a^2} - \frac{y^2}{b^2} = 1, \text{ where } b > 0 \text{ and } b^2 = c^2 - a^2$$

The foci and vertices are:

$$F_1 = (-c, 0) \text{ and } F_2 = (c, 0);\ V_1 = (-a, 0) \text{ and } V_2 = (a, 0)$$

b. The **standard form** of the equation of a hyperbola with center a the **origin**, foci on the Y-axis, and constant $\boldsymbol{2a}$, is:

$$\frac{y^2}{a^2} - \frac{x^2}{b^2} = 1, \text{ where } b > 0 \text{ and } b^2 = c^2 - a^2$$

The foci and vertices are:

$$F_1 = (0, -c) \text{ and } F_2 = (0, c);\ V_1 = (0, -a) \text{ and } V_2 = (0, a)$$

Remark

- For the ellipse, we always have that $a > b$, however, for the hyperbola, we can have:

$$a > b, \quad b > a \quad \text{or} \quad a = b$$

- We can determine on which coordinate axis the foci are located by finding out which of the variables has a positive sign(+) in the standard form of the hyperbola equation.

Example 3.4.1

Prove that the the graph of the following equation is a hyperbola. Find the vertices and the foci.

$$9y^2 - 25x^2 = 225$$

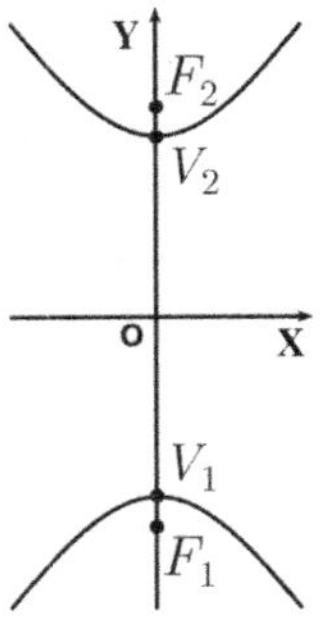

Solution

Dividing the equation by 225 and simplifying:

$$\frac{9y^2}{225} - \frac{25x^2}{225} = \frac{225}{225} \Rightarrow \frac{y^2}{25} - \frac{x^2}{9} = 1 \Rightarrow \frac{y^2}{5^2} - \frac{x^2}{3^2} = 1$$

This is the standard form of the equation of the hyperbola with center at the origin, and foci on the Y-axis. Moreover:

$$a = 5,\ b = 3 \ \text{ and } \ c = \sqrt{a^2 + b^2} = \sqrt{5^2 + 3^2} = \sqrt{34}$$

Hence, the vertices and the foci are:

$$V_1 = (0, -5), \quad V_2 = (0, 5); \quad F_1 = \left(0, -\sqrt{34}\right), \quad F_2 = \left(0, \sqrt{34}\right)$$

ECCENTRICITY AND LATUS RECTUM OF THE HYPERBOLA

The concepts of eccentricity and lactus rectum for a hyperbola are the same we established for the ellipse. That is:

- The **eccentricity** of a hyperbola is the ratio:

$$e = \frac{c}{a} = \frac{\sqrt{a^2 + b^2}}{a}, \quad \text{Observe that } \ e > 1$$

- The latus rectum of a hyperbola is any two perpendicular lines to the transverse axis passing through one of the foci, having its endpoints on the hyperbola. As with the ellipse, the length of the latus rectum is:

$$L = \frac{2b^2}{a}$$

Example 3.4.2

The transverse axis of a hyperbola is on the X-axis and its length is 18. One of the foci is 11 units away from the center. Find:

1. the standard form of the equation of the hyperbola.

2. the eccentricity.

3. the length of the latus rectum.

Solution

1. The standard form of the equation of the hyperbola is:

$$\frac{x^2}{a^2} - \frac{y^2}{b^2} = 1$$

We have that $2a = 18$, then $a = 9$.

On the other hand:

$$c = 11 \quad \text{and} \quad b^2 = c^2 - a^2 = 11^2 - 9^2 = 40$$

Therefore, the equation we are looking for is:

$$\frac{x^2}{81} - \frac{y^2}{40} = 1$$

2. The eccentricity is:

$$e = \frac{c}{a} = \frac{11}{9}$$

3. The length of the latus rectum is:

$$L = \frac{2b^2}{a} = \frac{2(40)}{9} = \frac{80}{9}$$

CONJUGATE AXIS AND CENTRAL BOX OF A HYPERBOLA

Definition

The **conjugate axis** of a hyperbola is the segment of length **$2b$** that is perpendicular to the transverse axis, having its midpoint at the center of the hyperbola.

The parallel lines to the coordinate axes that pass through the vertices, $V_1 = (-a, 0)$ and $V_2 = (a, 0)$, and through the endpoints of the conjugate axis, $B_1 = (0, -b)$ and $B_2 = (0, b)$, form the **central box** of the hyperbola.

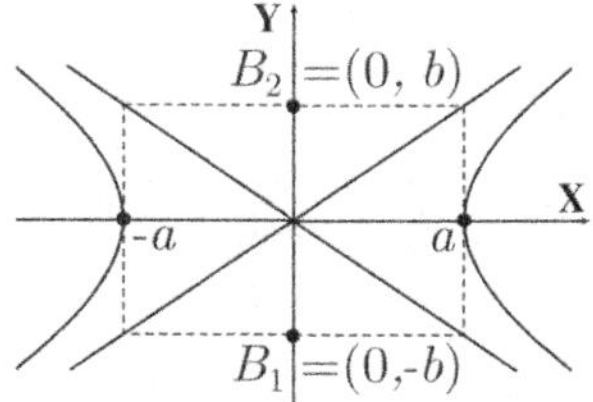

In other words, the conjugate axis is the segment $\overline{B_1B_2}$ of the hyperbola:

$$\frac{x^2}{a^2} - \frac{y^2}{b^2} = 1,$$

ASYMPTOTES OF A HYPERBOLA

We solve the equation $\frac{x^2}{a^2} - \frac{y^2}{b^2} = 1$ for y to obtain:

$$y = \pm\frac{b}{a}\sqrt{x^2 - a^2} \tag{1}$$

Neither of the two equations has a solution in the open interval $(-a,\ a)$. That means the hyperbola has two disjoint branches which are the graphs of the equation (1) on the intervals $(-\infty, a]$ and $[-a, +\infty)$, respectively.

Now, we take $x \geq a$ in (1), and then factor x^2, pulling it out of the radical:

$$y = \pm\frac{b}{a}x\sqrt{1 - \frac{a^2}{x^2}}$$

This equivalence indicates that, if x is very large, $\frac{a^2}{x^2}$ is close to 0, therefore, the radical is close to 1. Also, the point $P = (x, y)$ of the hyperbola will approach either of the two lines, $y = \frac{b}{a}x$ or $y = -\frac{b}{a}x$. We get the same result if $x \leq -a$. The lines $\boldsymbol{y = \frac{b}{a}x}$ and $\boldsymbol{y = -\frac{b}{a}x}$ are called **asymptotes** of the hyperbola:

$$\boldsymbol{\frac{y^2}{a^2} - \frac{x^2}{b^2} = 1}$$

If you check the central box of the hyperbola in the last figure, you will see that the diagonals of the box are $y = \pm\frac{b}{a}$. If we extend these lines, we obtain the asymptotes $y = \pm\frac{b}{a}x$. This is very helpful to plot the graph of a hyperbola.

We can plot the vertices and use the asymptotes as guides for sketching the branches of the hyperbola.

An easy approach to obtain the asymptotes of a hyperbola is to follow the two steps below:

1. Change the 1 by 0 in the standard form of the equation of a hyperbola.
2. Solve the the resulting equation.

That is:

$$\frac{x^2}{a^2} - \frac{y^2}{b^2} = 0 \Leftrightarrow \left(\frac{x}{a} - \frac{y}{b}\right)\left(\frac{x}{a} + \frac{y}{b}\right) = 0 \Leftrightarrow \frac{x}{a} - \frac{y}{b} = 0 \vee \frac{x}{a} + \frac{y}{b} = 0$$

$$\Leftrightarrow y = \frac{b}{a}x \quad \vee \quad y = -\frac{b}{a}x$$

Similarly, taking the hyperbola $\frac{y^2}{a^2} - \frac{x^2}{b^2} = 1$, we obtain the lines:

$$\boldsymbol{y = \frac{a}{b}x} \quad \text{and} \quad \boldsymbol{y = -\frac{a}{b}x},$$

These lines are the asymptotes of the hyperbola: $\dfrac{y^2}{a^2} - \dfrac{x^2}{b^2} = 1.$

Example 3.4.3 Given the hyperbola $4y^2 - 9x^2 = 36$, find:

1. the standard form of the equation.
2. the asymptotes.
3. the graph of the equation.

Solution

1. Dividing $4y^2 - 9x^2 = 36$ by 36:

$$\frac{y^2}{9} - \frac{x^2}{4} = 1$$

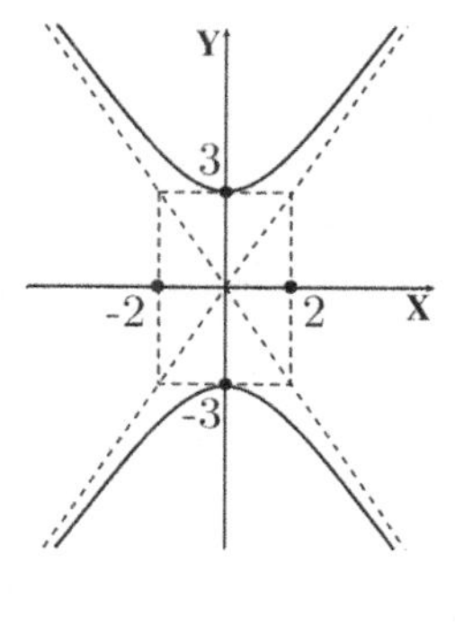

2. Applying the two-step approach to find the asymptotes:

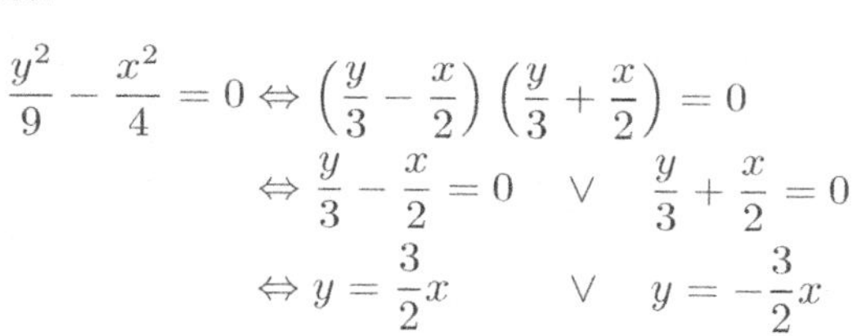

$$\frac{y^2}{9} - \frac{x^2}{4} = 0 \Leftrightarrow \left(\frac{y}{3} - \frac{x}{2}\right)\left(\frac{y}{3} + \frac{x}{2}\right) = 0$$
$$\Leftrightarrow \frac{y}{3} - \frac{x}{2} = 0 \quad \vee \quad \frac{y}{3} + \frac{x}{2} = 0$$
$$\Leftrightarrow y = \frac{3}{2}x \quad \vee \quad y = -\frac{3}{2}x$$

3. We can construct the central box extending the diagonals to intersect the asymptotes. Next, sketch the branches guided by the asymptotes, bearing in mind that this hyperbola does not intersect the X-axis.

STANDARD FORM OF THE EQUATION OF A SHIFTED HYPERBOLA

1. The **standard form** of the equation of a hyperbola with center (h, k), transverse axis parallel to the X-axis, and constant $2a$, is:

$$\frac{(x-h)^2}{a^2} - \frac{(y-k)^2}{b^2} = 1, \text{ where } b > 0 \text{ and } b^2 = c^2 - a^2$$

The foci and vertices are:

$$F_1 = ((-c+h), k) \text{ and } F_2 = ((c+h), k)$$
$$V_1 = ((-a+h), k) \text{ and } V_2 = ((a+h), k)$$

The asymptotes are:

$$y = \frac{b}{a}(x-h) + k, \quad y = -\frac{b}{a}(x-h) + k$$

2. The **standard form** of the equation of a hyperbola with center (h, k), transverse axis parallel to the Y-axis, and constant $2a$, is:

$$\frac{(y-k)^2}{a^2} - \frac{(x-h)^2}{b^2} = 1, \text{ where } b > 0 \text{ y } b^2 = c^2 - a^2$$

The foci and vertices are:

$$F_1 = (h, (-c+k)) \text{ y } F_2 = (h, (c+k))$$
$$V_1 = (h, (-a+k)) \text{ y } V_2 = (h, (a+k))$$

The asymptotes are:

$$y = \frac{a}{b}(x-h) + k, \quad y = -\frac{a}{b}(x-h) + k$$

The eccentricity of a shifted hyperbola is defined in the same way as before:

$$e = \frac{c}{a} = \frac{\sqrt{a^2+b^2}}{a}$$

It can be easily proved that the length of the latus rectum is also:

$$L = \frac{2b^2}{a}$$

Example 3.4.4 Given the equation:

$$16x^2 - 9y^2 - 64x + 54y - 161 = 0,$$

1. prove by graph that it is a hyperbola.
2. find the center, vertices and foci.
3. find the endpoints of the conjugate axis.
4. find the asymptotes.
5. find the eccentricity.
6. find the length of the latus rectum.

Solution

1. Completing squares:

$$16\left(x^2 - 4x \qquad\right) - 9\left(y^2 - 6y \qquad\right) = 161$$
$$\Leftrightarrow 16\left(x^2 - 4x + 4\right) - 9\left(y^2 - 6y + 9\right) = 161 + 64 - 81$$
$$\Leftrightarrow 16(x-2)^2 - 9(y-3)^2 = 144$$
$$\Leftrightarrow \frac{(x-2)^2}{9} - \frac{(y-3)^2}{16} = 1$$

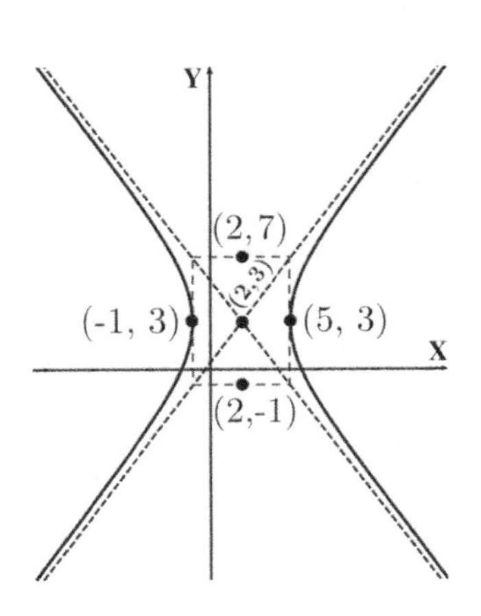

This is the standard form of the equation of a shifted hyperbola with center at (2,3) and transverse axis parallel to the X-axis.

2. We have:

$$a = 3, \quad b = 4 \quad \text{and} \quad c = \sqrt{a^2 + b^2} = \sqrt{3^2 + 4^2} = \sqrt{25} = 5$$

Hence, the center is $(h, k) = (2, 3)$,

Vertices:

$$\begin{aligned} V_1 &= ((-a + h), k) = ((-3 + 2), 3) = (-1, 3), \\ V_2 &= ((a + h), k) = ((3 + 2), 3) = (5, 3) \end{aligned}$$

Foci:

$$\begin{aligned} F_1 &= ((-c + h), k) = ((-5 + 2), 3) = (-2, 3), \\ F_2 &= ((c + h), k) = ((5 + 2), 3) = (7, 3) \end{aligned}$$

3. Endpoints of the conjugate axis:

$$\begin{aligned} B_1 &= (h, (-b + k)) = (2, (-4 + 3)) = (2, -1), \\ B_2 &= (h, (b + k)) = (2, (4 + 3)) = (2, 7) \end{aligned}$$

4. Asymptotes:

$$\begin{aligned} \frac{(x-2)^2}{9} - \frac{(y-3)^2}{16} = 0 &\Leftrightarrow \left(\frac{x-2}{3} - \frac{y-3}{4}\right)\left(\frac{x-2}{3} + \frac{y-3}{4}\right) = 0 \\ &\Leftrightarrow \frac{x-2}{3} - \frac{y-3}{4} = 0 \quad \vee \quad \frac{x-2}{3} + \frac{y-3}{4} = 0 \\ &\Leftrightarrow 3y - 4x - 1 = 0 \quad \vee \quad 3y + 4x - 17 = 0 \end{aligned}$$

5. Eccentricity:

$$e = \frac{c}{a} = \frac{5}{3}$$

6. Length of the latus rectum:

$$L = \frac{2b^2}{a} = \frac{2(4)^2}{3} = \frac{32}{3}$$

REFLECTION PROPERTY OF THE HYPERBOLA

This property states that a light ray, aimed at one focus of a hyperbolic mirror, is reflected toward the other focus. This will be proved in solved problem 3.4.5.

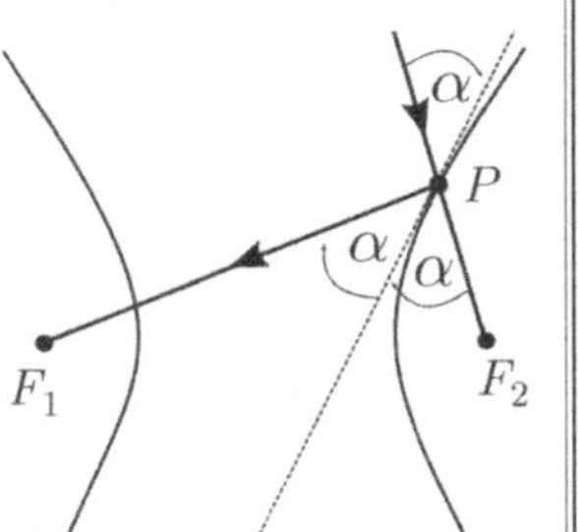

SOLVED PROBLEMS 3.4

Problem 3.4.1

Find the standard equation of the hyperbola of which the foci are $(\pm 5\sqrt{2},\, 0)$, and its asymptotes are the lines $y = \pm 2x$.

Solution

The equation is of the form:

$$\frac{x^2}{a^2} - \frac{y^2}{b^2} = 1 \qquad (1)$$

$$c = 5\sqrt{2} \text{ y } c^2 = a^2 + b^2$$

$$\Rightarrow a^2 + b^2 = 50 \qquad (2)$$

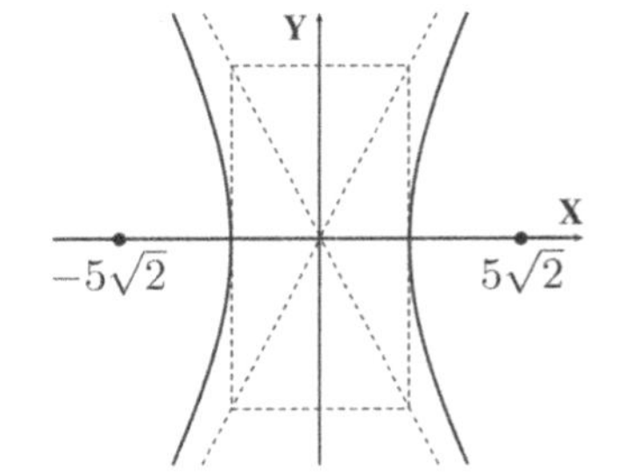

The asymptotes of the hyperbola (1) are:

$$y = \pm\frac{b}{a}x,$$

therefore:

$$\frac{b}{a} = 2 \Rightarrow b = 2a \qquad (3)$$

From (2) and (3), we get:

$$a^2 + (2a)^2 = 50 \Rightarrow 5a^2 = 50 \Rightarrow a^2 = 10 \quad \text{and} \quad b^2 = 40$$

Hence, the standard form of the equation of the hyperbola is:

$$\frac{x^2}{10} - \frac{y^2}{40} = 1$$

Problem 3.4.2

Find the standard equation of the hyperbola with vertices $V_1 = (-1, -2)$ and $V_2 = (-1, 8)$, where $F = (-1, 3 + \sqrt{34})$ is one focus.

Solution

The vertices and the focus have abscissa $x = -1$. Hence, the transverse axis is parallel to the Y-axis, meaning that the equation we are looking for has the form:

$$\frac{(y-k)^2}{a^2} - \frac{(x-h)^2}{b^2} = 1$$

The center of the hyperbola is the midpoint of the segment $\overline{V_1V_2}$. That is:

$$C = (h, k) = (-1, 3)$$

Besides:

$$2a = 8 - (-2) = 10 \Rightarrow a = 5$$

$$c = d(C, F) = 3 + \sqrt{34} - 3 = \sqrt{34}$$

$$b^2 = c^2 - a^2 = 34 - 25 = 9$$

Hence, the standard form of the equation is:

$$\frac{(y-3)^2}{25} - \frac{(x+1)^2}{9} = 1$$

Did you know this?

LORAN NAVIGATION SYSTEM

LORAN *(LOng RAnge Navigation) is a radio navigation system used by ships and air crafts to determine its location. Two ground stations, a primary and a secondary, are widely separated. Both stations broadcast some uninterrupted series of signals which are received by the ship on the ocean.*

The on-board computer converts the difference in reception time of these signals into distance differences from the stations. If the ship maintains a constant time difference while sailing, the distance difference also remains constant. Therefore, the route of the ship forms a hyperbola.

Another pair of stations deliver another hyperbola. The ship is located at the intersection of both hyperbolas.

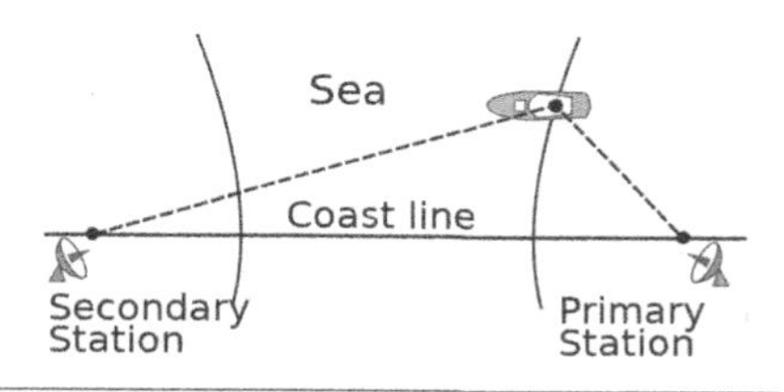

Problem 3.4.3

Two stations of a LORAN system are 400 km. apart on a straight coast. One ship receives the signal from the primary station 0.0008 seconds before the signal from secondary station. If the ship sails to the coast maintaining a constant time difference:

1. find the equation of the route.
2. at what distance from the primary station will the ship reach the coast?
3. find the time difference the ship must keep if the dock lies between the two stations, 110 kilometers away from the primary one.

Solution

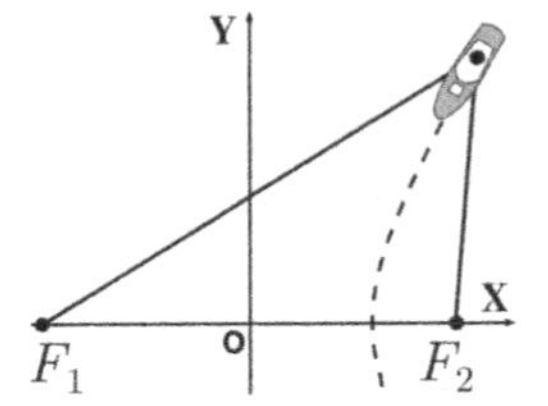

Let's take a coordinate system with the X-axis passing through the secondary station (F_1) and the primary station (F_2). The origin will be the midpoint of $\overline{F_1F_2}$.

1. The speed of the radio-electric signals is the same as the speed of light, that is 300,000 km/seg. Then, the constant of the distance difference of the signals is:

$$2a = \text{Distance} = \text{Speed} \times \text{Time}$$

$$= 300,000 \times 0.0008 = 240\, km \Rightarrow a = 120$$

The route is the hyperbola with foci at the stations. Hence:

$$2c = 400 \Rightarrow c = 200$$

Then, we have:

$$b^2 = c^2 - a^2 = (200)^2 - (120)^2 = 40,000 - 14,400 = 25,600$$

Therefore, the equation of the hyperbola is:

$$\frac{x^2}{14,400} - \frac{y^2}{25,600} = 1$$

2. The ship will reach the cost at the point $c - a = 200 - 120 = 80\, km$. from primary station.

3. We must have:

$$c - a = 110 \Rightarrow a = c - 110 = 200 - 110 = 90 \Rightarrow 2a = 180\, km.$$

Hence:

$$t = \frac{\text{Distance}}{\text{Speed}} = \frac{180}{300,000} = 0.0006\, seg.$$

Problem 3.4.4 A rifle shot hits one target 600 meters away.

Find the equation of the set of points P on the plane from where the shot and the hit on the target are herd simultaneously. *The speed of sound is 340 m/seg, and the speed of the bullet is 510 m/seg.*

Solution

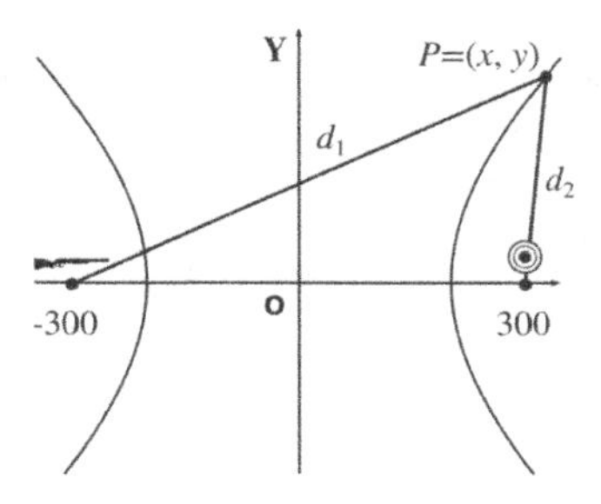

Let's take a coordinate system with the X-axis passing through the location of the rifle(F_1) and the location of target(F_2). The origin will be the midpoint of $\overline{F_1F_2}$.

Then:

- The rifle is at the point $F_1 = (-300, 0)$.
- The target at the point $F_2 = (300, 0)$.

Let P be a point in the set, and:

- $t_1 =$ the time it takes for the shot sound to reach P from the rifle.
- $t_2 =$ the time it takes for the hit sound to reach P from the target.
- $t_3 =$ the time it takes for the bullet to reach the target.

We have:

$$t_1 = t_2 + t_3 \Rightarrow t_1 - t_2 = t_3 \Rightarrow \frac{d(F_1, P)}{340} - \frac{d(F_2, P)}{340} = \frac{d(F_1, F_2)}{510}$$

$$\Rightarrow \frac{d(F_1, P)}{340} - \frac{d(F_2, P)}{340} = \frac{600}{510}$$

$$\Rightarrow d(F_1, P) - d(F_2, P) = 400 = 2a$$

This indicates that all the points P lie on a hyperbola of the form:

$$\frac{x^2}{a^2} - \frac{y^2}{b^2} = 1, \quad \text{where } a = 200$$

But, $c = 300$. Besides:

$$b^2 = c^2 - a^2 = (300)^2 - (200)^2 = 50,000$$

Thus, the set of points P on the plane, from where the shot and the hit on the target are herd simultaneously, are the points of the hyperbola:

$$\frac{x^2}{40,000} - \frac{y^2}{50,000} = 1$$

Problem 3.4.5 **Proof of the reflection property of the hyperbola.**

Let $P = (x, y)$ be a point of the hyperbola $\dfrac{x^2}{a^2} - \dfrac{y^2}{b^2} = 1$ with foci:

$$F_1 = (-c,\ 0) \text{ and } F_2 = (c,\ 0)$$

If α and β are the angles formed by the segments $\overline{F_1P}$ and $\overline{F_2P}$ with the line T, tangent to the hyperbola at the point P, then we must prove that:

$$\alpha = \beta$$

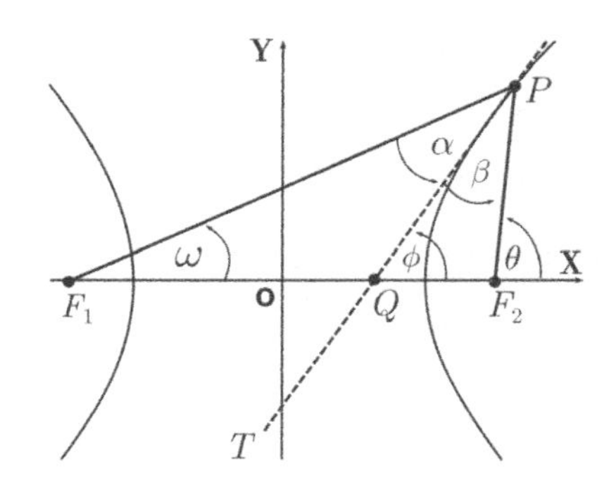

Solution

According to the statement of the exercise 23, we have that:

$$\tan\phi = \frac{b^2x}{a^2y} \qquad (1)$$

We also have:

$$(2) \qquad \tan\omega = \frac{y}{x+c} \qquad \text{and} \qquad (3) \qquad \tan\theta = \frac{y}{x-c}$$

From elementary geometry we know that, in a triangle, an exterior angle equals the sum of the non-adjacent interior angles. Applying this result on the triangle $\triangle F_1QP$, we obtain:

$$\phi = \alpha + \omega \Rightarrow \alpha = \phi - \omega \qquad \text{(supplementary angle)}$$
$$\Rightarrow \tan\alpha = \tan(\phi - \omega)$$

$$\tan(\phi - \omega) = \frac{\tan\phi - \tan\omega}{1 + \tan\phi\,\tan\omega} \qquad \text{(trig. form. 25)}$$

$$= \frac{\frac{b^2x}{a^2y} - \frac{y}{x+c}}{1 + \frac{b^2x}{a^2y}\cdot\frac{y}{x+c}} \qquad \text{(from (1) and (2))}$$

$$= \frac{(b^2x^2 - a^2y^2) + b^2cx}{(a^2+b^2)\,xy + a^2cy} = \frac{a^2b^2 + b^2cx}{c^2xy + a^2cy} \qquad \text{(def. of hyperbola)}$$

$$= \frac{b^2\,(a^2 + cx)}{cy\,(cx + a^2)} = \frac{b^2}{cy}$$

That is:

$$\tan\alpha = \frac{b^2}{cy} \tag{4}$$

We proceed in a similar way for triangle $\triangle QF_2P$:

$$\theta = \beta + \phi \Rightarrow \beta = \theta - \phi$$

$$\Rightarrow \tan\beta = \tan(\theta - \phi) = \frac{\tan\theta - \tan\phi}{1 + \tan\theta\,\tan\phi}$$

$$\begin{aligned}
\frac{\tan\theta - \tan\phi}{1 + \tan\theta\,\tan\phi} &= \frac{\frac{y}{x-c} - \frac{b^2x}{a^2y}}{1 + \frac{y}{x-c}\cdot\frac{b^2x}{a^2y}} && \text{(from (1) and (3))}\\
&= \frac{\left(a^2y^2 - b^2x^2\right) + b^2cx}{xy\left(a^2+b^2\right) - a^2cy} = \frac{-a^2b^2 + b^2cx}{c^2xy - a^2cy} && \text{(def. hyperbola)}\\
&= \frac{b^2\left(cx - a^2\right)}{cy\left(cx - a^2\right)} = \frac{b^2}{cy}
\end{aligned}$$

That is:

$$\tan\beta = \frac{b^2}{cy} \tag{5}$$

From (4) and (5), we get that $\tan\alpha = \tan\beta$, therefore, $\boldsymbol{\alpha = \beta}$.

Did you know this?

The first crewed spacecraft to reach space was Vostok 1, launched from Kazakhstan in 1961 by the Soviet Union. The Soviets determined the most efficient way for the rocket to reach an orbit 180 kilometers above the Earth's surface: by launching it along a ***hyperbolic*** *trajectory.*

Since then, space missions have been using hyperbolic trajectories to launch their spacecraft into space, such as the Space Shuttle, or even the Falcon 9 of Space X, which reaches orbit at a much lower altitude than all its predecessors.

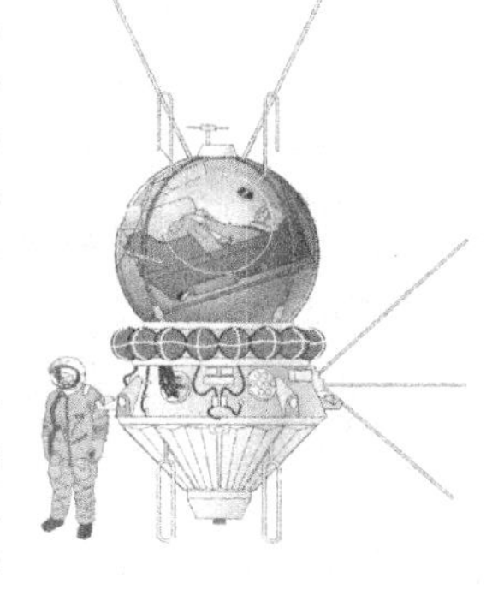

Vostok 1

EXERCISES 3.4

In the exercises 1 through 15, find the standard equation of the hyperbola satisfying the given conditions.

1. Foci: $(\pm 7, 0)$. Vertices: $(\pm 5, 0)$. **2.** Foci: $(\pm 13, 0)$. Vertices: $(\pm 5, 0)$.

3. Foci: $(0, \pm 6)$. Vertices: $(0, \pm 2)$. **4.** Foci: $(0, \pm 15)$. Vertices: $(0, \pm 4)$.

5. Foci: $(-2, 2)$, $(8, 2)$. Vertices: $(0, 2)$, $(6, 2)$.

6. One focus: $(-3, 3)$. Vertices: $(-3, 0)$, $(-3, -6)$.

7. Foci: $(-1, 2)$, $(5, 2)$. One vertex: $(4, 2)$.

8. Foci: $(\pm 3, 0)$. Asymptotes: $y = \pm 2x$.

9. Foci: $(0,\ \pm\sqrt{58})$. Asymptotes: $y = \pm\frac{5}{2}x$.

10. Asymptotes: $x = \pm\sqrt{3}y$. Passes trough (6, 4).

11. Foci: $(2, 2)$, $(6, 2)$, Asymptotes: $y = x + 2$, $y = -x + 6$.

12. Asymptotes: $y = 2x + 1$, $y = -2x + 3$. Passes trough (0, 0).

13. Vertices: $(-5, 3)$, $(1, 3)$. One asymptote: $2y - x + 7 = 0$.

14. Vertices: $(-1, 3)$, $(3, 3)$. Eccentricity: $e = \frac{3}{2}$.

15. Vertices: $(-2, -2)$, $(-2, 4)$. Latus rectum: $L = 2$.

In the exercises 16 through 19, completing squares, find:

a. the standard form of the hyperbola. **b.** the vertices.
c. the foci. **d.** the asymptotes.

16. $9x^2 - 16y^2 - 54x + 64y - 127 = 0$ **17.** $4x^2 - 9y^2 + 32x + 36y + 64 = 0$

18. $16x^2 - y^2 - 32x - 6y - 57 = 0$ **19.** $4x^2 - 9y^2 - 16x + 54y - 101 = 0$

20. Two stations A and B of a LORAN system are 200 km. away on a straight coast.

Station B is to the west, and station A is to the east.

One ship receives the signal from the station B 0.0004 seconds before the signal from the station A. The speed of the signal is 300,000 km/sec.

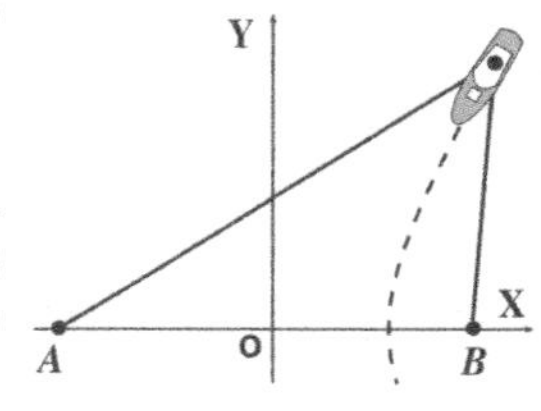

a. If the ship sails to the coast keeping a constant time difference, find the equation of the route.

b. At what point will the ship reach the coast?

c. If the dock is located between the two stations, 70 km. away from the station B, find the time difference the ship must keep.

21. Two observers stand at the points $F_1 = (-200, 0)$ and $F_2 = (200, 0)$ of the plane XY. An explosion at some point of the plane XY is heard by the observer located at F_2 one second before the observer of F_1. Find the equation of the hyperbola where the explosion occurred.

22. Find the equation of the set of points P of the plane such that the distance between them and the point $(-2, 1)$ is $\frac{2}{\sqrt{3}}$ the distance between them and the line $x = -\frac{3}{2}$.

23. Let $P = (x_1, y_1)$ be a point of the hyperbola $\dfrac{x^2}{a^2} - \dfrac{y^2}{b^2} = 1$.

a. Prove that the slope of the tangent line to the hyperbola at the point $P = (x_1, y_1)$ is:

$$m = \frac{b^2 x_1}{a^2 y_1}.$$

Hint: The line T: $y = m(x - x_1) + y_1$ pass through $P = (x_1, y_1)$. T is tangent to the hyperbola if they intersect at a single point. Follow the same steps given in the solved problem 3.2.6.

Another Hint: Wait until you learn derivatives.

b. Prove that the a equation of the tangent line T to the hyperbola at the point $P = (x_1, y_1)$ is:

$$\frac{x_1 x}{a^2} - \frac{y_1 y}{b^2} = 1$$

SECCION 3.5

GENERAL 2ND DEGREE EQUATION. ROTATIONS

The curves presented in this chapter have only been shown in their standard form, which makes it much more convenient for classification; however, it is important to clarify that all these curves are different variations of the same equation, known as the **Second Degree General Equation**:

$$\boldsymbol{Ax^2 + Bxy + Cy^2 + Dx + Ey + F = 0},$$

In earlier sections, the coefficient $\boldsymbol{B}$ of the term $\boldsymbol{Bxy}$ equals zero. In this respect, it is also important to point out that there are some special cases that we have not seen yet, in which this coefficient is not null. These cases can correspond to either **Rotated Conics** or **Degenerate Conics**.

In an effort to ease the understanding of this topic, we will present these curves from a geometrical perspective. In the introduction to this chapter we saw that conics are produced by intersecting a plane with a Double Right Circular Cone. All the curves we have seen so far, parabolas, ellipses and hyperbolas, have been produced when the plane intersects the Double Right Circular Cone *without making contact with the apex of the cones. When the plane meets the apex of the cones, it produces degenerate conics*, which have new geometrical representations like a **single point**, a **straight line** or **two straight lines** that can cross each other or be parallel.

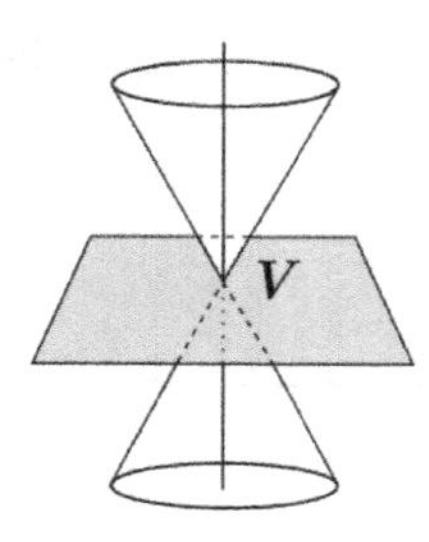

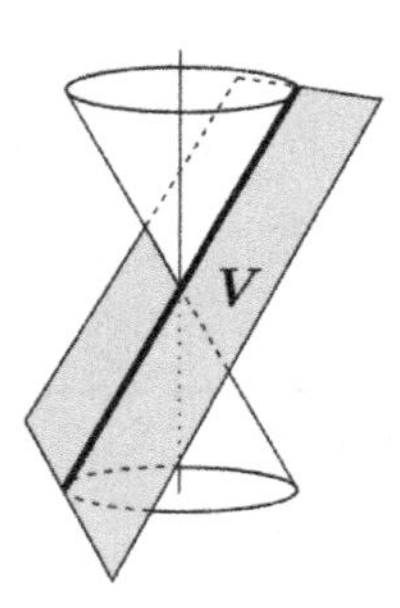

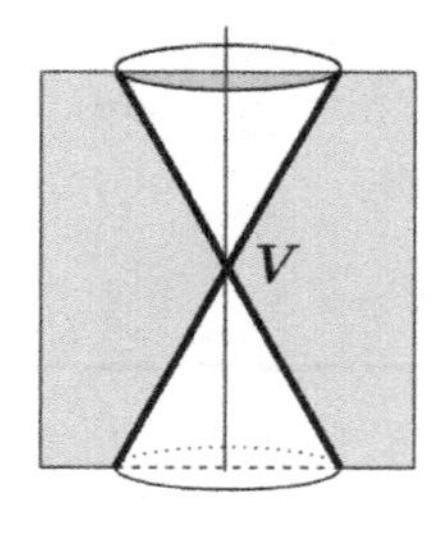

They are called "degenerate" because they are degenerations of the traditional conics. Even though the demonstration of these cases is beyond the scope of this book, we provide below a brief overview of these conics.

A Single Point

Like a circle, the point occurs when the plane cuts the cone while being perpendicular to its axis, however, it also intersects the apex.

The point is a degeneration of an ellipse. If we could be more specific, it is a circle of radius zero.

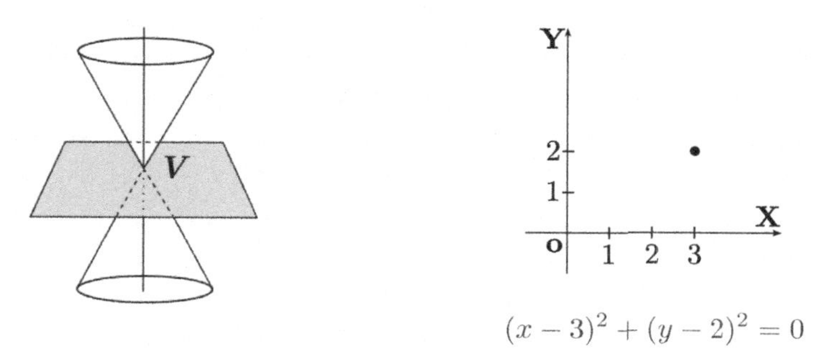

$(x-3)^2 + (y-2)^2 = 0$

A Straight Line or a Pair of Parallel Lines

When the plane cuts the entire surface of both cones, it produces a **straight line**. This degenerate conic resembles a first degree equation. **Two parallel lines** can also be generated, but its geometric representation with a Right Circular Cone is complex and goes beyond the scope of this book. However, we provide an example of this case in a Cartesian plane. Straight and parallel lines are degenerations of parabolas.

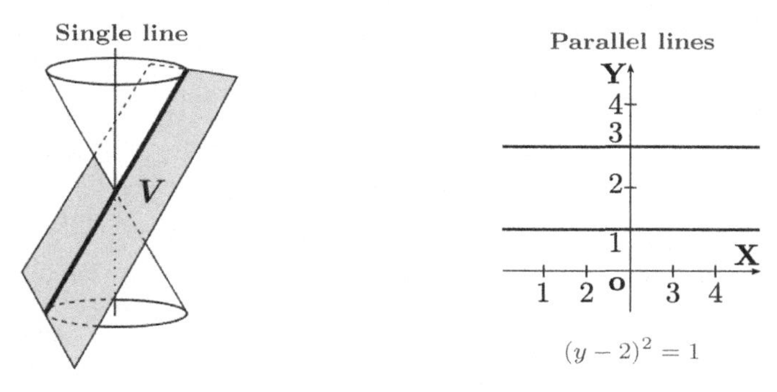

$(y-2)^2 = 1$

Two Crossing Lines

This case is a degeneration of the hyperbola. Empirically, we can describe it as a hyperbola with the left-hand side of its equation equal to zero ($\frac{y^2}{a^2} - \frac{x^2}{b^2} = 0$).

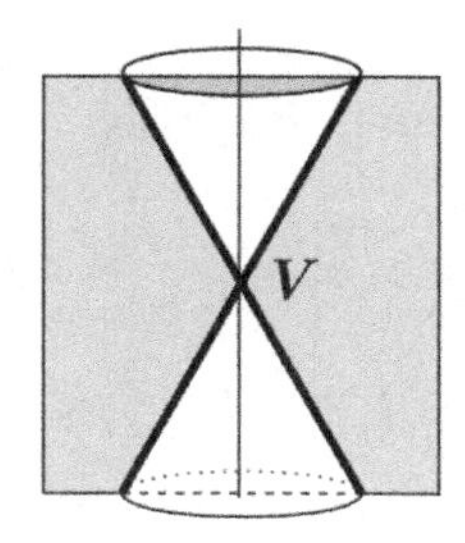

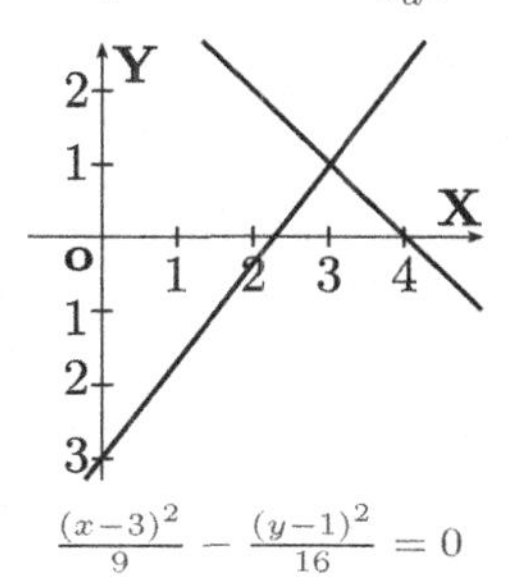

$\frac{(x-3)^2}{9} - \frac{(y-1)^2}{16} = 0$

Both, traditional and degenerate conics, can be defined in general terms with the next theorem.

Theorem 3.5.1 **Equation of a shifted conic.**

The graph of the equation $\boldsymbol{Ax^2 + Cy^2 + Dx + Ey + F = 0}$, where $\boldsymbol{A}$ and $\boldsymbol{C}$ are not both zero, is a conic or a degenerate conic. If it is not a degenerate conic, then its graph is:

a **parabola** if:	$AC = 0$
an **ellipse** if:	$AC > 0$
a **hyperbola** if:	$AC < 0$

Henceforth, we will devote ourselves to study the **General Second Degree Equation** of the form:

$$\boldsymbol{Ax^2 + Bxy + Cy^2 + Dx + Ey + F = 0},$$

This equation contains the term $\boldsymbol{Bxy}$, where $\boldsymbol{B \neq 0}$. We will find that the graph of this equation is also a conic, which can be identified by the discriminant of the equation, that is $\boldsymbol{B^2 - AC}$. To get these results, first, we first need to learn axis rotation.

ROTATION OF AXES

The coordinate axes X and Y are rotated at an acute positive angle θ to get the coordinates X′ and Y′.

Any point P has two representations, (x, y) in the old system, and (x', y') in the new one. Let's find the relation between these representations.

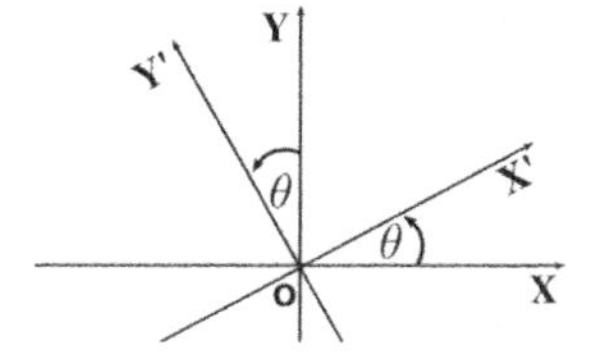

Let $\boldsymbol{r}$ be the length of the segment $\overline{OP}$, and α the angle that $\overline{OP}$ makes with the X′ axis. We have the following **trigonometric ratios**:

$$x' = r\cos\alpha \qquad y' = r\sin\alpha$$

$$x = r\cos(\theta + \alpha) \qquad y = r\sin(\theta + \alpha)$$

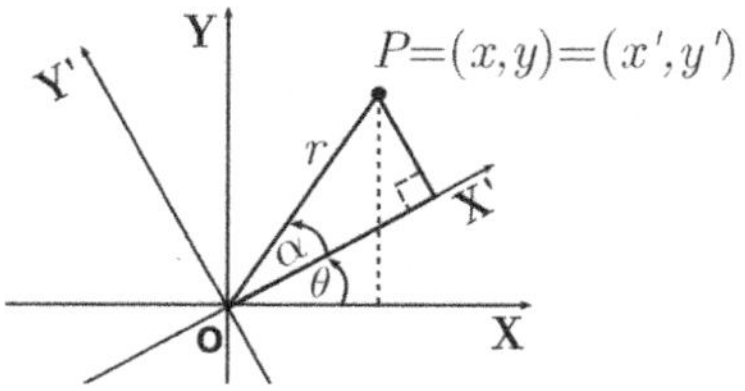

According to the trigonometric formula 24 (cosine of angle addition), we have:

$$\begin{aligned} x = r\cos(\theta+\alpha) &= r\cos\theta\cos\alpha - r\sin\theta\sin\alpha \\ &= (r\cos\alpha)\cos\theta - (r\sin\alpha)\sin\theta \\ &= x'\cos\theta - y'\sin\theta \end{aligned}$$

Thus, $$x = x'\cos\theta - y'\sin\theta \tag{1}$$

Similarly, $$y = x'\sin\theta - y'\cos\theta \tag{2}$$

Solving the system given by (1) and (2) for x' and y', we obtain:

(3) $x' = x\cos\theta + y\sin\theta$ (4) $y' = -x\sin\theta + y\cos\theta$

The above results are synthesized in the following theorem:

Theorem 3.5.2 **Formulas for rotation of axes.**

If the X and the Y axis in a coordinate plane are rotated at an acute angle θ to produce the X′ and the Y′ axis, then, the coordinates, (x, y) and $(x',' y)$, of a point in the systems XY and X′Y′, respectively, are related by:

$$\mathbf{I}\begin{cases} x = x'\cos\theta - y'\sin\theta \\ y = x'\sin\theta + y'\cos\theta \end{cases} \qquad \mathbf{II}\begin{cases} x' = x\cos\theta + y\sin\theta \\ y' = -x\sin\theta + y\cos\theta \end{cases}$$

Example 3.5.1

With a 45° rotation, prove that the graph of $\boldsymbol{xy = 1}$ is a **hyperbola**.

Solution

$$x = x'\cos 45° - y'\sin 45° = x'\frac{\sqrt{2}}{2} - y'\frac{\sqrt{2}}{2} = \frac{\sqrt{2}}{2}(x' - y')$$

$$y = x'\sin 45° + y'\cos 45° = x'\frac{\sqrt{2}}{2} + y'\frac{\sqrt{2}}{2} = \frac{\sqrt{2}}{2}(x' + y')$$

Replacing these expressions into the given equation:

$$xy = 1 \Rightarrow \left(\frac{\sqrt{2}}{2}(x' - y')\right)\left(\frac{\sqrt{2}}{2}(x' + y')\right) = 1$$

$$\Rightarrow \frac{1}{2}\left(x'^2 - y'^2\right) = 1 \Rightarrow \frac{x'^2}{2} - \frac{y'^2}{2} = 1$$

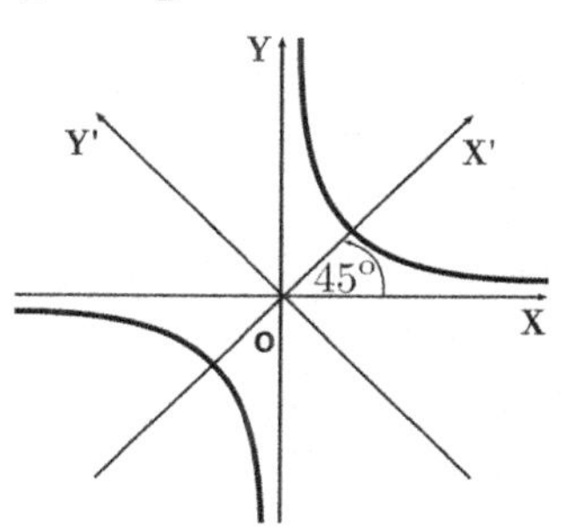

In the X′Y′ coordinate system, this is the standard equation of a hyperbola with center at the origin and foci on the X′ axis. The vertices are $(\sqrt{2}, 0)$ and $(-\sqrt{2}, 0)$. The asymptotes are $y' = \pm x'$.

Now, let's try to find a rotation to transform the second degree equation:

$$Ax^2 + Bxy + Cy^2 + Dx + Ey + F = 0, \tag{i}$$

into a second degree equation that contains no term Bxy in the X′Y′ system.

Replacing the values of x and y, given in the theorem 3.5.2, in the second degree equation, we have:

$$\begin{aligned}&A\left(x'\cos\theta - y'\sin\theta\right)^2 + B\left(x'\cos\theta - y'\sin\theta\right)\left(x'\sin\theta + y'\cos\theta\right) +\\&C\left(x'\sin\theta + y'\cos\theta\right)^2 + D\left(x'\cos\theta - y'\sin\theta\right) + E\left(x'\sin\theta + y'\cos\theta\right) + F\end{aligned}$$

Expending and collecting like terms, we obtain the following equations:

$$A'x'^2 + B'x'y' + C'y'^2 + D'x' + E'y' + F' = 0 \tag{ii}$$

Where:

$$\text{(iii)} \quad \begin{cases} A' = A\cos^2\theta + B\sin\theta\cos\theta + C\sin^2\theta \\ B' = 2(C - A)\sin\theta\cos\theta + B\left(\cos^2\theta - \sin^2\theta\right) \\ C' = A\sin^2\theta - B\sin\theta\cos\theta + C\sin^2\theta \\ D' = D\cos\theta + E\sin\theta \\ E' = -D\sin\theta + E\cos\theta \\ F' = F \end{cases}$$

If we want **(ii)** to not have the term $B'x'y'$, we must choose an angle θ, such that $B' = 0$. Then, according to the second equality of **(iii)**, this is:

$$\begin{aligned}&B' = 2(C - A)\sin\theta\cos\theta + B\left(\cos^2\theta - \sin^2\theta\right) = 0\\&\Rightarrow B' = (C - A)\sin 2\theta + B\cos 2\theta = 0 \qquad \text{(double angle formulas)}\\&\Rightarrow B\cos 2\theta = (A - C)\sin 2\theta\\&\Rightarrow \cot 2\theta = \frac{A - C}{B}\end{aligned}$$

The above results are synthesized in the following theorem.

Theorem 3.5.3 **Simplifying the general second degree equation.**

Given a general second degree equation of the form:

$$\boldsymbol{Ax^2 + Bxy + Cy^2 + Dx + Ey + F = 0}, \quad \text{where } B \neq 0,$$

this equation can be transformed into an equation of the form:

$$\boldsymbol{A'x'^2 + C'y'^2 + D'x' + E'y' + F' = 0},$$

by rotating the axes X and Y at an acute angle θ, given by:

$$\boldsymbol{\cot 2\theta = \frac{A - C}{B}}$$

Example 3.5.2 Rotating axes, eliminate the xy term in the equation:

$$8x^2 - 4xy + 5y^2 - 36 = 0$$

Identify the graph.

Solution

$$\cot 2\theta = \frac{A - C}{B} = \frac{8 - 5}{-4} = -\frac{3}{4}$$

According to the attached graph:

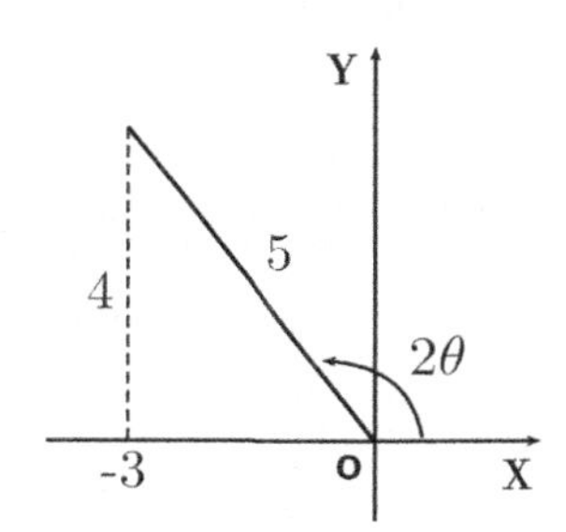

$$\cos 2\theta = -\frac{3}{5}$$

Using the half angle formulas we have:

$$\cos\theta = \sqrt{\frac{1 + (-\frac{3}{5})}{2}} = \frac{1}{\sqrt{5}}, \qquad \sin\theta = \sqrt{\frac{1 - (-\frac{3}{5})}{2}} = \frac{2}{\sqrt{5}}$$

Hence, the rotation formulas are:

$$x = \frac{1}{\sqrt{5}}x' - \frac{2}{\sqrt{5}}y' = \frac{1}{\sqrt{5}}(x' - 2y'), \quad y = \frac{2}{\sqrt{5}}x' + \frac{1}{\sqrt{5}}y' = \frac{1}{\sqrt{5}}(2x' + y')$$

Replacing these expressions into the equation:

$$8\left(\frac{1}{\sqrt{5}}(x' - 2y')\right)^2 - 4\left(\frac{1}{\sqrt{5}}(x' - 2y')\right)\left(\frac{1}{\sqrt{5}}(2x' + y')\right) + 5\left(\frac{1}{\sqrt{5}}(2x' + y')\right)^2 = 36$$

Expanding and simplifying:

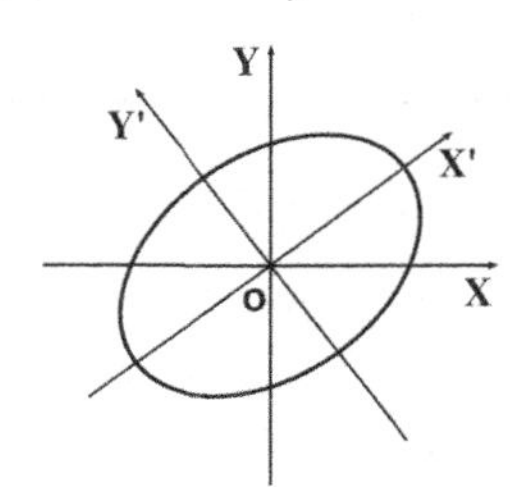

$$4x'^2 + 9y'^2 = 36 \Rightarrow \frac{x'^2}{9} + \frac{y'^2}{4} = 1$$

Clearly, this curve is a rotated ellipse.

Definition In the general second degree equation:

$$\boldsymbol{Ax^2 + Bxy + Cy^2 + Dx + Ey + F = 0},$$

the **discriminant** is $\boldsymbol{B^2 - 4AC}$

The next theorem states that the value of the discriminant can identify the conic, without the need of rotating axes. See the proof of this theorem in the solved problem 3.5.2.

Theorem 3.5.4 **Identifying a conic by the discriminant.**

The graph of the equation:

$$\boldsymbol{Ax^2 + Bxy + Cy^2 + Dx + Ey + F = 0},$$

is a conic or a degenerate conic. If it is not degenerate, then its graph is:

a **parabola**	if	$\boldsymbol{B^2 - 4AC = 0}$
an **ellipse**	if	$\boldsymbol{B^2 - 4AC < 0}$
a **hyperbola**	if	$\boldsymbol{B^2 - 4AC > 0}$

Example 3.5.3 Identify the following conic by its discriminant:

$$2x^2 - 3\sqrt{3}xy + 3y^2 + 5x - 6 = 0$$

Solution

We have that:

$$A = 2, \quad B = 3\sqrt{3} \quad \text{and} \quad C = 3$$

Then:

$$B^2 - 4AC = \left(3\sqrt{3}\right)^2 - 4(2)(3) = 27 - 24 = 3 > 0$$

Therefore, the graph of the equation is a hyperbola.

SOLVED PROBLEMS 3.5

Problem 3.5.1 Given the equation:

$$4x^2 - 12xy + 9y^2 - 6\sqrt{13}x - 4\sqrt{13}y = 0$$

1. By a rotation of axes, verify that the graph of this equation is a parabola.

2. Find the equation of the axis of the parabola in the coordinates XY.

3. Find the focus in both, the X′Y′ and XY coordinates.

4. Find the equation of the directrix in the XY coordinates.

Solution

1. We have:

$$\cot 2\theta = \frac{A-C}{B} = \frac{4-9}{-12} = \frac{5}{12}, \qquad \cos 2\theta = \frac{5}{13}$$

$$\cos\theta = \sqrt{\frac{1+\frac{5}{13}}{2}} = \frac{3}{\sqrt{13}}, \quad \sin\theta = \sqrt{\frac{1-\frac{5}{13}}{2}} = \frac{2}{\sqrt{13}}$$

13 12 2θ 5

Hence:

i. $x = \frac{1}{\sqrt{13}}\left(3x' - 2y'\right)$, **ii.** $y = \frac{1}{\sqrt{13}}\left(2x' + 3y'\right)$

Substituting equations i. and ii. into the original equation yields:

$$\frac{4}{13}\left(3x' - 2y'\right)^2 - \frac{12}{13}\left(3x' - 2y'\right)\left(2x' + 3y'\right)$$
$$+ \frac{9}{13}\left(2x' + 3y'\right)^2 - 6\sqrt{13}\frac{1}{\sqrt{13}}\left(3x' - 2y'\right)$$
$$- 4\sqrt{13}\frac{1}{\sqrt{13}}\left(2x' + 3y'\right) = 0$$

Y Y' X' X

Expanding and simplifying:

$$y'^2 = 2x',$$

This is the equation of a parabola with its vertex at the origin and its axis along the X′-axis.

2. The axis of the parabola (the X′ axis) in the XY system is the line that passes through the origin with slope:

$$m = \tan\theta = \frac{\sin\theta}{\cos\theta} = \frac{\frac{2}{\sqrt{13}}}{\frac{3}{\sqrt{13}}} = \frac{2}{3}$$

Then, its equation is:

$$y - 0 = \frac{2}{3}(x-0) \Rightarrow 2x - 3y = 0$$

3. $y'^2 = 2x' \Rightarrow 4px' = 2x' \Rightarrow p = \frac{1}{2}$

Hence, the focus in the X′Y′ coordinate system is:

$$F = (\frac{1}{2}, 0)$$

The coordinates of F in the XY coordinate system are:

$$x = x'\cos\theta - y'\sin\theta = \frac{1}{2}\frac{3}{\sqrt{13}} - 0\frac{2}{\sqrt{13}} = \frac{3}{2\sqrt{13}}$$

$$y = x'\sin\theta - y'\cos\theta = \frac{1}{2}\frac{2}{\sqrt{13}} + 0\frac{3}{\sqrt{13}} = \frac{1}{\sqrt{13}}$$

Hence, in the XY system, $F = \left(\frac{3}{2\sqrt{13}}, \frac{1}{\sqrt{13}}\right)$

4. The point where the directrix intersects the X′ axis is $(-p, 0) = \left(-\frac{1}{2}, 0\right)$.

In XY coordinate system, this point is $\left(-\frac{3}{2\sqrt{13}}, -\frac{1}{\sqrt{13}}\right)$.

Besides, the directrix is perpendicular to the axis of the parabola.

The slope of the axis of the parabola is $\frac{2}{3}$, so, the slope of the directrix is:

$$m' = -\frac{3}{2}$$

Hence, the equation of the directrix in the XY system is:

$$y - \left(-\frac{1}{\sqrt{13}}\right) = -\frac{3}{2}\left(x - \left(-\frac{3}{2\sqrt{13}}\right)\right) \Rightarrow 6x + 4y = -\sqrt{13}$$

Problem 3.5.2 **Prove the theorem 3.5.4.**

The graph of the equation:

$$\boldsymbol{Ax^2 + Bxy + Cy^2 + Dx + Ey + F = 0},$$

is a conic or a degenerate conic. If it is not degenerate, then its graph is:

a **parabola**	if	$\boldsymbol{B^2 - 4AC = 0}$
an **ellipse**	if	$\boldsymbol{B^2 - 4AC < 0}$
a **hyperbola**	if	$\boldsymbol{B^2 - 4AC > 0}$

Solution

We know that a rotation of the axes by an angle θ transforms the given equation into an equation of the form:

$$A'x'^2 + B'x'y' + C'y'^2 + D'x' + E'y' + F' = 0$$

The relations between the coefficients $A, B, \ldots$ and $A', B', \ldots$ are given in the group (iii), prior to theorem 3.5.3.

Using these equalities, we can prove that the discriminants of this equation remain constant after the rotation. That is:

$$B^2 - 4AC = B'^2 - 4A'C'$$

In particular, if the la rotation is such that $B' = 0$, we get the equality:

$$B^2 - 4AC = -4A'C'$$

Now, we can apply the theorem 3.5.1:

$$B^2 - 4AC = 0 \Rightarrow -4A'C' = 0 \Rightarrow A'C' = 0$$

The graph is a parabola.

$$B^2 - 4AC < 0 \Rightarrow -4A'C' < 0 \Rightarrow A'C' > 0$$

The graph is an ellipse.

$$B^2 - 4AC > 0 \Rightarrow -4A'C' > 0 \Rightarrow A'C' < 0$$

The graph is a hyperbola.

EXERCISES 3.5

In the exercises 1 through 3, the coordinates of a point are given in the XY system, and the axes are rotated at the given angle. Find the coordinates of the point in the X′Y′ system.

1. $\left(1, -\sqrt{3}\right)$, $60°$ **2.**$(-2, 6)$, $45°$ **3.** $\left(-2\sqrt{3}, 4\right)$, $30°$

In the exercises 4 through 5, the coordinates of a point are given in the X′Y′ system, obtained rotating the XY system at the given angle. Find the coordinates of the point in the XY system.

4. $\left(2 - \sqrt{3}, -1 - 2\sqrt{3}\right)$, $60°$ **5.** $\left(-3 + \frac{3\sqrt{2}}{2}, -3 - \frac{3\sqrt{2}}{2}\right)$, $45°$

In the exercises 6 and 7, find the transformed equation if the XY system is rotated at the given angle. Identify the conic.

6. $2xy = -1$, $\frac{\pi}{4}$ rad **7.** $x^2 + 4\sqrt{3}xy - 3y^2 = 30$, $\frac{\pi}{6}$ rad

In the exercises 8 and 9, use the discriminant to identify the conic. Use rotation of axes to eliminate the *xy* term, find the transformed equation and plot it.

8. $2x^2 + \sqrt{3}xy + y^2 = 5$ **9.** $9x^2 + 12xy + 4y^2 + 2\sqrt{13}x - 3\sqrt{13}y = 0$

10. Let $13x^2 - 8xy + 7y^2 - 45 = 0$

- **a.** By rotation of axes, verify that the graph of the equation is an ellipse.
- **b.** Find the vertices in both, X′Y′ and XY, coordinate system.
- **c.** Find the foci in both, X′Y′ and XY, coordinate system.
- **d.** Find the line containing the major axis in the XY system.
- **e.** Find the line containing the minor axis in the XY system.

11. Let $4x^2 - 24xy + 11y^2 + 56x - 58y + 95 = 0$

- **a.** By a rotation of axes verify that the graph of the equation is a hyperbola.
- **b.** Find the center in both, the X′Y′ and XY, coordinate system.
- **c.** Find the foci in both, the X′Y′ and XY, coordinate system.

4

REAL FUNCTIONS

Arquímedes (287 - 212 A. C.)

ARCHIMEDES was born in Syracuse, a city located in the south of the Italian peninsula, which was then part of the Hellenic Empire. He received his education in Alexandria, which was the pinnacle of science at the time.

Historians consider Archimedes to be one of the three greatest geniuses in history, alongside the Englishman Isaac Newton (1642-1727) and the German Carl Friedrich Gauss (1777-1855). The scholar calculated the areas of plane figures, anticipating the invention of Calculus by Newton and Leibniz, which took place 2000 years later.

One of his fascinating anecdotes is about Hieron, the king of Syracuse, who requested his jeweler to create a gold crown for him. The king suspected that the jeweler had tricked him by blending gold with silver. Mindful of Archimedes' intellect, he tasked him with finding proof of the fraud without damaging the crown. The sage pondered over this for quite some time.

While ruminating in his bathtub one day, he noticed his legs feeling lighter as he submerged them in the water. This was the piece of the puzzle he had been searching for.

This discovery is known today in the field of hydrostatics as Archimedes' Principle.

He was so enthusiastic about his discovery that he rushed naked into the streets shouting "Eureka! Eureka!" ("I've got it!").

One day, the Romans seized Syracuse after three years of siege. It is said that Archimedes, immersed in solving a problem, did not notice the entrance of an invading soldier. The vile man, annoyed at seeing the wise man ignoring him, stabbed him with his sword.

SECCION 4.1

REAL FUNCTIONS AND THEIR GRAPHS

Definition

A **function** is a triad of objects $(\boldsymbol{X}, \boldsymbol{Y}, \boldsymbol{f})$, where $\boldsymbol{X}$ and $\boldsymbol{Y}$ are two sets and $\boldsymbol{f}$ is a rule assigning a **unique** element, y of Y, to each element x of X.

The set X is called the **domain** of the function and the set Y is the **co-domain** of the function.

The most usual notations for a function (X, Y, f) are the following:

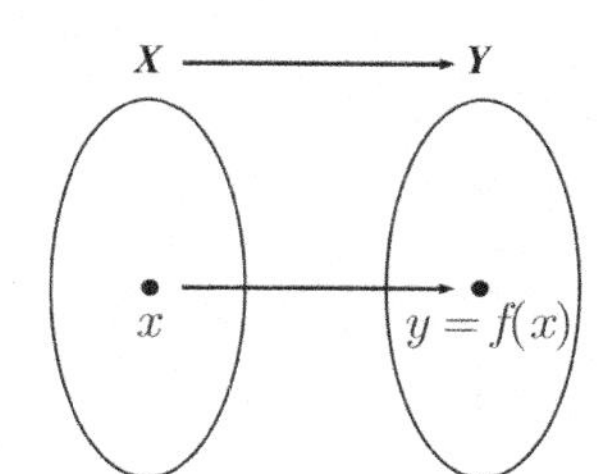

$$f : X \to Y \quad \text{or} \quad X \xrightarrow{f} Y$$

and is read: "the function **f** from **X** to **Y**".

To point out that f makes correspond an element, y of Y, to an element, x of X, we write the following expression:

$$\boldsymbol{y = f(x)},$$

which is read "**y** is equal to **f** of **x**". We also state that $\boldsymbol{y}$ is the value of $\boldsymbol{f}$ at $\boldsymbol{x}$, or $\boldsymbol{y}$ is the **image** of $\boldsymbol{x}$ under $\boldsymbol{f}$. The element x, in this case, is a **preimage** of the element y.

The **independent variable** represents the elements of the domain, while the **dependent variable** represents the images. In the above notation ($y = f(x)$), the independent variable is x, and the dependent variable is y.

The variables x and y can be exchanged by any pair of letters. Thus, we can write $z = f(t)$. In this case, the independent variable is t, and the dependent variable is z. The range of the function $f : X \to Y$ is the set of all images. That is:

$$\textbf{Range of } \boldsymbol{f} = \{\boldsymbol{f(x)} \in \boldsymbol{Y} \,/\, \boldsymbol{x} \in \boldsymbol{X}\}$$

The range may be the entire set Y or a part of it.

We will abbreviate both, domain and range of a function $f : X \to Y$, by **Dom(*f*)** and **Rang(*f*)**, respectively.

Remark

Two terms require special attention in the definition of function. One of the them is "**each**", which indicates that every element of the domain must have an image. The other is "**unique**", which indicates that all the elements of the domain have exactly one image.

Example 4.1.1 Given the function $f : X \to Y$, where:

$$X = \{a, b, c, d\}, \quad Y = \{1, 2, 3, 4, 5\}$$

If the rule f is given by the adjoining graph, we have:

- **Domain** $= \text{Dom}(f) = X = \{a, b, c, d\}$
- **Co-domain** $= Y = \{1, 2, 3, 4, 5\}$
- **Range** $= \text{Rang}(f) = \{3, 4, 5\}$

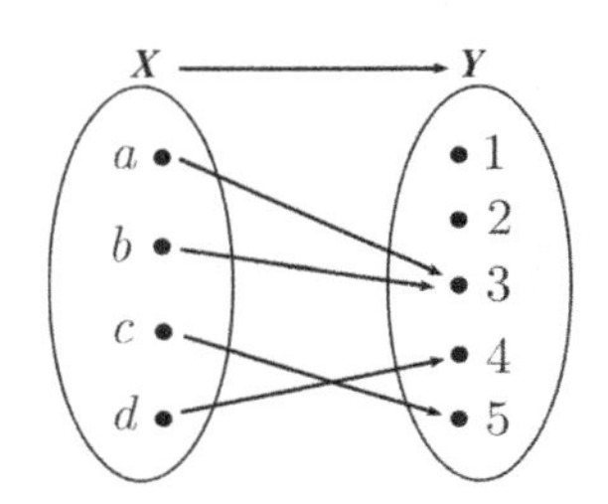

The rule f establishes that:

$$f(a) = 3, \quad f(b) = 5, \quad f(c) = 3, \quad f(d) = 4$$

Example 4.1.2 **The Identity Function.**

Let X be any set. The following function is called the **identity function** of the set X:

$$I_X : X \to X$$

$$I_X(x) = x$$

In this function, the domain, co-domain and range, are equal to X. That is:

$$\text{Dom}(I_X) = \text{Codom} = \text{Rang}(I_X) = X$$

The rule I_X assigns the element x to each element x.

Definition **Equal functions.**

If $f : X \to Y$ and $g : X \to Y$ are two functions with the same domain and co-domain, then:

$$\boldsymbol{f = g \Leftrightarrow f(x) = g(x), \ \forall x \in X}$$

REAL FUNCTIONS

In this Precalculus course our main focus are the **real functions of real variable**. A real function of real variable is a function whose domain and co-domain are subsets of $\mathbb{R}$. Thus, the following are real functions:

a. $f : \mathbb{R} \to \mathbb{R}$, $f(x) = x$

b. $g : \mathbb{R} - \{0\} \to \mathbb{R}$, $g(x) = \dfrac{1}{x}$

c. $h : \mathbb{R} \to \mathbb{R}$, $h(x) = 5$

CONVENTION FOR THE DOMAIN OF A REAL FUNCTION

Frequently, in order to simplify the notation to represent a real function of real variable $f : X \to \mathbb{R}$, we will only specify the rule (formula) f, omitting the domain X and the co-domain $\mathbb{R}$. For this purpose, we shall accept the following convention.

Convention

When a real function of real variable is defined only giving the rule or formula f, omitting the domain, we will assume that the domain is the set of real numbers x such that the value $f(x)$ is defined and is also a real number.

Example 4.1.3 Find the domain of the function:

$$f(x) = \frac{1}{x-2}$$

Solution

The domain of the function $f(x) = \frac{1}{x-2}$ is the set of real numbers, except for $x = 2$. We discard $x = 2$ because $f(2) = \frac{1}{0}$, and the quotient of a rational with zero denominator does not exist. Hence:

$$\text{Dom}(f) = \mathbb{R} - \{2\} = (-\infty, 2) \cup (2, +\infty)$$

Example 4.1.4 Find the domain and the range of the functions:

1. $f(x) = x - 3$ **2.** $g(x) = \sqrt{x-3}$

Solution

1. Since $f(x) = x - 3$ is defined for all $x \in \mathbb{R}$, we have:

- $\text{Dom}(f) = \mathbb{R}$
- $\text{Rang}(f) = \mathbb{R}$

Indeed, given $y \in \mathbb{R}$, let's take $x = y + 3$.

It follows that $x \in \mathbb{R} = \mathrm{Dom}(f)$, besides:

$$f(x) = x - 3 = (y + 3) - 3 = y$$

2. The radicand of $g(x) = \sqrt{x - 3}$ must be non-negative. Then:

$$x - 3 \geq 0 \Leftrightarrow x \geq 3$$

$$\Leftrightarrow x \in [3, +\infty)$$

So, $\mathrm{Dom}(g) = [3, +\infty)$.

$\mathrm{Rang}(g) = [0, +\infty)$. Indeed, given $y \in [0, +\infty)$, let's take $x = y^2 + 3$.

It follows that $x \geq 3$, so, $x \in [3, +\infty)$, besides:

$$g(x) = \sqrt{x - 3} = \sqrt{(y^2 + 3) - 3} = \sqrt{y^2} = |y| = y$$

GRAPHS OF FUNCTIONS

The **graph** of a function $\boldsymbol{f : X \to \mathbb{R}}$, is the set:

$$\boldsymbol{G = \{(x,\ f(x)) \in \mathbb{R}^2 \,/\, x \in X\}}$$

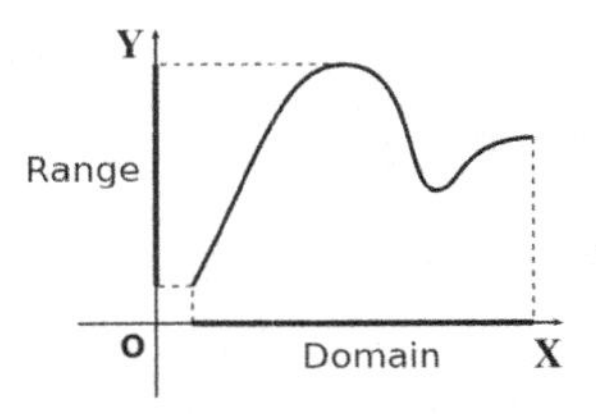

Some curves in the plane do not represent graphs of a function. In order to recognize the curves corresponding to graphs of functions, the following geometric criterion is very helpful.

THE VERTICAL LINE TEST

A curve in the plane is the graph of a function
if and only if
every vertical line intersects the curve, at most, at one point.

This criterion is very easy to demonstrate, which is why we believe it is convenient to leave it as a challenge for the reader.

According to this criterion, only the third of the following curves is the graph of a function.

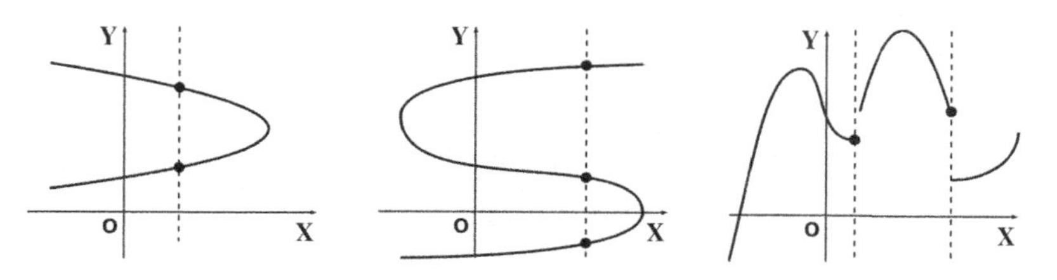

Example 4.1.5 Graph and find the domain and range of the function:

$$f(x) = \frac{x^2 - x - 6}{x - 3}$$

Solution

Clearly, $\text{Dom}(f) = \mathbb{R} - \{3\}$.

On the other hand, factoring and simplifying:

$$f(x) = \frac{(x-3)(x+2)}{x-3} = x + 2$$

Then, the function $f(x) = \frac{x^2-x-6}{x-3}$ equals the linear function $y = x + 2$, except for $x = 3$, where f is not defined.

Hence, the range of f equals the range of $y = x + 2$, without the number $y = (3) + 2 = 5$. That is:

$$\text{Rang}(f) = \mathbb{R} - \{5\}$$

PIECEWISE-DEFINED FUNCTIONS

Some functions are defined by parts, as in the two following examples.

Example 4.1.6 Given the **absolute value** function:

$$f(x) = |x| = \begin{cases} x, & \text{if } x \geq 0 \\ -x, & \text{if } x < 0 \end{cases}$$

Graph and find the domain and the range of the function.

Solution

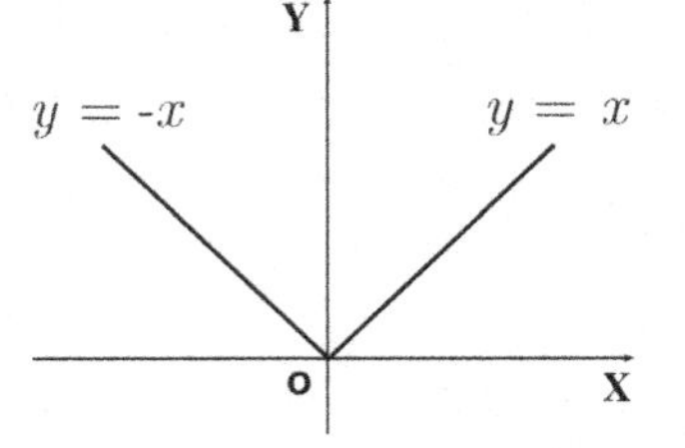

The graph of this function is made up by two half-lines:

- $y = x, \ x \geq 0,$ to the right of the Y-axis.
- $y = -x, \ x < 0,$ to the left of the Y-axis.

Domain: $\mathbb{R}$ Range: $[0, +\infty)$

Example 4.1.7 **The Greatest Integer Function.**

Graph and find domain and range of the greatest integer function:

$$f(x) = \lfloor x \rfloor = n, \text{ if } n \leq x < n + 1, \text{ where } n \text{ is an integer.}$$

This function is also called *stair* or *floor* function.

Solution

In more explicit terms, this function can be defined as follows:

$$\lfloor x \rfloor = \begin{cases} \vdots \\ -2, \text{ if } -2 \leq x < -1 \\ -1, \text{ if } -1 \leq x < 0 \\ 0, \text{ if } 0 \leq x < 1 \\ 1, \text{ if } 1 \leq x < 2 \\ 2, \text{ if } 2 \leq x < 3 \\ \vdots \end{cases}$$

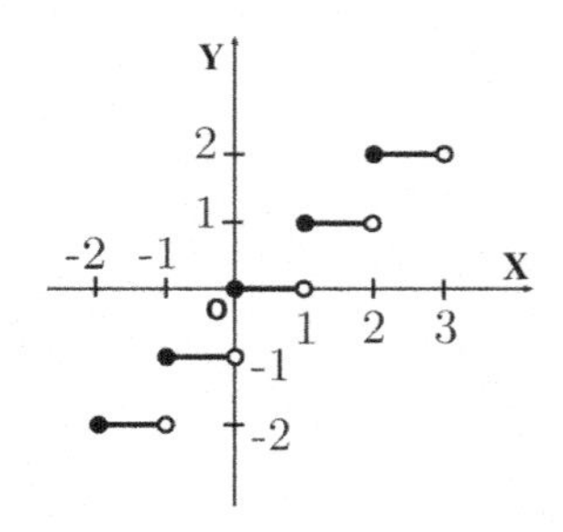

Domain: $\mathbb{R}$, Range: $\mathbb{Z}$

EVEN AND ODD FUNCTIONS. SYMMETRY

1. A function f is **even** if, for all x in the domain of f, it is satisfied that:

$$\boxed{f(-x) = f(x)}$$

2. A function f is **odd** if, for all x in the domain of f, it is satisfied that:

$$\boxed{f(-x) = -f(x)}$$

Example 4.1.8 Graph the following functions and prove that:

a. $f(x) = x^2$ is even **b.** $f(x) = x^3$ is odd

Solution

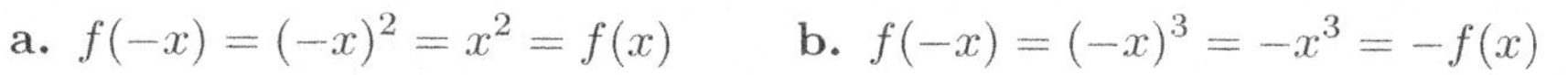

a. $f(-x) = (-x)^2 = x^2 = f(x)$ **b.** $f(-x) = (-x)^3 = -x^3 = -f(x)$

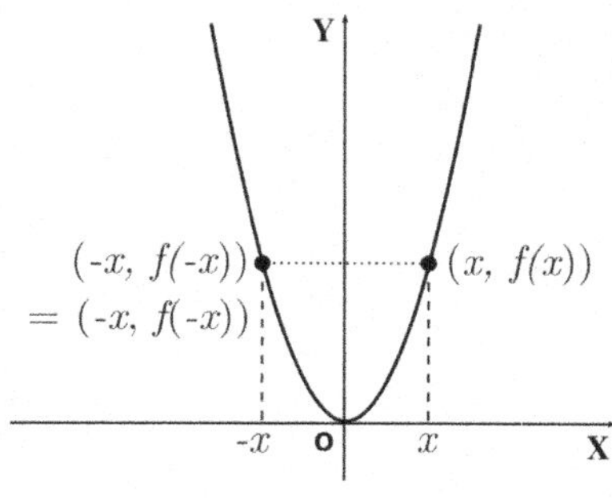

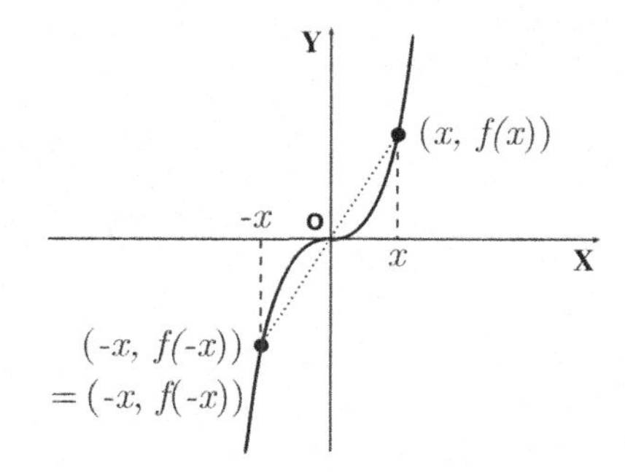

We can see that:

f is **even** $\Leftrightarrow$ the graph of f is **symmetric respect to the Y-axis**

f is **odd** $\Leftrightarrow$ the graph of f is **symmetric respect to the origin**

The terms *even* and *odd* follow from the fact that the function $f(x) = x^n$ is even if n is even, and is odd if n is odd.

INCREASING AND DECREASING FUNCTIONS

Definition Let f be a function defined on an interval I.

1. f **is increasing** on I if $\forall x_1, x_2 \in I$, it is satisfied that:

$$x_1 < x_2 \Rightarrow f(x_1) < f(x_2),\ \forall x_1, x_2 \in I$$

2. f **es decreasing** on I if $\forall x_1, x_2 \in I$, it is satisfied that:

$$x_1 < x_2 \Rightarrow f(x_1) > f(x_2)$$

3. f **is monotonic** on I if f is either increasing or decreasing on I.

Increasing

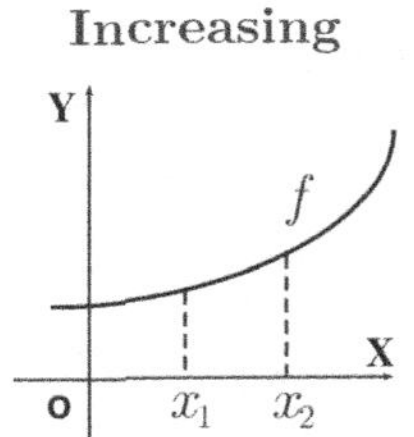

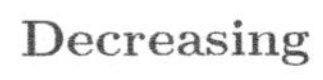

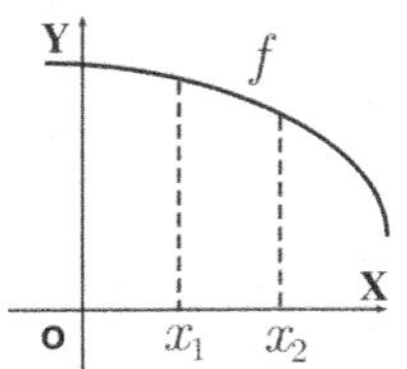

The function $f(x) = x^2$, given in the example 4.1.8, is decreasing on the interval $(-\infty, 0]$, and is increasing on the interval $[0, +\infty)$. On the other hand, the function $f(x) = x^3$ is increasing on all its domain, $\mathbb{R}$.

BRIEF CATALOG OF FUNCTIONS

CONSTANT FUNCTION

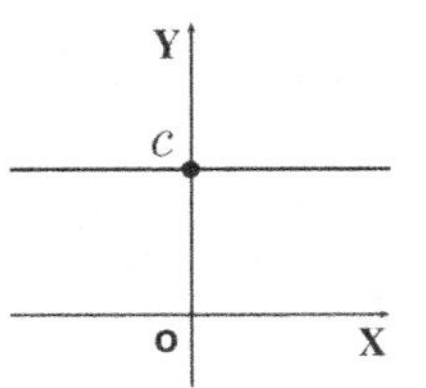

If c is a fixed real number, then the below function is a **constant function**:

$$f(x) = c, \ \forall x \in \mathbb{R}$$

- Its domain is $\mathbb{R}$, and its range the unitary set $\{c\}$.
- Its graph is horizontal line through the point $(0, c)$.

POWER FUNCTION

The **power function** is the function $\boldsymbol{f(x) = x^{\alpha}}$, where $\boldsymbol{\alpha}$ is a constant.

Example 4.1.9 What happens if $\alpha = 0$, $\alpha = 1$, $\alpha = 2$ or $\alpha = 3$?

If $\alpha = 0$ we have the constant function $f(x) = x^0 = 1$.

If $\alpha = 1$ we have the identity function.

if $\alpha = 2$ or $\alpha = 3$ we have a parabola or a cubic parabola.

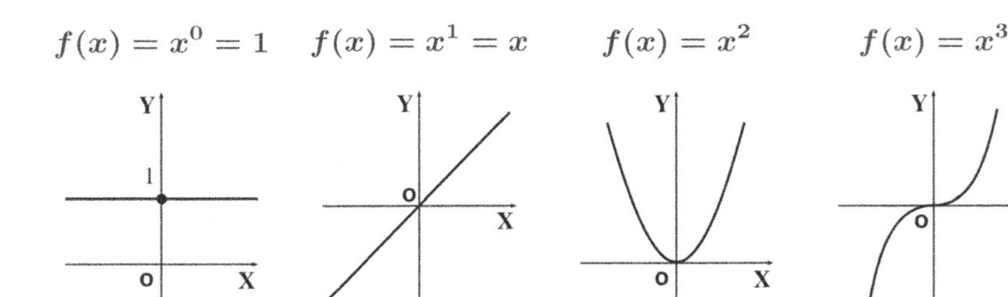

Notice how the graphs differ when n is even or odd.

Example 4.1.10 If $\alpha = \frac{1}{n}$, where $n \neq 0$ is a natural number, we have:

$$f(x) = x^{1/n} = \sqrt[n]{x}, \qquad \text{the } \boldsymbol{n}\textbf{th root function}$$

The following are cases for $n = 2$ and $n = 3$:

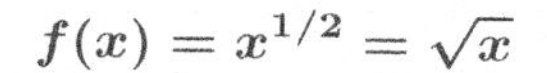

$$f(x) = x^{1/2} = \sqrt{x} \qquad\qquad f(x) = x^{1/3} = \sqrt[3]{x}$$

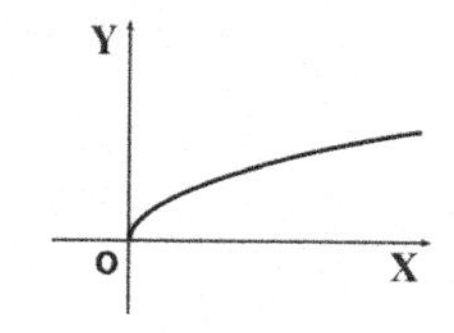

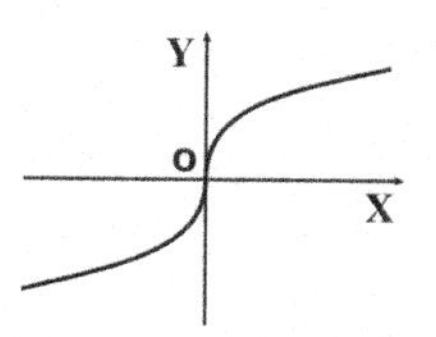

$\mathbf{Dom}(f) = \mathbf{Rang}(f) = [0, +\infty)$ $\qquad$ $\mathbf{Dom}(f) = \mathbf{Rang}(f) = \mathbb{R}$

Example 4.1.11 If $\alpha = -n$, where $n \neq 0$ is a natural number, we have:

$$f(x) = x^{-n} = \frac{1}{x^n}, \qquad \mathbf{Dom}(f) = \mathbf{Rang}(f) = \mathbb{R} - \{0\}$$

The following are cases for $n = 1$ and $n = 2$:

$$f(x) = \frac{1}{x}$$

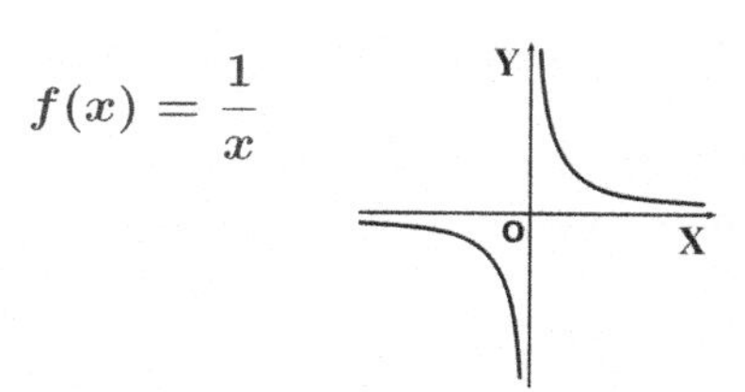
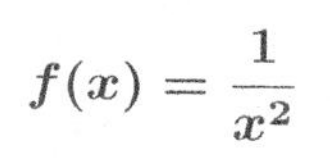

$$f(x) = \frac{1}{x^2}$$

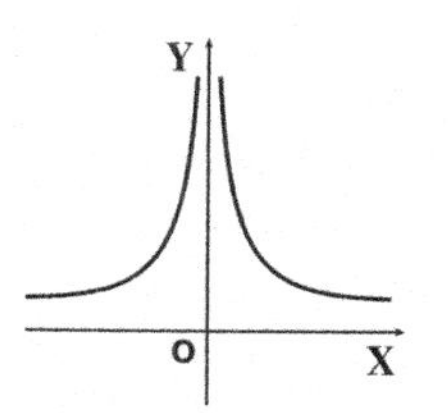

If n is odd the graph of $f(x) = \frac{1}{x^n}$ resembles the graph of $f(x) = \frac{1}{x}$.

If n is even the graph of $f(x) = \frac{1}{x^n}$ resembles the graph of $f(x) = \frac{1}{x^2}$.

POLYNOMIAL FUNCTION

A **polynomial of degree n** is a function of the form:

$$p(x) = a_n x^n + a_{n-1}x^{n-1} + \ldots + a_2 x^2 + a_1 x + a_0,$$

where n is a natural number, $a_0, a_1, \ldots, a_n$ are real numbers, and $a_n \neq 0$.

The numbers $a_0, a_1, \ldots, a_n$ are called **coefficients** of the polynomial. the **constant coefficient** is a_0, and a_n is the **leading coefficient**. Polynomials of degree 1, 2, 3:

$$\boldsymbol{p(x) = ax + b, \quad p(x) = ax^2 + bx + c, \quad p(x) = ax^3 + bx^2 + cx + d,}$$

are called **linear**, **quadratic** and **cubic** functions, respectively.

A polynomial of degree 0 is a constant function. The graph of a linear function is a non-vertical line, and the graph of a quadratic function is a parabola with axis parallel to the Y-axis.

RATIONAL FUNCTION

A **rational** function is the quotient of two polynomials. That is:

$$\boldsymbol{r(x) = \frac{p(x)}{q(x)}}$$

For instance, $r(x) = \frac{2-3x+8x^2}{4-x^2}$ is a rational function. The domain of a rational function is $\mathbb{R}$ minus the set of all numbers where the denominator becomes 0. Therefore, the domain of this function is:

$$\mathbb{R} - \{2, -2\}$$

ALGEBRAIC FUNCTIONS

An **algebraic** function is one that can be created from polynomials using operations such as addition, subtraction, multiplication, division, and the raising of powers or taking roots. Polynomial and rational functions are the simplest algebraic functions. Here are two examples:

$$\textbf{a.}\ f(x) = \sqrt{x^2 - 1} \qquad \textbf{b.}\ g(x) = \frac{2}{1 + \sqrt{x}}$$

TRANSCENDENTAL FUNCTIONS

A **transcendental** function is a function that is not algebraic. The most elementary transcendental functions are the following:

- Trigonometric functions and their inverses.
- Exponential functions
- Logarithmic functions.

We will discuss these functions in more detail in the upcoming sections.

FUNCTIONS AS MATHEMATICAL MODELS

Functions can display some relationships or patterns in non-mathematical fields, as well as in everyday life. Such formulations are called **Mathematical Models.** Let's explore some examples.

Example 4.1.12 **Product Manufacturing.**

A certain kind of article is produced by a factory. If the production of this article does not exceed 800 units, the factory earns a profit of 300 dollars for each unit it manufactures. However, once the production exceeds 800 units, the profit decreases by 2 dollars for each additional unit manufactured.

a. Express the profit $P(x)$ of the factory as a function of x units produced.

b. Find the profit if 1200 units are produced.

Solution

a. If $0 \leq x \leq 800$, the profit is $P(x) = 300x$

If $x > 800$, the surplus over 800 is $x - 800$, then the profit per unit has decreased:

$$2(x - 800) = 2x - 1,600$$

Hence:

$$\text{Profit per unit} = 300 - (2x - 1,600) = 1,900 - 2x,$$

Then:

$$P(x) = (\text{profit for the first } 800) + (\text{profit for exceeding } 800)$$

$$= 300(800) + (1,900 - 2x)(x - 800) = -2x^2 + 3,500x - 1,280,000$$

Thus, the profit, as function of x units of production, is:

$$P(x) = \begin{cases} 300x, & \text{if } 0 \leq x \leq 800 \\ -2x^2 + 3,500x - 1,280,000, & \text{if } \quad x > 800 \end{cases}$$

b. $P(1,200) = -2(1,200)^2 + 3,500(1,200) - 1,280,000$

$$= -2,880,000 + 4,200,000 - 1,280,000 = 40,000$$

Example 4.1.13 **Carpentry.**

A rectangular beam is cut from a cylindrical log with a radius of 3 dm. Express the area of the beam in terms of the length x of the base of the rectangle.

Solution

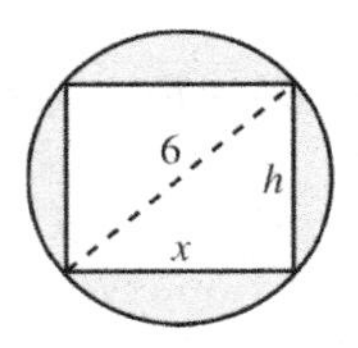

Let x, h and A be the base, height and the area of the rectangle, respectively. We have:

$$A = xh \qquad (1)$$

Now, we must express the height h in terms of x. The diameter of the circle divides the rectangle into two right triangles with a hypotenuse length of 6 dm. By the Pythagoras theorem, we have:

$$h = \sqrt{6^2 - x^2} \qquad (2)$$

Since $A(x)$ is the area of the rectangle, from (1) and (2), we have:

$$A(x) = x\sqrt{36 - x^2}$$

Example 4.1.14 **Container Factory.**

Four squares of equal size are cut at the four corners of a square sheet of metal to build a box without a lid, folding the sides up after the small squares are removed. If the big square sheet of metal has 72 cm of side and x is the length of the side of the small squares, express:

a. the volume of the box as a function of x.

b. the area of the box (without top) as a function of x.

Solution

1. We have:

$$\text{Volume} = (\text{area of the base})(\text{height})$$

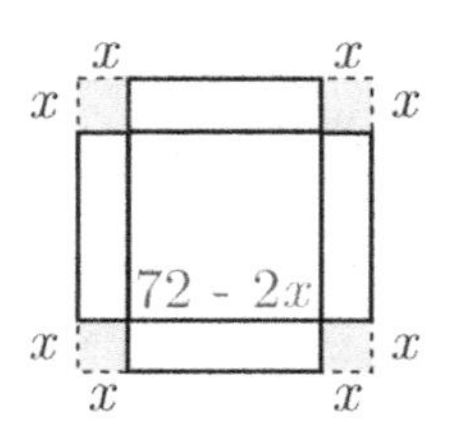

The base of the box is a square of side $72 - 2x$.

So, its area is $(72 - 2x)^2$.

The height of the box is x.

Hence, the volume of the box is:

$$V = (72 - 2x)^2(x) = x(72 - 2x)^2$$

2. The area of the box equals the area of the original square sheet, less the area of the 4 small squares. Hence, if $A(x)$ is the area of the box, then:

$$A(x) = (72)^2 - 4x^2 = 5,184 - 4x^2$$

Example 4.1.15 **Water tank construction.**

A water tank of 16 m^3 will be constructed. The base is required to be a rectangle with a height that is double its width. The lateral walls are perpendicular to the base. The cost of one m^2 of the base is 80 dollars, and the cost of one m^2 of the walls is 50 dollars. Express the cost of the tank as a function of the width of the base.

Solution

Let be:

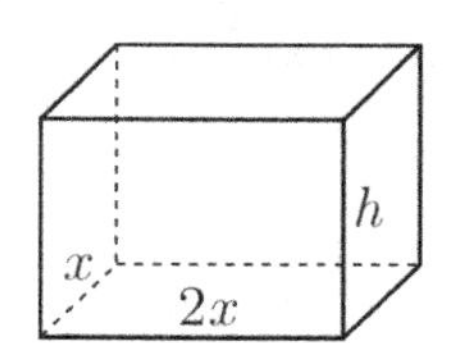

- x, the width of the base.
- h, the height of the water tank.
- $C(x)$, the cost in dollars.

The height of the base is $2x$, and its area is $2x(x) = 2x^2$. Hence:

$$\text{Cost of the base} = 80\left(2x^2\right) = 160x^2 \qquad (1)$$

The volume of the tank is 16 m^3. If h is the height of the tank, then:

$$16 = V = (\text{base height})(\text{width})(\text{tank height}) = 2x(x)h = 2x^2h$$

Solving for h:

$$h = \frac{16}{2x^2} = \frac{8}{x^2}$$

The area of the 4 lateral walls is:

$$2xh + 2(2x)h = 6xh = 6x\left(\frac{8}{x^2}\right) = \frac{48}{x}$$

Hence:

$$\text{Cost of the lateral walls} = 50\left(\frac{48}{x}\right) = \frac{240}{x} \qquad (2)$$

The cost of the tank is the sum of (1) and (2), that is:

$$C(x) = 160x^2 + \frac{240}{x} \text{ dollars.}$$

SOLVED PROBLEMS 4.1

Problem 4.1.1 Find the domain and the range of the function:

$$f(x) = \sqrt{9 - \frac{2}{x}}$$

Solution

$$x \in \text{Dom}(f) \Leftrightarrow 9 - \frac{2}{x} \geq 0 \Leftrightarrow \frac{9x-2}{x} \geq 0$$

+ + + + + + - - - - - - - + + + + + + +

0 $\frac{2}{9}$

Hence, $\text{Dom}(f) = (-\infty, 0) \cup \left[\frac{2}{9}, +\infty\right)$.

Range:

$$y \in \text{Rang}(f) \Leftrightarrow \exists x \in \text{Dom}(f) \text{ such that } f(x) = y$$

$$\Leftrightarrow \exists x \in \text{Dom}(f) \text{ such that } \sqrt{9 - \frac{2}{x}} = y$$

Solving for x in terms of y:

$$\sqrt{9 - \frac{2}{x}} = y \quad \Leftrightarrow \quad 9 - \frac{2}{x} = y^2 \quad \wedge \quad y \geq 0$$

$$\Leftrightarrow \quad \frac{2}{x} = 9 - y^2 \quad \wedge \quad y \geq 0$$

$$\Leftrightarrow \quad x = \frac{2}{9 - y^2} \quad \wedge \quad y \geq 0$$

Observe carefully the following expression $x = \frac{2}{9-y^2}$.

Notice that we can find x if the denominator $9 - y^2$ is different from 0, i.e. when $y \neq 3$ or $y \neq -3$. Now, we have:

$$y \in \text{Rang}(f) \Leftrightarrow (y \neq 3 \text{ or } y \neq -3) \ \wedge \ y \geq 0 \Leftrightarrow y \in [0, +\infty) - \{3\}$$

Hence:

$$\text{Rang}(f) = [0, +\infty) - \{3\}$$

Problem 4.1.2 Find the domain, range and graph of the function:

$$S(x) = x - \lfloor x \rfloor$$

Solution

Domain: $\mathbb{R}$

Let's analyze the function S on each interval of the form $[n,\ n+1)$, where n is an integer.

$$n \leq x < n+1 \Rightarrow \lfloor x \rfloor = n \Rightarrow S(x) = x - n$$

Then:

$$S(n) = n - n = 0$$

Meaning that, on the interval $[n,\ n+1)$, S is the part of the line $y = x - n$ with slope 1, and passing through the point $(n,\ S(n)) = (n, 0)$.

Hence, the **range** of S is the interval $\mathbf{[0,\ 1)}$.

Problem 4.1.3

Find the linear function $f(x) = ax + b$ that satisfies the following conditions:

1. $f(x+z) = f(x) + f(z),\ \forall x, z \in \mathbb{R}$ **2.** $f(-2) = -6$

Solution

Using the condition (1), we get:

$$f(x+z) = f(x) + f(z) \Rightarrow a(x+z) + b = (ax+b) + (az+b)$$

$$\Rightarrow ax + az + b = ax + b + az + b$$

$$\Rightarrow b = b + b \Rightarrow b = 0$$

Therefore, $f(x) = ax$.

Now, with respect to the condition (2):

$$f(-2) = -6 \Rightarrow a(-2) = -6$$

$$\Rightarrow a = 3$$

Hence, the linear function we are looking for is: $f(x) = 3x$

Problem 4.1.4

A soft drink company needs to manufacture an aluminum can shaped like a right circular cylinder to hold $250\pi\, cm^3$ of liquid. Express the amount of aluminum (area) of each can as a function of the radius of the base.

Solution

Let r be the radius of the base, h the height, and A the total area of the can. The total area A is the sum the areas of the two bases, which is $2\pi r^2$, plus the area of the lateral surface, $2\pi rh$. Hence:

$$A = 2\pi r^2 + 2\pi rh \qquad (1)$$

On the other hand, the volume of the cylinder is:

$$V = \pi r^2 h$$

Since the problem says that $V = 250\pi$, we have:

$$\pi r^2 h = 250\pi \Rightarrow r^2 h = 250 \Rightarrow h = \frac{250}{r^2}$$

Replacing this value of h in (1), we get:

$$A(r) = 2\pi r^2 + 2\pi r \frac{250}{r^2} = 2\pi \left(r^2 + \frac{250}{r^2} \right)$$

EXERCISES 4.1

1. If $f(x) = \frac{x}{x+1}$, find:

   a. $f(3)$ **b.** $f\left(1+\sqrt{x}\right)$ **c.** $f(2+h) - f(2)$ **d.** $f(a+h) - f(a)$

2. if $g(x) = x + \frac{(x-2)^2}{4}$, find:

   a. $g(2)$ **b.** $g(a+2)$ **c.** $g(a+h) - g(a)$

In the exercises 3 through 8, find the domain and range of the given function.

3. $f(x) = \sqrt{x-9}$ **4.** $g(x) = \frac{\sqrt{16-x^2}}{3}$ **5.** $h(x) = \frac{\sqrt{x^2-4}}{2}$

6. $u(x) = \sqrt[3]{x-2}$ **7.** $f(x) = \frac{x^2-4}{x}$ **8.** $y = \sqrt{x(x-2)}$

In the exercises 9 through 14, find the domain of the function.

9. $g(x) = \frac{6}{\sqrt{9-x}-2}$ **10.** $y = \frac{1}{\sqrt{x^2-4}-2}$ **11.** $y = \sqrt{4 - \frac{1}{x}}$

12. $y = \frac{1}{4-\sqrt{1-x}}$ **13.** $y = \sqrt{\frac{x+1}{2-x}}$ **14.** $y = \sqrt[4]{\frac{x+5}{x-3}}$

In the exercises 15 and 16, find the domain, range and graph the function.

15. $g(x) = \begin{cases} |x|, & \text{if } |x| \leq 1 \\ 1, & \text{if } |x| > 1 \end{cases}$ **16.** $f(x) = \begin{cases} \sqrt{-x}, & \text{if } x < 0 \\ x, & \text{if } 0 \leq x \leq 2 \\ \sqrt{x-2}, & \text{if } x > 2 \end{cases}$

17. Prove that:

a. If the graph of f is symmetric with respect to the Y-axis, then f is even.

b. If the graph of f is symmetric with respect to the origin, then f is odd.

18. If $f(x+1) = (x-3)^2$, find $f(x-1)$.

19. Find the quadratic function:

$$f(x) = ax^2 + bx \quad \text{such that} \quad f(x) - f(x-1) = x, \ \forall x \in \mathbb{R}$$

20. A hotel has 40 rooms. The manager knows that when the price of a room is 30 dollars, all the rooms get rented. However, for every 5 dollars he increases the rent, a room goes unoccupied. If the maintenance cost of an occupied room is 4 dollars, express the profit of the hotel as a function of the number x of occupied rooms.

21. When the daily production of certain article does not exceed 1,000 units, the profit is 4,000 dollars per unit. If the number of articles produced exceed 1,000, the profit decreases by 10 dollars for each article exceeding 1,000 units. Express the daily profit as a function of the number x of produced articles.

22. A farm is planting orange trees. If 80 trees per hectare are planted, each plant produces an average of 960 oranges. For each additional plant sown, the production drops by an average of 10 oranges per plant. Express the production $p(x)$ of oranges per hectare as a function of the number x of orange trees per hectare.

23. For sending a box by mail, the administration requires that the base must be a square, for which the sum of its dimensions (length + width + height) cannot exceed 150 *cm*. Express the volume of the box with the maximum sum of its dimensions as a function of the length x of the base side.

24. A wire of 12 *m.* of length is cut into two pieces.

One of them is used to build a circle, and the other, to build a square.

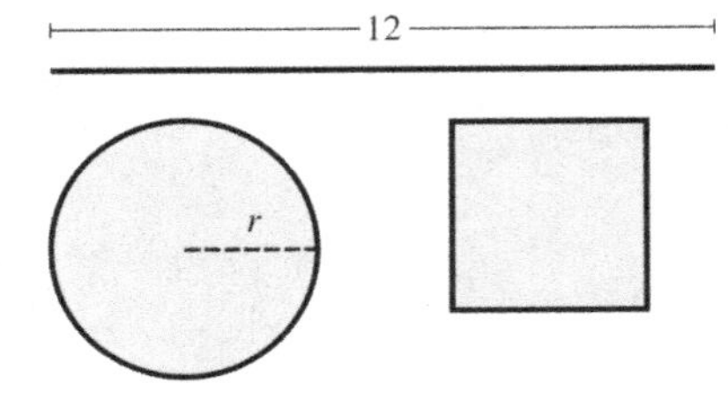

Express the area enclosed by the two figures as a function of the radium r of the circle.

25. The perimeter of an isosceles triangle is 36 *cm*. Express the area of the triangle as a function of the length x of one of the two equal sides.

26. A window has the form of a rectangle crowned by a semicircle.

The window has a perimeter of 7 *m*.

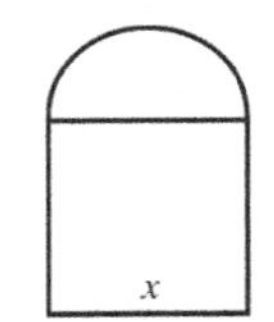

Express the area of the window as a function of the width x of the rectangle.

27. A factory requires to build boxes with an open top.

Metal sheets of 80 *cm* by 50 *cm* will be implemented as raw material.

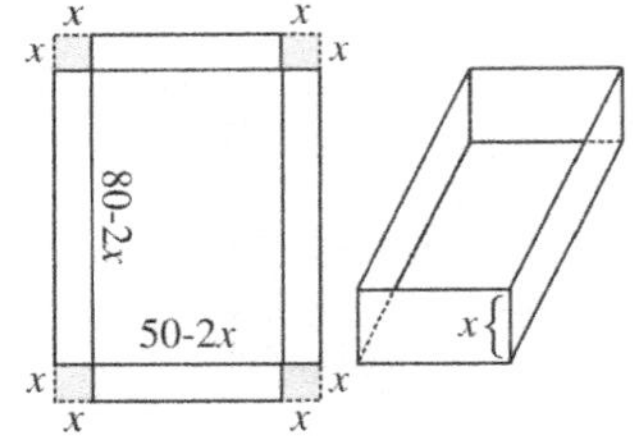

Equal squares will be cut out at each corner. Then, the sides will be folded upward, as shown in the figure.

If x is the length of the side of the small square, express the volume of the box as a function of x.

28. A book will be published. Each page must have 3 *cm.* of top and button margins, and 2 *cm.* of lateral margins.

The written area of the pages must be 252 cm^2.

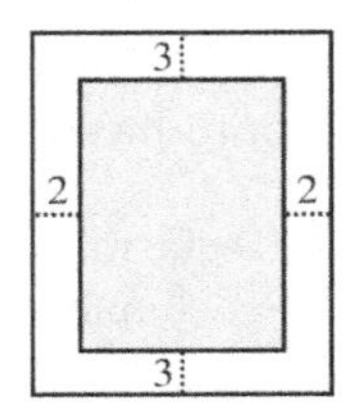

Express the area as a function of the width x of the written part of the page.

SECCION 4.2

TRIGONOMETRIC FUNCTIONS

Trigonometry has been in existence since the time of the ancient Babylonians and Egyptians; in fact, the earliest findings in this field were used to build the majestic Pyramids of Egypt. In this section we will not look at classical trigonometry, but at its more modern form, the **trigonometric functions**. Nowadays these functions have endless applications in fields like astronomy, architecture, navigation, mechanics, electronics, physics and 3D animation.

SINE AND COSINE FUNCTIONS

Let C be the circle of radius 1, with center at the origin. The standard formula of this circle will be:

$$x^2 + y^2 = 1,$$

This circumference is called:

Trigonometric Circle

To gain a deep understanding of this concept, we will proceed as follows:

- Define a function $L : \mathbb{R} \to C$.
- Fix $Q = (1, 0)$ as a reference point and any $t \in \mathbb{R}$.

If $t = 0$, then $L(0) = Q = (1, 0)$.

If $t > 0$, starting at $Q = (1, 0)$, we move in a counterclockwise direction on C, to form an arc of length t. The end point of the arc is $L(t)$.

If $t < 0$, starting at $Q = (1, 0)$, we move in a clockwise direction on C to form an arc of length t. The end point of the arc is also $L(t)$.

Thus:

$$L\left(\frac{\pi}{2}\right) = (0, 1) \quad \text{y} \quad L\left(-\frac{\pi}{2}\right) = (0, -1)$$

Considering that the length of C is 2π, we have:

$$L(t + 2\pi) = L(t), \ \forall t \in \mathbb{R}$$

Furthermore, 2π is the minimum positive number satisfying this equality; that is, L is a periodic function with period 2π.

In general, a function f is **periodic** if there exists a real number $k > 0$, such that:

$$f(t+k) = f(t),\ \forall t \in \mathbb{R}$$

The **minimum number** $\boldsymbol{k}$ that satisfies this condition is the *period.*

Definition

Sine and **Cosine** functions are given by:

$\mathbf{sin} : \mathbb{R} \to \mathbb{R},\ \mathbf{sin}(t) =$ ordinate of $L(t)$

$\mathbf{cos} : \mathbb{R} \to \mathbb{R},\ \mathbf{cos}(t) =$ abscissa of $L(t)$

That is $L(t) = (\cos(t), \sin(t))$

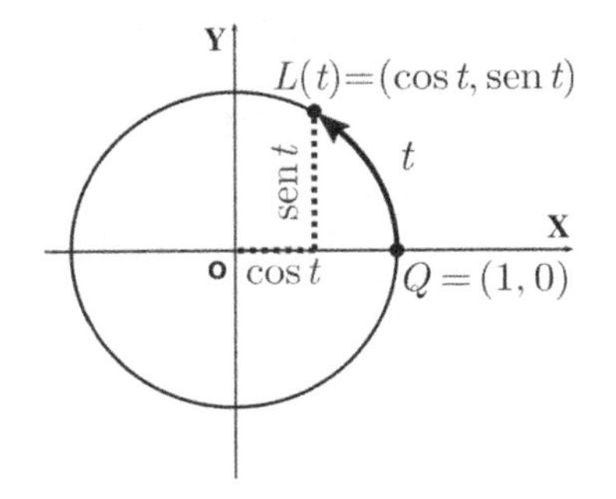

GRAPHS OF SINE AND COSINE

Sine function: $y = \sin t$

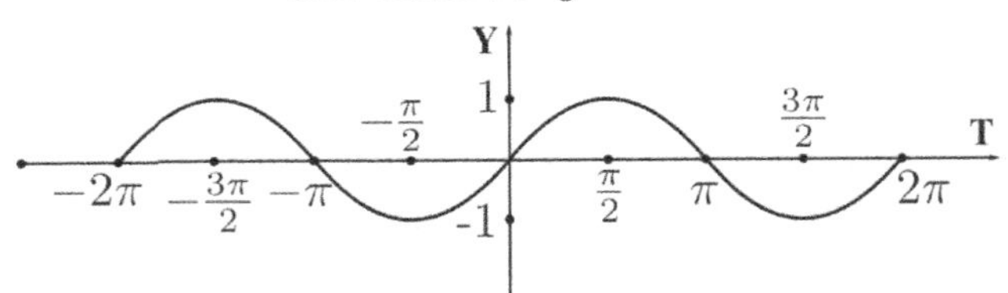

Cosine function: $y = \cos t$

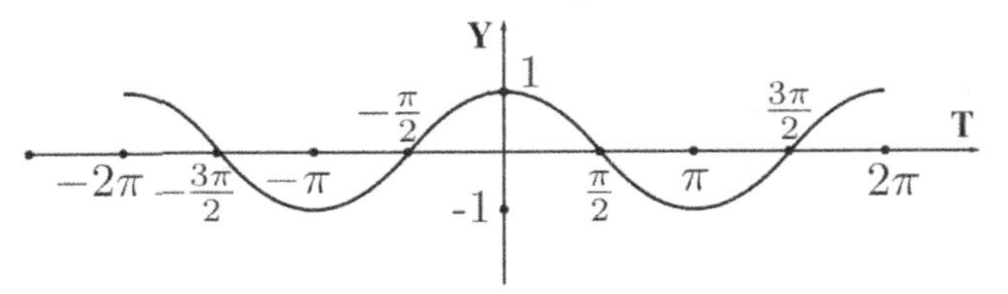

Sometimes we will write $\cos t$ and $\sin t$, instead of $\cos(t)$ y $\sin(t)$.

The trigonometric circle plays an important role in the definition of the sine and cosine functions. For this reason, trigonometric functions are also called **circular functions**.

Theorem 4.2.1

If t is any real number, then:

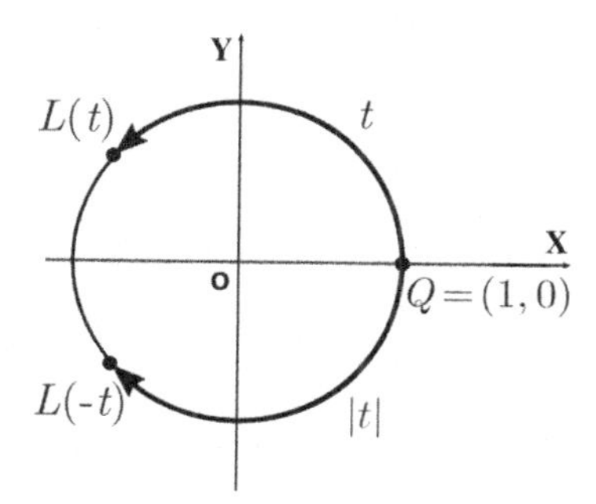

1. $\sin(t+2\pi) = \sin t, \quad \cos(t+2\pi) = \cos t$

2. $\sin(-t) = -\sin t, \quad \cos(-t) = \cos t$

3. $\sin\left(\frac{\pi}{2} - t\right) = \cos t, \quad \cos\left(\frac{\pi}{2} - t\right) = \sin t$

4. $\sin^2 t + \cos^2 t = 1$

5. $|\sin t| \leq 1, \quad |\cos t| \leq 1$

Proof

1. This property is a result of the periodicity of the L function.

2. These identities result from the fact that the following points are symmetric about the X-axis.

$$L(t) = (\cos t, \sin t) \qquad \text{y} \qquad L(-t) = (\cos(-t), \sin(-t),$$

3. The next points are symmetric about the diagonal $y = x$:

$$L(t) = (\cos t, \sin t)$$

and

$$L\left(\frac{\pi}{2} - t\right)$$

$$= \left(\cos\left(\frac{\pi}{2} - t\right), \sin\left(\frac{\pi}{2} - t\right)\right),$$

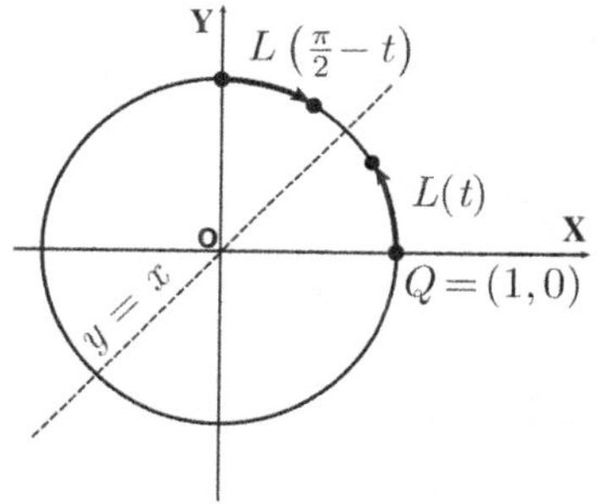

Hence, their coordinates become inverted.

4. $L(t) = (\cos t, \sin t)$ is a point of the trigonometric circle. Hence:

$$\cos^2 t + \sin^2 t = 1$$

5. From $\cos^2 t + \sin^2 t = 1$, we get $\sin^2 t \leq 1$ and $\cos^2 t \leq 1$. Taking square root we obtain these two inequalities.

The property (1) states that the functions sine and cosine are periodic.

It is proved that the period is 2π. The property (2) states that the sine function is odd, and the cosine function is even.

Example 4.2.1 Find all real numbers t such that:

1. $\sin t = 0$ **2.** $\cos t = 0$

Solution

1. $\sin t = 0$

$$\Leftrightarrow L(t) = (1,0) \text{ ó } L(t) = (-1,0)$$
$$\Leftrightarrow t = 2n\pi \text{ ó } t = \pi + 2n\pi, \ \forall n \in \mathbb{Z}$$
$$\Leftrightarrow t = n\pi, \ \forall n \in \mathbb{Z}$$

2. $\cos t = 0 \Leftrightarrow L(t) = (0,1) \text{ ó } L(t) = (0,-1)$

$$\Leftrightarrow t = \frac{\pi}{2} + 2n\pi \text{ ó } t = \frac{3}{2}\pi + 2n\pi, \ \forall n \in \mathbb{Z}$$
$$\Leftrightarrow t = \frac{\pi}{2} + n\pi, \ \forall n \in \mathbb{Z}$$

THE OTHER TRIGONOMETRIC FUNCTIONS

There are other trigonometric functions that derive from the sine and cosine functions; indeed, these functions are defined in terms of these two. These functions are: tangent, cotangent, secant and cosecant; abbreviated by tan, cot, sec and csc, respectively.

Definition **Other trigonometric functions.**

$$\tan t = \frac{\sin t}{\cos t} \qquad \cot t = \frac{\cos t}{\sin t} \qquad \sec t = \frac{1}{\cos t} \qquad \csc t = \frac{1}{\sin t}$$

According to the previous example we have:

1. $\text{Dom}(\tan) = \text{Dom}(\sec) = \{t \in \mathbb{R} / t \neq \frac{\pi}{2} + n\pi, \ n \in \mathbb{Z}\}$

2. $\text{Dom}(\cot) = \text{Dom}(\csc) = \{t \in \mathbb{R} / t \neq n\pi, \ n \in \mathbb{Z}\}$

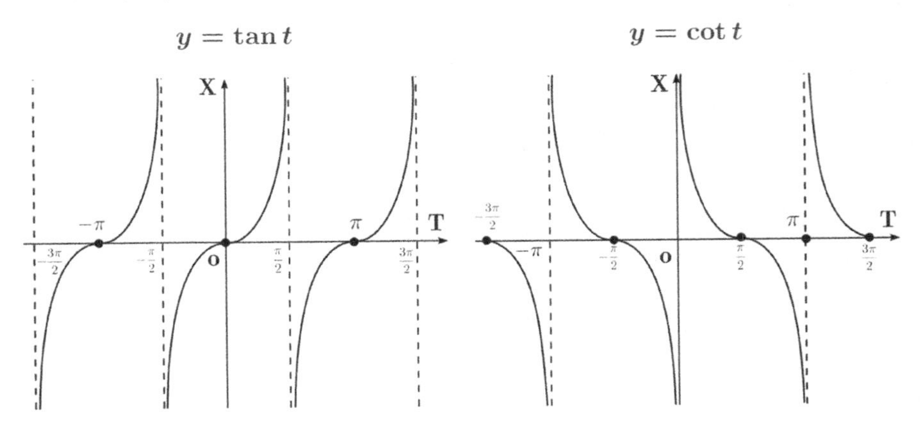

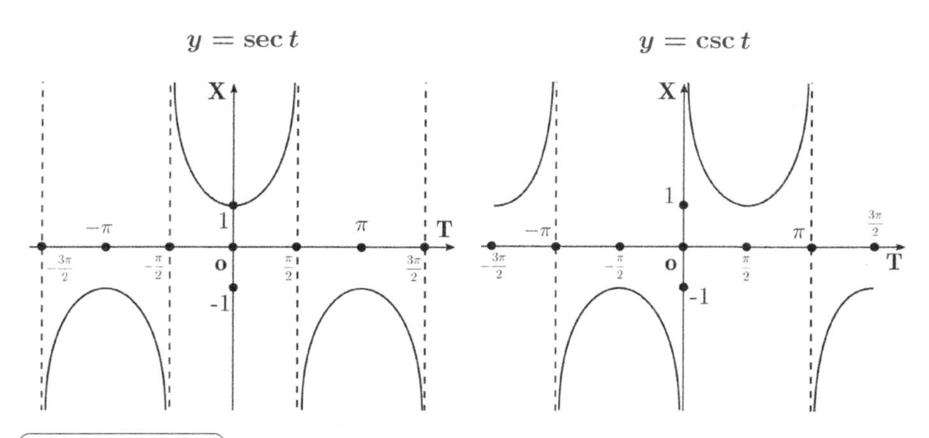

Example 4.2.2

Find the value of every trigonometric function at $\boldsymbol{t = -9\pi}$.

Solution

We have $L(-9\pi) = L(-\pi + (-4)2\pi) = L(-\pi) = (-1, 0)$

Hence:

a. $\sin(-9\pi) = 0$

b. $\cos(-9\pi) = -1$

c. $\tan(-9\pi) = \dfrac{\sin(-9\pi)}{\cos(-9\pi)} = \dfrac{0}{-1} = 0$

d. $\cot(-9\pi)$ is not defined

e. $\sec(-9\pi) = \dfrac{1}{\cos(-9\pi)} = \dfrac{1}{-1} = -1$

f. $\csc(-9\pi)$ is not defined

ORIENTED ANGLES

An angle is considered to be in **normal position** if it is drawn in the XY-plane as follows:

- Its vertex is at the origin of the XY-plane.
- One of its two sides, which will be called **initial side**, is on the positive half of the X-axis.
- The other side will be the **terminal side**.

The next adjoining figures show the angles $\angle AOB$ and $\angle AOC$ in normal position. The initial side is $\overline{OA}$, and terminal side is $\overline{OB}$.

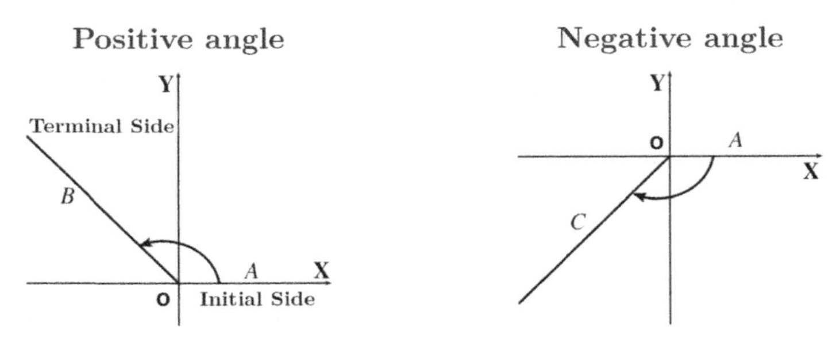

The concept of angle from elementary geometry is not relevant in Calculus. This field requires we consider that each angle is generated by a rotation to get an oriented angle. Thus, the oriented angle $\angle AOB$ is obtained by rotating, in counterclockwise direction, the initial side $\overline{OA}$ to reach the terminal side $\overline{OB}$. On the other hand, the oriented angle $\angle AOC$ is obtained by rotating, in clockwise direction, the initial side $\overline{OA}$ to reach the terminal side $\overline{OC}$.

An oriented angle is **positive** if the rotation is counterclockwise, and is **negative** if the rotation is clockwise. That said, in the above figures, the angle $\angle AOB$ is positive and the angle $\angle AOC$ is negative.

The rotation of the point A, to reach the point B or C (in both figures), describes an arc of certain length. We also consider this length positive if the rotation is counterclockwise, and negative if it is clockwise.

It is clear that, for every angle, there exits another congruent angle in normal position. This result allows us to concentrate our work on angles in normal position, without loosing generality.

The angles can be measured in degrees or radians (abbreviated *rad.*). In Calculus, the formulas get simpler when using radians, that is what makes this measurement system so popular in this field.

Definition

If a central angle with vertex at the center of a circle subtends an arc of length s on a circle of radius r, then the measure of this angle in radians is:

$$\theta = \frac{s}{r} \textbf{ radians} \qquad (1)$$

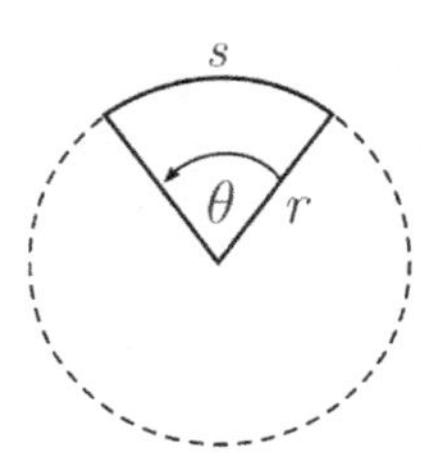

If an angle subtends an arc equal to the entire circle, then the angle measures:

$$\frac{2\pi r}{r} \text{ radians} = 2\pi \text{ rad}$$

Hence, $360° = 2\pi$ rad. or simplifying:

$$\mathbf{180° = \pi\ rad.} \qquad (2)$$

Therefore:

$$\mathbf{1° = \frac{\pi}{180}\ rad. \approx 0.017\ rads.} \qquad (3)$$

$$\mathbf{1\ rad. = \frac{180°}{\pi} \approx 57.3°} \qquad (4)$$

To gain a geometric understanding of an angle measuring 1 radian, let's consider a central angle θ that subtends an arc of the length of one radius.

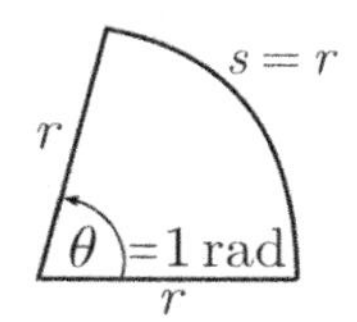

By (1) we have:

$$\theta = \frac{r}{r} = 1\ \text{rad.}$$

Hence, an angle measures 1 radian when it subtends an arc of length r.

Example 4.2.3

Find the length of the arc subtended by the central angle $\theta = 1.8$ radians in a circle of radius 12 cm.

Solution

$$s = \theta r = 1.8(12\,cm.) = 21.6\,cm.$$

We will use the formulas (3) and (4), given in the previous definition, to convert degrees into radians, and radians into degrees, respectively.

Example 4.2.4 Express:

a. $60°$ in radians **b.** $-\frac{5}{2}\pi$ radians in degrees

Solution

a. $60° = 60\left(\frac{\pi}{180}\right)\ \text{rad} = \frac{\pi}{3}\ \text{rad}$

b. $-\frac{5}{2}\ \text{rad} = -\frac{5}{2}\pi\left(\frac{180°}{\pi}\right) = -450°$

TRIGONOMETRIC FUNCTIONS OF ANGLES

Although we said earlier that the elementary Geometry definition of angle is not relevant in Calculus, it is important to make an exception with respect to the ancient **trigonometric ratios** defined for the acute angle of a right triangle. These are:

$$\sin\theta = \frac{\textbf{Op}}{\textbf{Hip}} \qquad \cos\theta = \frac{\textbf{Ady}}{\textbf{Hip}}$$

$$\tan\theta = \frac{\textbf{Op}}{\textbf{Ady}} \qquad \cot\theta = \frac{\textbf{Ady}}{\textbf{Op}}$$

$$\sec\theta = \frac{\textbf{Hip}}{\textbf{Ady}} \qquad \csc\theta = \frac{\textbf{Hip}}{\textbf{Op}}$$

Hypotenuse
Opposite side
θ
Adjacent side

We will attempt to harmonize both approaches, the *trigonometric circle* and the *trigonometric ratios.*

Definition

If an oriented angle θ measures t radians, then:

$$\sin\theta = \sin t$$

If the measure of the angle is given in degrees, we convert the degrees into radians.

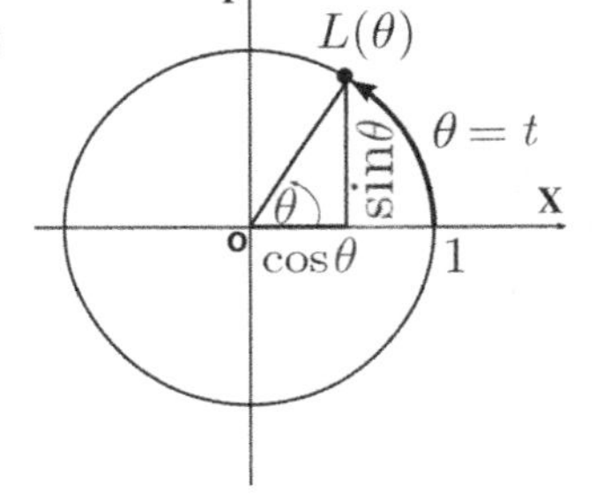

Assume the angle A° equals t radians, then:

$$\sin(A^\circ) = \sin t$$

We proceed the same way with the other trigonometric functions. Now, let's focus on the trigonometric circle.

If a central angle θ, with a measure of θ radians, subtends an arc of length t, then, according to the formula (1), we have:

$$\theta = \frac{t}{1} = t$$

In the trigonometric circle, ***the radian measure of an angle equals the length of the subtended arc.***

Now, observe carefully the last figure. Notice the small triangle inside the trigonometric circle. Evidently, the old definition of trigonometric functions for rectangle triangles coincides with the new one of the trigonometric circle.

In fact, we have that:

$$(\text{Old definition}) \sin\theta = \frac{\text{Opposite side}}{\text{Hypotenuse}} = \frac{\sin\theta}{1}$$

$$= \sin\theta = \text{ ordinate of } L(\theta)(\text{new definition})$$

Theorem 4.2.2 **Laws of sines and cosines**

- **Law of sines**

$$\frac{\sin A}{a} = \frac{\sin B}{b} = \frac{\sin C}{c}$$

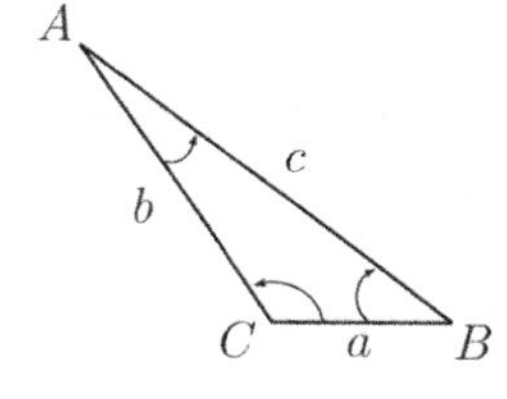

- **Law of cosines**

$$a^2 = b^2 + c^2 - 2bc\cos A$$
$$b^2 = a^2 + c^2 - 2ac\cos B$$
$$c^2 = a^2 + b^2 - 2ab\cos C$$

Proof

See the solved problem 4.2.5

Theorem 4.2.3 **Addition and Subtraction formulas**

1. $\sin(x+y) = \sin x\cos y + \cos x\sin y$
2. $\cos(x+y) = \cos x\cos y - \sin x\sin y$
3. $\sin(x-y) = \sin x\cos y - \cos x\sin y$
4. $\cos(x-y) = \cos x\cos y + \sin x\sin y$
5. $\tan(x+y) = \dfrac{\tan x + \tan y}{1 - \tan x\tan y}$
6. $\tan(x-y) = \dfrac{\tan x - \tan y}{1 + \tan x\tan y}$

Proof

See the solved problem 4.2.6.

ANGLE OF INCLINATION

The **angle of inclination** of a non-horizontal line is the positive angle generated by the line and the positive side of the X-axis. The angle of inclination of a horizontal line is the angle of measure 0.

If the measure of the angle of inclination is α radians, then:

$$0 \leq \alpha < \pi$$

If L is a non-vertical line of slope m, with an angle of inclination α, then:

$$m = \tan \alpha$$

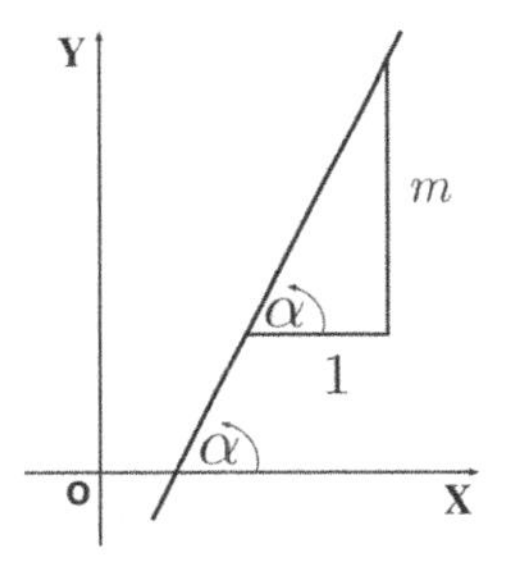

Indeed, just by looking at triangle of the figure, we have:

$$\tan \alpha = \frac{\text{Op}}{\text{Ady}} = \frac{m}{1} = m$$

This result coincides with the proof given in the solved problem 2.3.11.

If a line is vertical, its angle of inclination measures $\frac{\pi}{2}$. But $\tan\left(\frac{\pi}{2}\right)$ is not defined. This result is plausible since vertical lines do not have slope.

ANGLE BETWEEN TWO LINES

Let L_1 and L_2 be two intersecting lines with angles of inclination α_1 and α_2, respectively. These angles will form supplementary angles at the intersection.

One of the angles is:

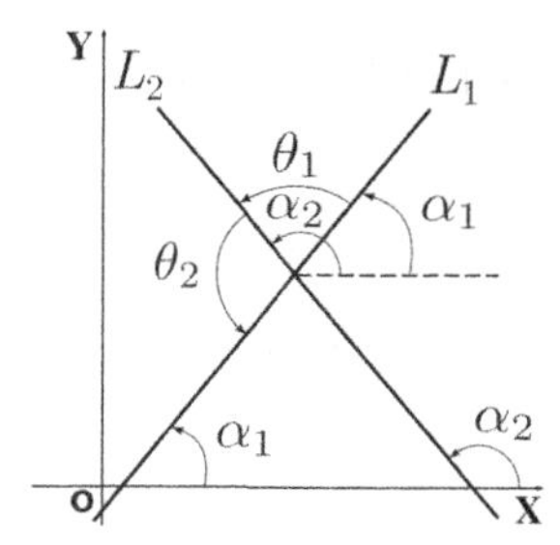

$$\theta_1 = \begin{cases} \alpha_2 - \alpha_1, & \text{if } \alpha_2 \geq \alpha_1 \\ \\ \alpha_1 - \alpha_2, & \text{if } \alpha_1 \geq \alpha_2 \end{cases}$$

The other angle is:

$$\theta_2 = \pi - \theta_1$$

If the lines are not perpendicular, only one of these angles is acute. The next theorem shows how to calculate this acute angle.

Theorem 4.2.4

Let L_1 and L_2 be neither perpendicular nor vertical lines. If L_1 and L_2 have slopes m_1 and m_2, respectively, and θ is the acute angle generated by L_1 and L_2, we have:

$$\boldsymbol{\tan\theta = \left|\frac{m_2 - m_1}{1 + m_1 m_2}\right|}$$

Proof

Let θ_1 and θ_2 be the supplementary angles formed by the two lines. If θ is the acute angle, then θ is θ_1 if $\tan\theta_1 \geq 0$, or θ is θ_2 if $\tan\theta_2 \geq 0$.

Let α_1 and α_2 be the inclination angles of L_1 and L_2, respectively. Assume that $\alpha_2 \geq \alpha_1$. Then, we have:

$$\theta_1 = \alpha_2 - \alpha_1, \quad \theta_2 = \pi - \theta_1, \quad \tan\alpha_2 = m_2 \quad \text{and} \quad \tan\alpha_1 = m_1$$

According to the trigonometric formula 25, and relying on the fact that the tangent function has period π, we have:

$$\tan\theta_1 = \tan(\alpha_2 - \alpha_1) = \frac{\tan\alpha_2 - \tan\alpha_1}{1 + \tan\alpha_1 \tan\alpha_2} = \frac{m_2 - m_1}{1 + m_1 m_2}$$

$$\tan\theta_2 = \tan(\pi - \theta_1) = \tan(-\theta_1) = -\tan\theta_1 = -\frac{m_2 - m_1}{1 + m_1 m_2}$$

Hence,

$$\tan\theta = \left|\frac{m_2 - m_1}{1 + m_1 m_2}\right|$$

Example 4.2.5 Find the acute angles generated by the lines:

$$L_1 : 9y - 2x - 30 = 0, \quad \text{and} \quad L_2 : 3y - 8x + 12 = 0$$

Solution

The slope of L_1 is $m_1 = \dfrac{2}{9}$ and the slope of L_2 is $m_2 = \dfrac{8}{3}$

If θ is the acute angle between the lines, then:

$$\tan\theta = \left|\frac{m_2 - m_1}{1 + m_1 m_2}\right| = \left|\frac{\frac{8}{3} - \frac{2}{9}}{1 + \left(\frac{2}{9}\right)\left(\frac{8}{3}\right)}\right| = \left|\frac{72 - 6}{27 + 16}\right| = \frac{66}{43}$$

Hence,

$$\theta = \arctan\left(\frac{66}{43}\right) \approx 0.993 \text{ rads.} \approx 56^\circ\, 54'\, 54''$$

The other angle is:

$$\theta' = \pi - 0.993 = 2.1486 \text{ rads.} \approx 123^\circ\, 5'\, 6''$$

SOLVED PROBLEMS 4.2

Problem 4.2.1

The adjoining figure consists of an isosceles triangle with a semicircle on top. The length of the congruent sides is 10 cm. and they form the angle θ. Express the area A of the figure as a function of the angle θ.

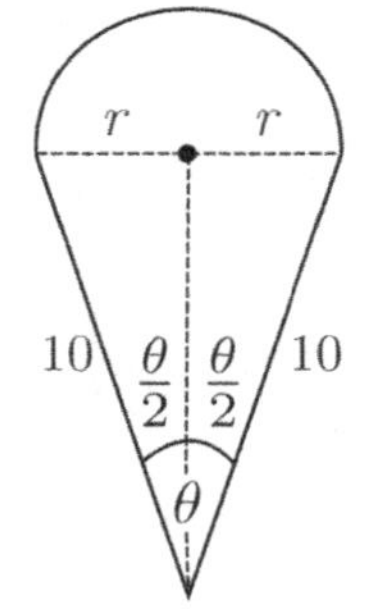

Solution

If A_1 is the area enclosed by the semicircle, and A_2 is the area of the triangle, then:

$$A = A_1 + A_2$$

Let's find A_1:

The radius of the semicircle is $r = 10\sin\left(\frac{\theta}{2}\right)$.

So:

$$A_1 = \frac{1}{2}\pi r^2 = \frac{1}{2}\pi\left[10\sin\left(\frac{\theta}{2}\right)\right]^2$$

$$= 50\pi\sin^2\left(\frac{\theta}{2}\right)$$

Let's find A_2:

The base b and the height h of the triangle are:

$$b = 2r = 2\left(10\sin\left(\frac{\theta}{2}\right)\right) = 20\sin\left(\frac{\theta}{2}\right), \quad h = 10\cos\left(\frac{\theta}{2}\right)$$

So:

$$A_2 = \frac{1}{2}bh = \frac{1}{2}\left[20\sin\left(\frac{\theta}{2}\right)\right]\left[10\cos\left(\frac{\theta}{2}\right)\right]$$

$$= 50\left[2\sin\left(\frac{\theta}{2}\right)\cos\left(\frac{\theta}{2}\right)\right] = 50\sin\theta \qquad \text{(Trig. formula 27)}$$

Now we find A:

$$A = A_1 + A_2 = 50\pi\sin^2\left(\frac{\theta}{2}\right) + 50\sin\theta = 50\left[\pi\sin^2\left(\frac{\theta}{2}\right) + \sin\theta\right]$$

Hence:

$$A = \left[\pi\sin^2\left(\frac{\theta}{2}\right) + \sin\theta\right]$$

Problem 4.2.2

Prove that the tangent, cotangent and cosecant functions are odd, and the secant function is even. That is, prove that:

a. $\tan(-t) = -\tan t$ **b.** $\cot(-t) = -\cot t$

c. $\sec(-t) = \sec t$ **d.** $\csc(-t) = -\csc t$

Solution

We are just proving **(a)** and **(c)**. The others can be proven using the same approach.

a. $\tan(-t) = \dfrac{\sin(-t)}{\cos(-t)} = \dfrac{-\sin t}{\cos t} = -\dfrac{\sin t}{\cos t} = -\tan t$

c. $\sec(-t) = \dfrac{1}{\cos(-t)} = \dfrac{1}{\cos t} = \sec t$

Problem 4.2.3

If A is the area of a circular sector of a circle of radius r, and a central angle of θ radians, prove that:

$$\boldsymbol{A = \frac{1}{2}\theta r^2}$$

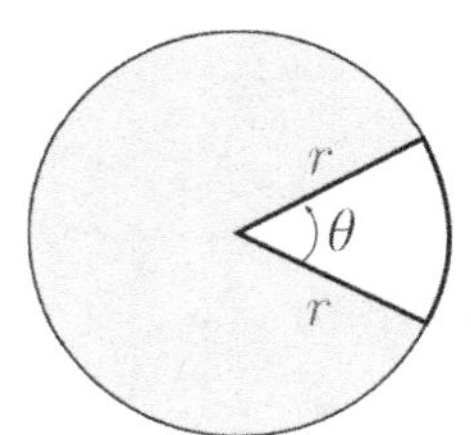

Solution

Clearly, the areas of two circular sectors of the same circle are proportional to their respective central angles.

A a circle, or disk, could be described as a circular sector with angle 2π; moreover, the area of a circle of radius r is πr^2

According to the previous results, we have that the ratio between the area A and the area of the circle of radius r is the same as the ratio between θ and 2π. That is:

$$\frac{A}{\pi r^2} = \frac{\theta}{2\pi} \Rightarrow A = \frac{1}{2}\theta r^2$$

Problem 4.2.4

The two gears of a bicycle have 10 $cm.$ and 3 $cm.$ of radius:

a. how many revolutions per minute does the small gear (the one that spins the rear wheel) spin if the big gear (the one of the pedals) spins 75 revolutions per minute?

b. find the speed of the bicycle if the wheels have a radius of 45 $cm.$

Solution

a. The circumference of the big gear is $2\pi(10)\,cm.$

So, after one minute, any point on circle of the gear travels:

$$2\pi(10)(75)\,cm$$

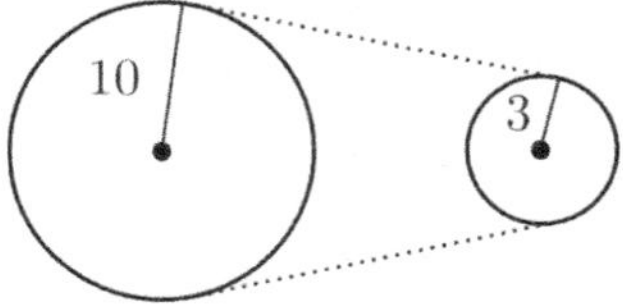

On the other hand, the circumference of the small gear is $2\pi(3)\,cm.$ Then, this gear spins:

$$\frac{2\pi(10)(75)}{2\pi(3)} = 250 \text{ revolutions per minute.}$$

b. The rear wheel of the bicycle, as the small gear, spins 250 revolutions per minute, which gives the bicycle a speed of:

$$2\pi(45)(250)\ cm/min. = 22,500\pi\ cm/min. \approx 706.86\ m/min.$$

Problem 4.2.5 Prove the law of cosines given in theorem 4.2.2.

Law of Cosines

$$\mathbf{a^2 = b^2 + c^2 - 2bc\cos A}$$
$$\mathbf{b^2 = a^2 + c^2 - 2ac\cos B}$$
$$\mathbf{c^2 = a^2 + b^2 - 2ab\cos C}$$

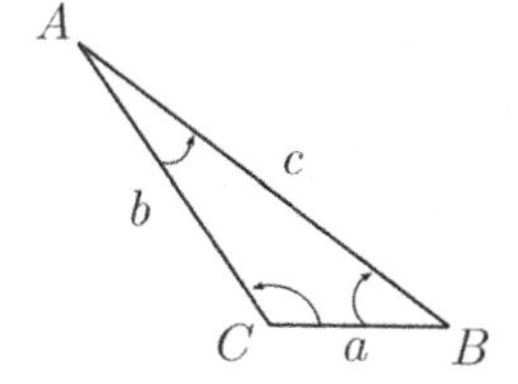

Solution

We will only prove the third equality. The demonstration of the others can be achieved following the same procedure.

Let's take a coordinate system placing the angle C in normal position, with side a over the X-axis. Let $A = (x, y)$.

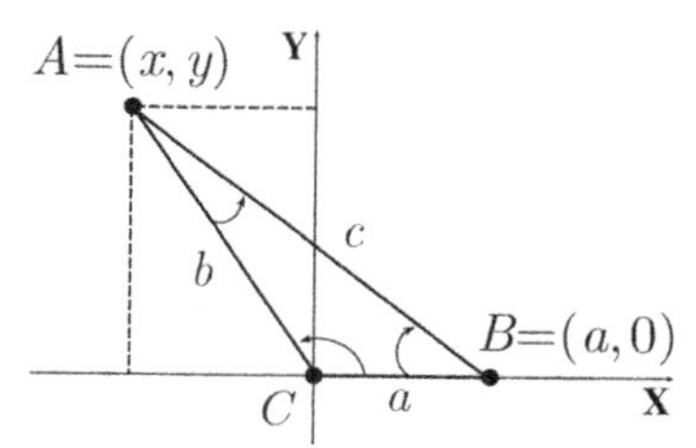

We have that:

$$y = b\sin C \quad \text{and} \quad x = b\cos C$$

Applying the distance formula to the vertices of the side c:

$$\begin{aligned} c^2 &= (x-a)^2 + (y-0)^2 = (b\cos C - a)^2 + (b\sin C - 0)^2 \\ &= b^2\cos^2 C - 2ab\cos C + a^2 + b^2\sin^2 C \\ &= a^2 + b^2(\cos^2 C + \sin^2 C) - 2ab\cos C \\ &= a^2 + b^2 - 2ab\cos C \end{aligned}$$

Problem 4.2.6 Prove the formulas of the theorem 4.2.3.

1. $\sin(x+y) = \sin x\cos y + \cos x\sin y$
2. $\cos(x+y) = \cos x\cos y - \sin x\sin y$
3. $\sin(x-y) = \sin x\cos y - \cos x\sin y$
4. $\cos(x-y) = \cos x\cos y + \sin x\sin y$

5. $\tan(x+y) = \dfrac{\tan x + \tan y}{1 - \tan x \tan y}$

6. $\tan(x-y) = \dfrac{\tan x - \tan y}{1 + \tan x \tan y}$

Solution

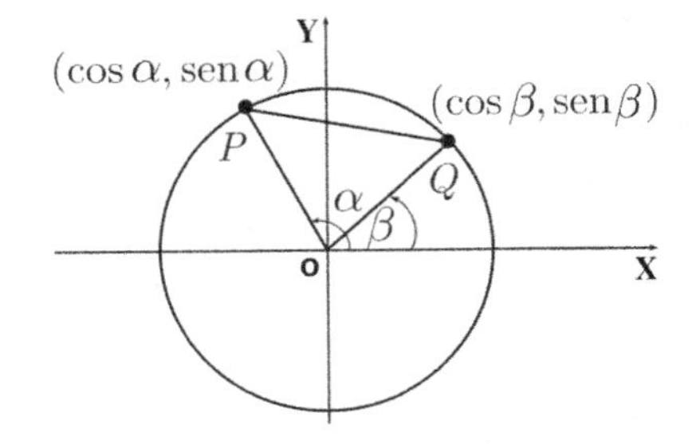

We will only prove the formulas 1, 3, 4 and 5. The demonstration of the others can be achieved following the same procedure.

Let α and β be angles in normal position. Let P and Q be the intersection points between the terminal sides and the trigonometric circle. We have:

$$P = (\cos\alpha,\ \sin\beta) \quad \text{and} \quad Q = (\cos\beta,\ \sin\beta)$$

4. The square of the length of the segment $\overline{PQ}$ is:

$$\begin{aligned}
(d(P,Q))^2 &= (\cos\beta - \cos\alpha)^2 + (\sin\beta - \sin\alpha)^2 && \text{(distance formula)}\\
&= \left(\sin^2\alpha + \cos^2\alpha\right) + \left(\sin^2\beta + \cos^2\beta\right) - 2\cos\alpha\cos\beta - 2\sin\alpha\sin\beta\\
&= 2 - 2\cos\alpha\cos\beta - 2\sin\alpha\sin\beta && \text{(trigonometric formula 5)}
\end{aligned}$$

On the other hand, by the law of cosines:

$$\begin{aligned}
(d(P,Q))^2 &= (d(\mathrm{O},P))^2 + (d(\mathrm{O},Q))^2 - 2\,(d(\mathrm{O},P))\,(d(\mathrm{O},Q))\cos(\alpha-\beta)\\
&= 2 - 2\cos(\alpha-\beta)
\end{aligned}$$

Hence:

$$\begin{aligned}
2 - 2\cos(\alpha-\beta) &= 2 - 2\cos\alpha\cos\beta - 2\sin\alpha\sin\beta\\
&\Rightarrow \cos(\alpha-\beta) = \cos\alpha\cos\beta + \sin\alpha\sin\beta
\end{aligned}$$

3. The part 3 of the theorem 4.2.1 says that:

$$\sin t = \cos\left(\frac{\pi}{2} - t\right) \quad \textbf{and} \quad \cos t = \sin\left(\frac{\pi}{2} - t\right)$$

According to these formulas we have:

$$\begin{aligned}\sin(x-y) &= \cos\left[\frac{\pi}{2}-(x-y)\right]\\ &= \cos\left[\left(\frac{\pi}{2}-x\right)-(-y)\right]\\ &= \cos\left(\frac{\pi}{2}-x\right)\cos(-y)+\sin\left(\frac{\pi}{2}-x\right)\sin(-y)\\ &= \sin x\cos y-\cos x\sin y\end{aligned}$$

1. $\sin(x+y)=\sin(x-(-y))=\sin x\cos(-y)-\cos x\sin(-y)$

$$\begin{aligned}&= \sin x\cos y+\cos x\sin y\\ &= \sin x\cos y-\cos x\sin y\end{aligned}$$

5. $\tan(x+y)=\dfrac{\sin(x+y)}{\cos(x+y)}=\dfrac{\sin x\cos y+\cos x\sin y}{\cos x\cos y-\sin x\sin y}$

Now, dividing both, numerator and denominator, by $\cos x\cos y$:

$$\tan(x+y)=\frac{\frac{\sin x}{\cos x}+\frac{\sin y}{\cos y}}{1-\left(\frac{\sin x}{\cos x}\right)\left(\frac{\sin y}{\cos y}\right)}=\frac{\tan x+\tan y}{1-\tan x\tan y}$$

Did you know this?

The Irresistible Beat of the Sine Function

What our brains interpret as musical notes are sound waves generated by the air vibrations produced by, let's say, the speakers of your headphones, an acoustic guitar or the vocal cords of your favorite singer.

Higher wave frequency ***Lower wave frequency***

Whether a musical note is high or low is defined by the ***wave frequency****, which is the number of oscillations of air vibrations in a time span, or better said, the* ***period*** *of the sine function.*

EXERCISES 4.2

1. Without using a calculator, find:

a. $\cot \dfrac{5\pi}{3}$ **b.** $\sin \dfrac{7\pi}{6}$ **c.** $\tan\left(-\dfrac{\pi}{3}\right)$

d. $\sec\left(-\dfrac{7\pi}{6}\right)$ **e.** $\csc\left(-\dfrac{241\pi}{6}\right)$

2. Find $\alpha \in \mathbb{R}$ such that:

a. $\tan\alpha = 0$ **b.** $\cot\alpha = 0$ **c.** $\sec\alpha = 0$ **d.** $\csc\alpha = 0$

e. $\sin\alpha = -\dfrac{\sqrt{3}}{2}$

3. Prove that:

a. $\cot(\alpha + \pi) = \cot\alpha$ **b.** $\sec(\alpha + \pi) = -\sec\alpha$

c. $\csc(\alpha + \pi) = -\csc\alpha$

4. Prove that:

a. $\cos(n\pi) = (-1)^n$ **b.** $\cos(\alpha + n\pi) = (-1)^n \cos\alpha$

c. $\sin(\alpha + n\pi) = (-1)^n \sin\alpha$

5. Let $P = (x, y) \neq (0, 0)$ be a point of the plane with a distance of r from the origin. If $L(t)$ is the point of intersection between the segment $\overline{OP}$ and the trigonometric circle, prove that:

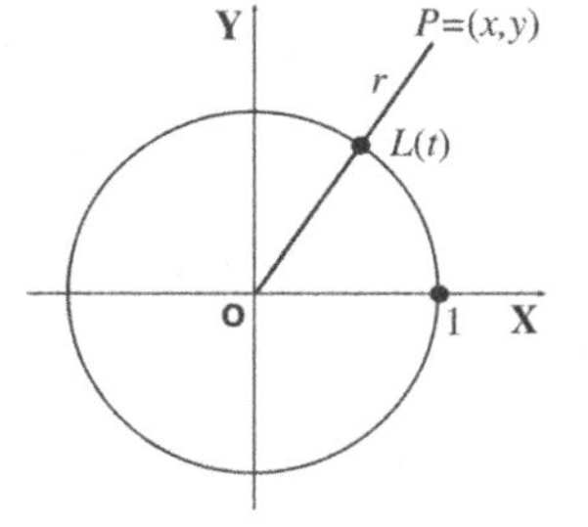

a. $\sin t = \dfrac{y}{r}$ **b.** $\cos t = \dfrac{x}{r}$

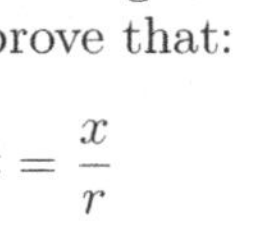

c. $\tan t = \dfrac{y}{x}$, $x \neq 0$

6. Find the value of $\sin(-23\pi/2)\cos(31\pi)$.

7. If $\alpha + \beta + \gamma = \pi$, simplify:

a. $\sin(2\alpha + \beta + \gamma)$ **b.** $\sin(2\alpha + \beta + \gamma) + \sin(\beta + \gamma)$

8. We know that the period of $y = \sin x$ is 2π, and the period of $y = \cot x$ is π. With that in mind, find the period of the following functions:

a. $f(x) = \sin(\gamma x)$, where $\gamma > 0$. **b.** $g(x) = \cot(2x)$

9. A circle has a radius of 18 cm. Find the measure, in radians, of a central angle with an arc length of:

a. $6\,cm$ **b.** $1.8\,cm$ **c.** $6\pi\,cm$

10. Find the length of the arc subtended, on a 9 cm. radius circle, by a central angle of:

a. $\frac{\pi}{6}$ radians **b.** $\frac{5}{4}\pi$ radians **c.** $50°$

11. The distance of two points, A and B, on the Earth's surface is the length of the arc formed by these points and the center of the Earth, C. Since the radius of the Earth is 6.367 Km, find the distance between A and B if the angle $\angle ACB$ measures:

a. $1°$ **b.** $30°$ **c.** $45°$ **d.** $80°45'$

12. In the previous problem, if the angle $\angle ACB$ measures $1'$ (one minute), then the distance between A and B is a nautical mile. How many kilometers does a nautical mile have?

13. How many radians does the minute hand of a clock turn in a time span of 20 minutes?

14. Find the measure in degrees of the angle that is supplementary to an angle of $\frac{\pi+1}{2}$ radians.

15. Two angles of a triangle measure $\frac{\pi+1}{2}$ and $\frac{3\pi-4}{8}$ radians, respectively. Find the measure in degrees of the remaining angle.

16. In the figure, the arc $\overset{\frown}{QP}$ has a length of $\frac{7\pi}{3}$ cm.

Find the point P.

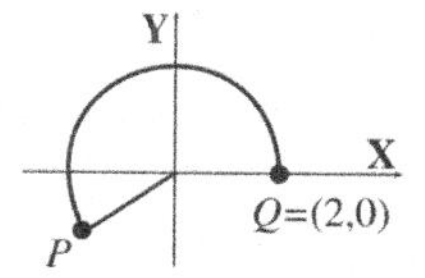

17. In the figure, the radius of the circle is 3 cm. and the length of the arc $\overset{\frown}{QP}$ is 2π.

Find the point P.

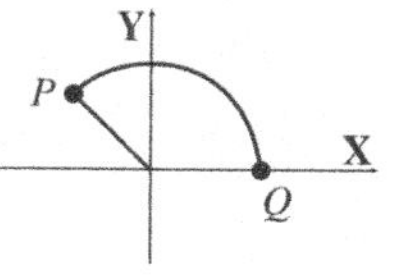

18. The terminal side of an oriented angle in normal position is the segment $\overline{OP}$, where O is the origin, and $P = (-2, 6)$. If the measure of this angle is α radians, find the value of: $(\sin\alpha - 3\cos\alpha)(\tan\alpha)(\sec\alpha)$.

19. Find the value of:

a. $\dfrac{\sin(-750°)}{\cos(-150°)}$ **b.** $\dfrac{\cos(-1,290°)}{\tan(7,515°)}$

20. Find the value of: $\left(\cos\frac{11\pi}{6}+\sin\frac{26\pi}{4}\right)\left(\tan\frac{\pi}{6}+\cos\frac{14\pi}{3}\right)$

21. Find the length of the side of a regular polygon of n sides inscribed in a circle of radius r.

22. The tires of a car have a diameter of 60 cm. How many revolutions per minute does each tire spin when the car runs at 90 Kms. per hour?

23. Two gears are linked by a belt, as the figure shows. The radii of the gears are 14 cm. and 8 cm. respectively.

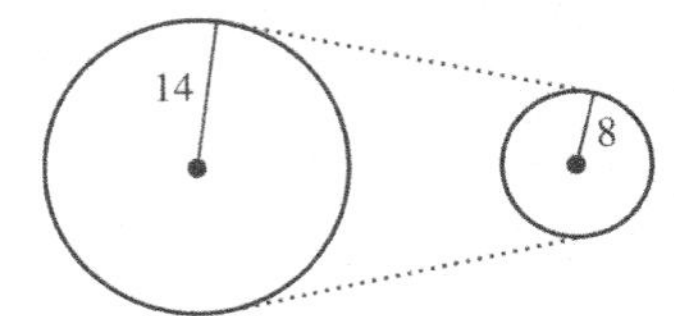

How many revolutions per second does the small gear spin when the big gear spins 28 revolutions per second?

24. An isosceles triangle is inscribed in a circle of radius 5 cm. Find a function that expresses the perimeter P of the triangle in terms of the angle θ.

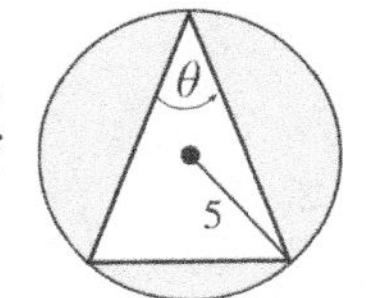

25. In order to construct a conic cup, a circular sector is cut out from a circular plate of radius 10 cm. Find a function to express the volume of the cup in terms of the central angle θ.

The volume of a cone is: $V=\frac{1}{3}\pi r^2 h$

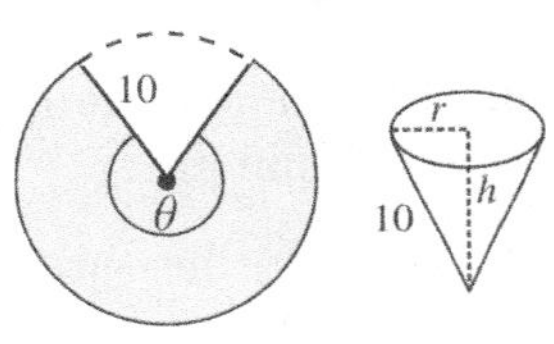

26. The inclination angle of a line, which does not intersect the second quadrant, measures $\frac{\pi}{4}$ radians. If the distance between the origin and the line is 4, find the equation of the line.

27. Find the acute angle generated by the lines:

$$3x+2y=0 \quad \text{and} \quad 5x-y+7=0$$

28. Find the equation of the line passing through the point $Q=(2,1)$ that generates an angle of $\pi/4$ radians with the line $3y+2x+4=0$ (two solutions).

29. The points (6, 2) and (-1, 3) are opposite vertices of a square. Find the equations of the lines that contain the sides of this square.

SECCION 4.3

NEW FUNCTIONS FROM OLD FUNCTIONS

NEW GRAPHS FROM KNOWN GRAPHS

If we already know the graph of a function $y = f(x)$, then, we can obtain the graph of the following functions with the aid of geometric transformations, where c is a positive constant:

$$y = f(x) + c \qquad y = f(x) - c \qquad y = f(x + c) \qquad y = f(x - c)$$

$$y = -f(x) \qquad y = f(-x) \qquad y = cf(x) \qquad y = f(cx)$$

The suggested transformations are of three types:

- Vertical and horizontal translations.
- Stretches and compressions.
- Reflections.

VERTICAL AND HORIZONTAL TRANSLATIONS

Let $c > 0$ be a constant. To obtain the graph of:

$y = f(x) + c$: shift the graph of $y = f(x)$, c units **upward**.

$y = f(x) - c$: shift the graph of $y = f(x)$, c units **downward**.

$y = f(x + c)$: shift the graph of $y = f(x)$, c units to the **left**.

$y = f(x - c)$: shift the graph of $y = f(x)$, c units to the **right**.

Example 4.3.1 Using the graph of the function $y = |\, x \,|$, graph:

a. $y = |\, x \,| + 2$ **b.** $y = |\, x \,| - 3$

c. $y = |\, x - 1 \,|$ **d.** $y = |\, x + 2 \,|$

Solution

a. $y = |\, x \,| + 2$ **b.** $y = |\, x \,| - 3$ **c.** $y = |\, x - 1 \,|$ **d.** $y = |\, x + 2 \,|$

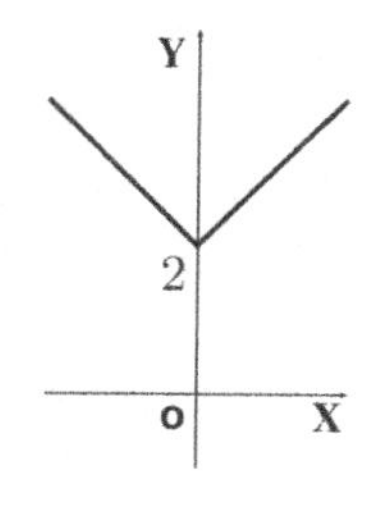

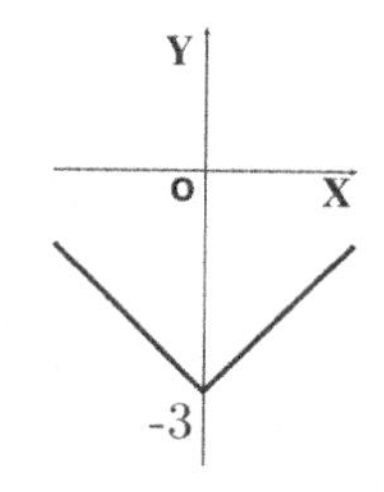

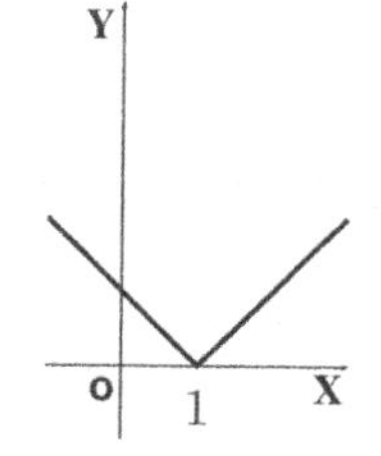

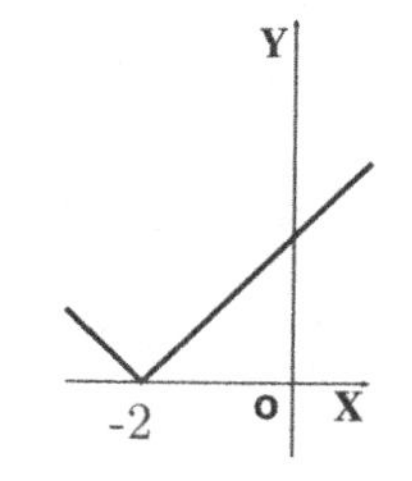

REFLECTIONS

To obtain the graph of:

$\boldsymbol{y = -f(x)}$**:** reflect the graph of $y = f(x)$ about the **X-axis.**

$\boldsymbol{y = f(-x)}$**:** reflect the graph of $y = f(x)$ about the **Y-axis.**

Example 4.3.2

Graph the next functions using the graphs of $y = \mid x \mid$ and $y = \sqrt{x}$:

a. $y = - \mid x \mid$ **b.** $y = \sqrt{-x}$

Solution

a. To obtain the graph of $y = - \mid x \mid$ we can reflect the graph $y = \mid x \mid$ about the X-axis.

b. To obtain the graph of $y = \sqrt{-x}$ we can reflect the graph of $y = \sqrt{x}$ about the Y-axis.

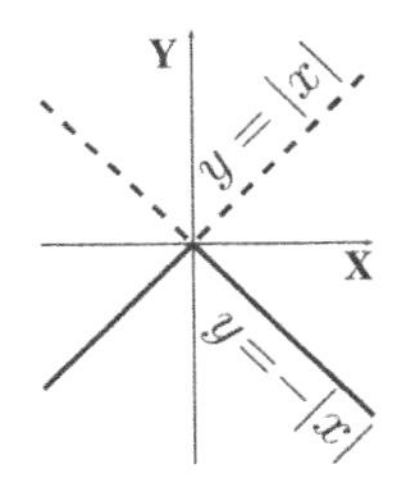

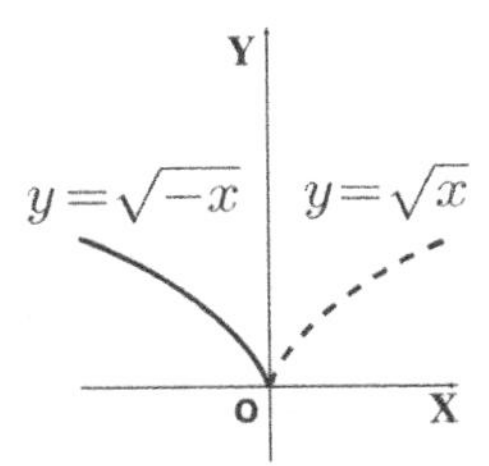

STRETCHES AND COMPRESSIONS

Let $c > 0$ be a constant. To obtain the graph of:

$\boldsymbol{y = cf(x)}$**, where** $\boldsymbol{c > 1}$**:** stretch the graph of $y = f(x)$ vertically by the factor c.

$\boldsymbol{y = cf(x)}$**, where** $\boldsymbol{c < 1}$**:** compress the graph of $y = f(x)$ vertically by the factor c.

$\boldsymbol{y = f(cx)}$**, where** $\boldsymbol{c > 1}$**:** compress the graph of $y = f(x)$ horizontally by the factor $\frac{1}{c}$.

$\boldsymbol{y = f(cx)}$**, where** $\boldsymbol{c < 1}$**:** stretch the graph of $y = f(x)$ horizontally by the factor $\frac{1}{c}$.

A proof of these criteria is given in the solved problem 4.3.6.

Example 4.3.3 Using the graph of $y = \sqrt{1-x^2}$, graph the functions:

a. $g(x) = 2\sqrt{1-x^2}$ **b.** $h(x) = \frac{1}{2}\sqrt{1-x^2}$

Solution

The graph of $y = \sqrt{1-x^2}$ is the upper part of the circle:

$$x^2 + y^2 = 1$$

a. By the first rule, since $c = 2 > 1$, we can obtain this graph by stretching the graph of $y = \sqrt{1-x^2}$ vertically by a factor $c = 2$.

b. By the second rule, since $c = \frac{1}{2} < 1$, we can obtain this graph by compressing the graph of $y = \sqrt{1-x^2}$ vertically by the factor $c = \frac{1}{2}$.

$y = \sqrt{1-x^2}$ **a.** $g(x) = 2\sqrt{1-x^2}$ **b.** $h(x) = \frac{1}{2}\sqrt{1-x^2}$

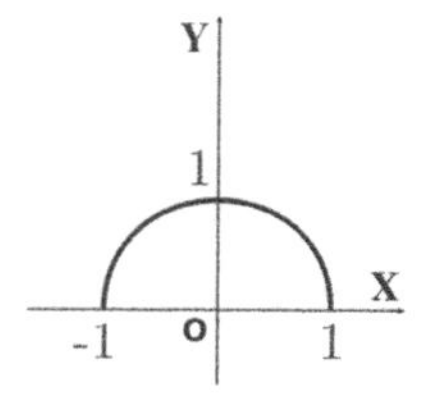

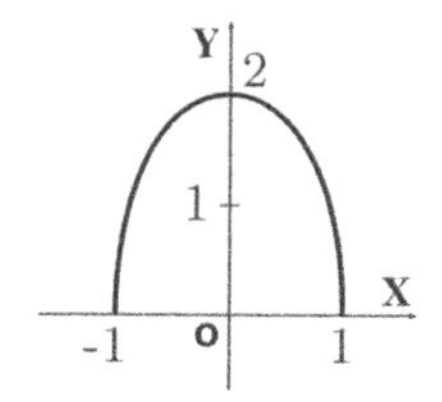

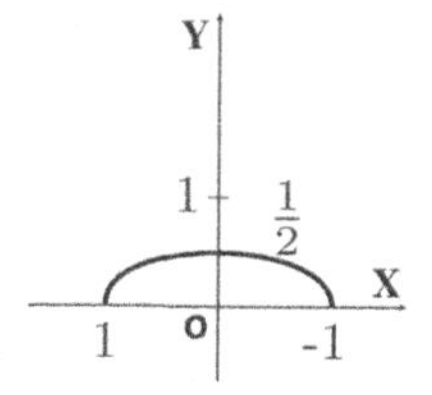

Example 4.3.4 Using the graph of $y = \sqrt{1-x^2}$, graph the functions:

a. $g(x) = \sqrt{1-4x^2}$ **b.** $h(x) = \sqrt{1 - \frac{x^2}{4}}$

Solution

a. By the third rule, since $c = 2 > 1$, we can obtain this graph compressing the graph of $y = \sqrt{1-x^2}$ horizontally by the factor $c = \frac{1}{2}$.

b. By the fourth rule, since $c = \frac{1}{2} < 1$, we can obtain this graph stretching the graph of $y = \sqrt{1-x^2}$ horizontally by the factor:

$$\frac{1}{c} = \frac{1}{\frac{1}{2}} = 2$$

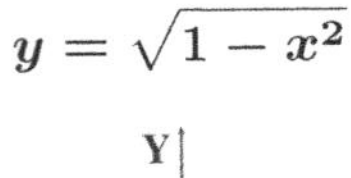

a. $g(x) = \sqrt{1 - 4x^2}$

b. $h(x) = \sqrt{1 - \dfrac{x^2}{4}}$

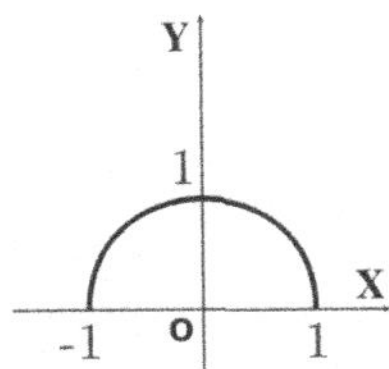

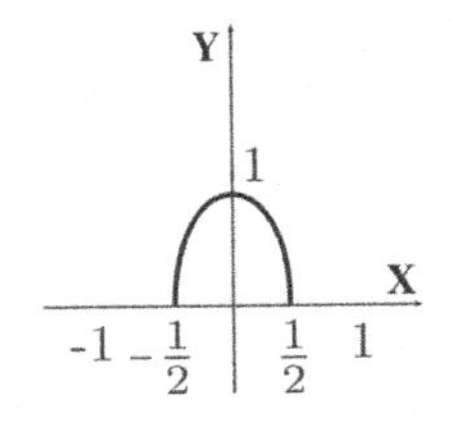

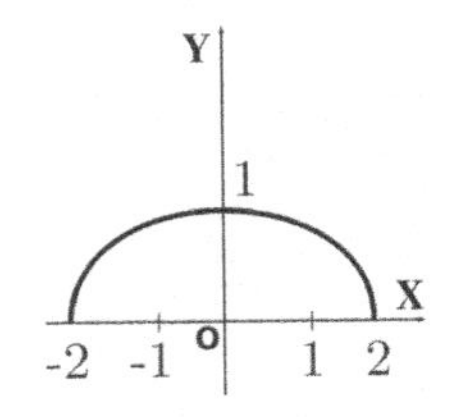

ALGEBRA OF FUNCTIONS

Functions also obey the laws of addition, subtraction, multiplication and division. These operations are described in the next definition, in which $\boldsymbol{f}$ and $\boldsymbol{g}$ are real functions, and $\boldsymbol{r}$ is a real number. In this manner, the operations to be defined are the sum $\boldsymbol{f + g}$, the difference $\boldsymbol{f - g}$, the quotient $\frac{\boldsymbol{f}}{\boldsymbol{g}}$ and the products, $\boldsymbol{fg}$ and $\boldsymbol{rf}$.

Definition Let f and g be real functions, and r a real number.

a. $(f + g)(x) = f(x) + g(x)$, $\quad \text{Dom}(f + g) = \text{Dom}(f) \cap \text{Dom}(g)$

b. $(f - g)(x) = f(x) - g(x)$, $\quad \text{Dom}(f - g) = \text{Dom}(f) \cap \text{Dom}(g)$

c. $(fg)(x) = f(x)g(x)$, $\quad \text{Dom}(fg) = \text{Dom}(f) \cap \text{Dom}(g)$

d. $(rf)(x) = rf(x)$, $\quad \text{Dom}(rf) = \text{Dom}(f)$

e. $\left(\frac{f}{g}\right)(x) = \frac{f(x)}{g(x)}$, $\quad \text{Dom}\left(\frac{f}{g}\right) = \text{Dom}(f) \cap \text{Dom}(g) - \{x \,/\, g(x) = 0\}$

Example 4.3.5 If $f(x) = \sqrt{x}$, $g(x) = \sqrt{9 - x^2}$ and $r = 5$, find:

a. $f + g$ **b.** $f - g$ **c.** fg **d.** rf **e.** $\dfrac{f}{g}$

Solution

Let's find the domains of f and g:

$$x \in \text{Dom}(f) \Leftrightarrow x \geq 0. \text{ Hence, } \text{Dom}(f) = [0, +\infty)$$
$$x \in \text{Dom}(g) \Leftrightarrow 9 - x^2 \geq 0 \Leftrightarrow x^2 \leq 9 \Leftrightarrow -3 \leq x \leq 3$$

Hence, $\text{Dom}(g) = [-3, 3]$

The intersection of these domains is:

$$\mathrm{Dom}(f) \cap \mathrm{Dom}(g) = [0, +\infty) \cap [-3, 3] = [0, 3]$$

Now,

a. $(f+g)(x) = f(x) + g(x) = \sqrt{x} + \sqrt{9-x^2}$, with domain $= [0, 3]$.

b. $(f-g)(x) = f(x) - g(x) = \sqrt{x} - \sqrt{9-x^2}$, with domain $= [0, 3]$

c. $(fg)(x) = f(x)g(x) = \sqrt{x}\sqrt{9-x^2} = \sqrt{9x-x^3}$, with domain $= [0, 3]$.

d. $(5f)(x) = 5f(x) = 5\sqrt{x}$, with domain $= \mathrm{Dom}(f) = [0, +\infty)$

e. $\left(\frac{f}{g}\right)(x) = \frac{f(x)}{g(x)} = \frac{\sqrt{x}}{\sqrt{9-x^2}} = \sqrt{\frac{x}{9-x^2}}$, with domain $= [0, 3] - \{3\} = [0, 3)$

COMPOSITION OF FUNCTIONS

Definition

Given two functions f and g, the **composite function**, or the **composition** of f with g, is the function $f \circ g$ defined by:

$$(f \circ g)(x) = f(g(x))$$

$$\mathrm{Dom}(f \circ g) = \{x \in \mathrm{Dom}(g) \,/\, g(x) \in \mathrm{Dom}(f)\}$$

Observe that the rang of g must have a non-empty intersection with the domain of f in order to have the composition $f \circ g$.

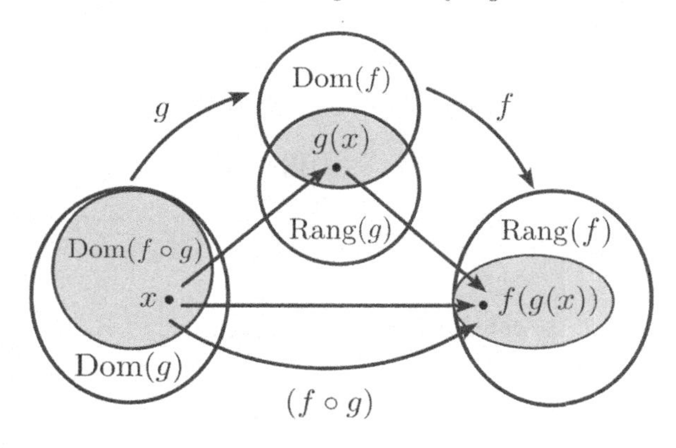

Example 4.3.6 If $f(x) = \sqrt{1 - x^2}$ and $g(x) = \frac{1}{x}$, find:

a. $f \circ g$ **b.** $g \circ f$ **c.** $g \circ g$ **d.** $f \circ f$

Solution

a. $(f \circ g)(x) = f(g(x)) = f\left(\frac{1}{x}\right) = \sqrt{1 - \left(\frac{1}{x}\right)^2} = \sqrt{1 - \frac{1}{x^2}}$

We have $\text{Dom}(g) = \mathbb{R} - \{0\}$, so:

$$(f \circ g)(x) = \sqrt{1 - \frac{1}{x^2}} \text{ is a real number} \Leftrightarrow 1 - \frac{1}{x^2} \geq 0 \Leftrightarrow x^2 \geq 1$$

$$\Leftrightarrow | x | \geq 1 \Leftrightarrow x \leq -1 \lor x \geq 1$$

$$\Leftrightarrow x \in (-\infty, 1] \cup [1, +\infty)$$

Therefore,

$$\text{Dom}(f \circ g) = (\mathbb{R} - \{0\}) \cap ((-\infty, -1] \cup [1, +\infty)) = (-\infty, -1] \cup [1, +\infty)$$

b. $(g \circ f)(x) = g(f(x)) = g\left(\sqrt{1 - x^2}\right) = \dfrac{1}{\sqrt{1 - x^2}}$

$$(g \circ f)(x) = \frac{1}{\sqrt{1 - x^2}} \text{ is a real number} \Leftrightarrow 1 - x^2 > 0 \Leftrightarrow x^2 < 1$$

$$\Leftrightarrow x \in (-1, 1)$$

Besides, we have that $\text{Dom}(f) = [-1, 1]$.

Therefore, $\text{Dom}(g \circ f) = [-1, 1] \cap (-1, 1) = (-1, 1)$

c. $(g \circ g)(x) = g(g(x)) = g\left(\frac{1}{x}\right) = \dfrac{1}{\frac{1}{x}} = x$

$(g \circ g)(x) = x$ is defined for all $\mathbb{R}$. Therefore:

$$\text{Dom}(g \circ g) = (\mathbb{R} - \{0\}) \cap \mathbb{R} = \mathbb{R} - \{0\}$$

d. $(f \circ f)(x) = f(f(x)) = f\left(\sqrt{1 - x^2}\right) = \sqrt{1 - \left(\sqrt{1 - x^2}\right)^2} = \sqrt{x^2} = | x |$

$(f \circ f)(x) = | x |$ is defined for all $\mathbb{R}$. Therefore:

$$\text{Dom}(f \circ f) = [-1, 1] \cap \mathbb{R} = [-1, 1]$$

Remark The composition of functions is not commutative. That is:

$$(g \circ f) \neq (f \circ g).$$

Indeed, according to the previous example:

$$(g \circ f)(x) = \sqrt{1 - \frac{1}{x^2}} \neq \frac{1}{\sqrt{1 - x^2}} = (f \circ g)(x)$$

Example 4.3.7 If $f(x) = \dfrac{x}{1+x}$, $g(x) = x^3$ and $h(x) = x - 2$, find:

a. $f \circ g \circ h$ **b.** $f \circ h \circ g$ **c.** $h \circ g \circ f$

Solution

a. $(f \circ g \circ h)(x) = (f \circ g)(h(x)) = f(g(h(x))) = f(g(x-2)) = f((x-2)^3)$

$$= \frac{(x-2)^3}{1+(x-2)^3}$$

b. $(f \circ h \circ g)(x) = (f \circ h)(g(x)) = f(h(g(x))) = f(h(x^3)) = f(x^3 - 2)$

$$= \frac{x^3 - 2}{1 + x^3 - 2} = \frac{x^3 - 2}{x^3 - 1}$$

c. $(h \circ g \circ f)(x) = (h \circ g)(f(x)) = h(g(f(x))) = h\left(g\left(\dfrac{x}{1+x}\right)\right)$

$$= h\left(\left(\frac{x}{1+x}\right)^3\right) = \left(\frac{x}{1+x}\right)^3 - 2 = \frac{x^3}{(1+x)^3} - 2$$

Example 4.3.8 If $F(x) = \frac{-5}{\sqrt{x^2-3}}$, find the functions f, g and h such that:

$$F = f \circ g \circ h$$

Solution

Let $f(x) = \dfrac{-5}{x}$, $g(x) = \sqrt{x}$ and $h(x) = x^2 - 3$, we have:

$$(f \circ g \circ h)(x) = (f \circ g)(h(x)) = f(g(h(x))) = f(g(x^2 - 3))$$

$$= f\left(\sqrt{x^2 - 3}\right)$$

$$= \frac{-5}{\sqrt{x^2 - 3}}$$

This is not the only solution. The next functions also satisfy the required conditions:

$$f(x) = \frac{-5}{\sqrt{x}}, \quad g(x) = x - 3 \quad \text{and} \quad h(x) = x^2$$

SOLVED PROBLEMS 4.3

Problem 4.3.1

Using the transformation techniques and the graph of $y = \lfloor x \rfloor$ (example 4.1.6), sketch the graph of:

a. $y = \lfloor -x \rfloor$ **b.** $y = \left\lfloor \frac{x}{2} \right\rfloor$

Solution

a. The graph of $y = \lfloor -x \rfloor$ can be obtained by reflecting the graph of the function $y = \lfloor x \rfloor$ about the Y-axis.

b. The graph of $y = \lfloor \frac{x}{2} \rfloor$ can be obtained by stretching the graph of $y = \lfloor x \rfloor$ horizontally by the factor $\frac{1}{c} = \frac{1}{\frac{1}{2}} = 2$.

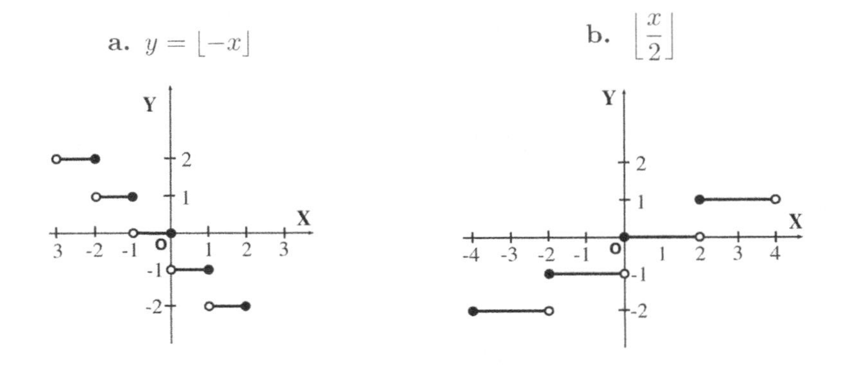

Problem 4.3.2 Using transformation techniques, sketch the graph of:

$$y = -\sqrt{\frac{1}{2}x} + 3$$

Solution

We must proceed as follows:

1. Take the graph of $y = \sqrt{x}$ that we already know.
2. Construct the graph of $y = \sqrt{\frac{x}{2}}$ by horizontally stretching the graph of $y = \sqrt{x}$ by the factor $\frac{1}{c} = \frac{1}{1/2} = 2$.
3. Construct the graph of $y = -\sqrt{\frac{x}{2}}$ by reflecting the graph of $y = \sqrt{\frac{x}{2}}$ about the X-axis.
4. Construct the graph of $y = -\sqrt{\frac{x}{2}} + 3$ by shifting the graph of $y = -\sqrt{\frac{x}{2}}$ three units upward.

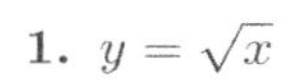

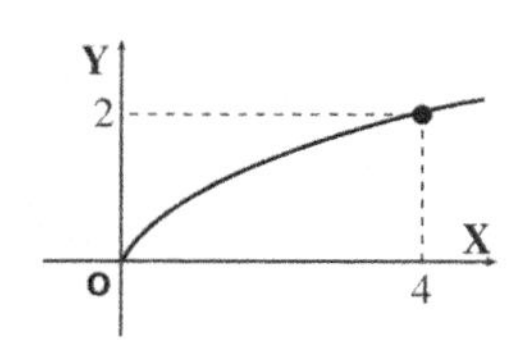

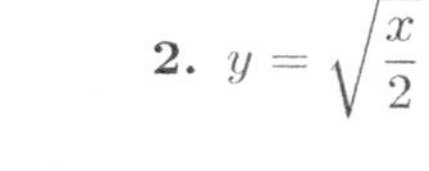

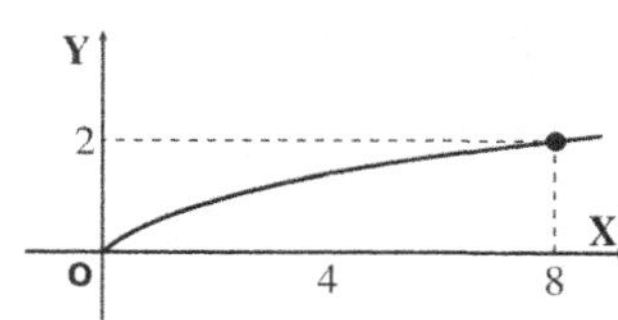

3. $y = -\sqrt{\frac{x}{2}}$

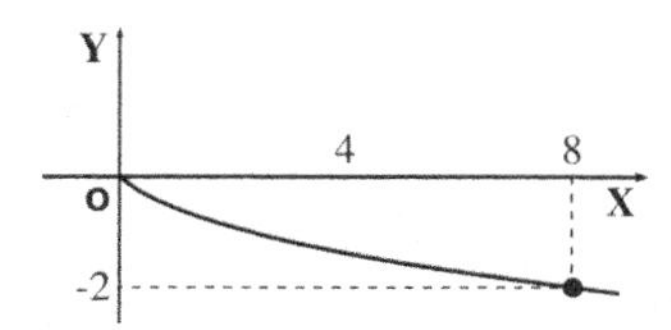

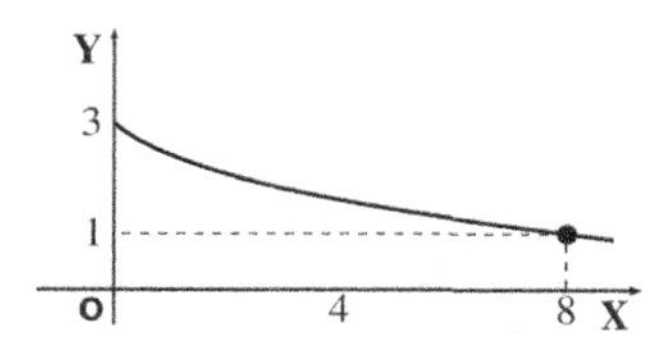

Problem 4.3.3 Using the transformation techniques, graph the functions:

a. $f(x) = 2\cos x$ **b.** $g(x) = \cos 2x$

Consider the graph of $y = \cos x$.

Solution

a. The graph of $f(x) = 2\cos x$ can be obtained by stretching the graph of $y = \cos x$ vertically by a factor $c = 2$.

b. The graph of $g(x) = \cos 2x$ can be obtained by compressing the graph of $y = \cos x$ horizontally by a factor $\frac{1}{2}$.

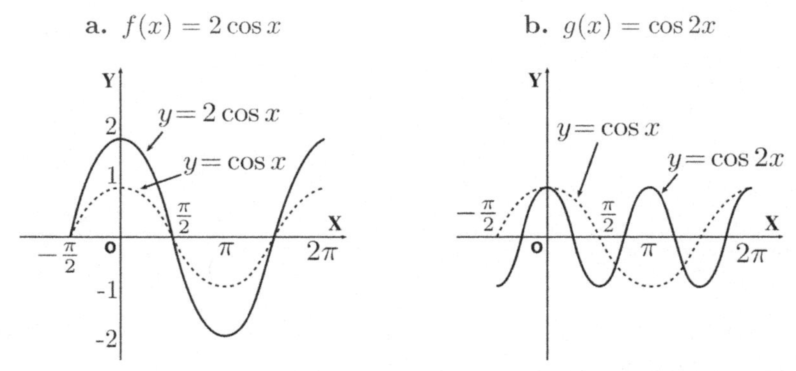

Notice that the period of $g(x) = \cos 2x$ is $\boldsymbol{\pi}$, which is half the period of $y = \cos x$. In general terms, the period of $y = \cos cx$ is $\frac{2\pi}{c}$.

Problem 4.3.4 Given the function:

$$h(x) = \sqrt{4 - x^2} + \frac{1}{4 - x^2}$$

a. find the domain of h.

b. find two functions f and g such that $h = (g \circ f)$

Solution

a. Since $\sqrt{4 - x^2}$ must be a real number, we must have $4 - x^2 \geq 0$.

Moreover, since $4 - x^2$ is a denominator, we must have $4 - x^2 \neq 0$. These two conditions are satisfied if:

$$4 - x^2 > 0 \Leftrightarrow x^2 < 4 \Leftrightarrow | x | < 2 \Leftrightarrow -2 < x < 2$$

Hence, the domain of h is the interval $(-2, 2)$.

b. If $f(x) = 4 - x^2$ and $g(y) = \sqrt{y} + \frac{1}{y}$, we have:

$$(g \circ f)(x) = g(f(x)) = g\left(4 - x^2\right) = \sqrt{4 - x^2} + \frac{1}{4 - x^2} = h(x)$$

Problem 4.3.5 Given the functions $g(x) = x - 1$ and $h(x) = x^2$:

a. find a function p such that $g \circ p = h$.

b. find a function f such that $f \circ g = h$

Solution

a. $g \circ p = h \Rightarrow g(p(x)) = h(x) \Rightarrow p(x) - 1 = x^2 \Rightarrow p(x) = x^2 + 1$

b. $f \circ g = h \Rightarrow f(g(x)) = h(x) \Rightarrow f(x-1) = x^2$

Hence:

$$f(x-1) = f(x+1-1) = f((x+1)-1)$$

Therefore:

$$f(x-1) = x^2 \Leftrightarrow f(x) = (x+1)^2$$

Problem 4.3.6 Given the functions:

$$f(x) = \frac{1}{x^2 - 1} \quad \text{and} \quad g(x) = \sqrt{16 - x^2}$$

Find $g \circ f$ and its domain.

Solution

$$(g \circ f)(x) = g(f(x)) = g\left(\frac{1}{x^2-1}\right) = \sqrt{16 - \left(\frac{1}{x^2-1}\right)^2}$$

$$= \sqrt{16 - \frac{1}{(x^2-1)^2}}$$

$\text{Dom}(f) = \mathbb{R} - \{-1, 1\}$ and:

$$(g \circ f)(x) \text{ is defined} \Leftrightarrow 16 - \frac{1}{(x^2-1)^2} \geq 0$$

$$\Leftrightarrow \quad 16\left(x^2-1\right)^2 \geq 1 \qquad \Leftrightarrow \quad 4\left|x^2-1\right| \geq 1$$

$$\Leftrightarrow \quad \left|x^2-1\right| \geq \frac{1}{4} \qquad \Leftrightarrow \quad x^2 - 1 \leq -\frac{1}{4} \quad \vee \quad \frac{1}{4} \leq x^2 - 1$$

$$\Leftrightarrow \quad x^2 \leq \frac{3}{4} \quad \vee \quad \frac{5}{4} \leq x^2 \qquad \Leftrightarrow \quad |\, x \,| \leq \frac{\sqrt{3}}{2} \quad \vee \quad \frac{\sqrt{5}}{2} \leq |\, x \,|$$

$$\Leftrightarrow \quad -\frac{\sqrt{3}}{2} \le x \le \frac{\sqrt{3}}{2} \quad \vee \quad x \le -\frac{\sqrt{5}}{2} \quad \vee \quad x \ge \frac{\sqrt{5}}{2}$$

$$\Leftrightarrow \quad x \le -\frac{\sqrt{5}}{2} \quad \vee \quad -\frac{\sqrt{3}}{2} \le x \le \frac{\sqrt{3}}{2} \quad \vee \quad x \ge \frac{\sqrt{5}}{2}$$

Hence, $(g \circ f)(x)$ is defined on the set:

$$B = \left(-\infty, -\frac{\sqrt{5}}{2}\right] \cup \left[-\frac{\sqrt{3}}{2}, \frac{\sqrt{3}}{2}\right] \cup \left[\frac{\sqrt{5}}{2}, +\infty\right)$$

Finally:

$$\begin{aligned} \mathrm{Dom}(g \circ f) &= \mathrm{Dom}(f) \cap B = B \\ &= \left(-\infty, -\frac{\sqrt{5}}{2}\right] \cup \left[-\frac{\sqrt{3}}{2}, \frac{\sqrt{3}}{2}\right] \cup \left[\frac{\sqrt{5}}{2}, +\infty\right) \end{aligned}$$

Problem 4.3.7 Justify the stretch and compress criterion of a graph.

Solution

1. Let's take any point $(x, f(x))$ from the graph of$y = f(x)$.

By multiplying the **ordinate** of this point by c, we obtain the point $(x, cf(x))$ of the graph of $y = cf(x)$.

However, if we multiply only the ordinates of the points $(x, f(x))$ by c, it will vertically stretch (if $c > 1$) or compress (if $c < 1$) the graph of $y = f(x)$ by a factor c.

2. Let's take any point $(x, f(x))$ from the graph of $y = f(x)$.

By multiplying the **abscissa** of this point by $\frac{1}{c}$, we obtain the point:

$$\left(\frac{x}{c}, f(x)\right)$$

If $z = \frac{x}{c}$, then we get:

$$x = cz \quad \text{and} \quad \left(\frac{x}{c}, f(x)\right) = (z, f(cz)),$$

which belongs to the graph of $y = f(cx)$.

However, if we multiply only the abscissa of the points $(x, f(x))$ by $\frac{1}{c}$, it will horizontally compress (if $c > 1$) or stretch (if $c < 1$) the graph of $y = f(x)$ by a factor $\frac{1}{c}$.

EXERCISES 4.3

1. Sketch the following graphs using the graph of $f(x) = x^3$:

a. $y = x^3 - 3$ **b.** $y = (x-1)^3$ **c.** $y = -x^3 + 1$

d. $y = -(x-1)^3 + 1$

2. Sketch the following graphs using the graph of $f(x) = \dfrac{1}{x}$:

a. $y = \dfrac{1}{x} - 2$ **b.** $y = \dfrac{1}{x-2}$ **c.** $y = -\dfrac{1}{x}$ **d.** $y = \dfrac{1}{x-2} + 5$

3. Sketch the following graphs using the graph of $y = \lfloor x \rfloor$:

a. $y = -\lfloor x \rfloor$ **b.** $y = \lfloor 2x \rfloor$ **c.** $y = \dfrac{1}{2}\lfloor x \rfloor$

4. Using the translation and reflection techniques, and the graph of $y = \sin x$, graph the function $y = 1 - \sin(x - \frac{\pi}{2})$.

5. Considering the graph of $y = \cos x$:

a. sketch the graph of $y = -3\cos 4x$ using transformation techniques.

b. find the period of $y = -3\cos 4x$.

In the exercises 6, 7 and 8, find $f+g$, $f-g$, fg and f/g, with their respective domains.

6. $f(x) = \dfrac{1}{1-x}$, $g(x) = \sqrt{2-x}$ **7.** $f(x) = \sqrt{16 - x^2}$, $g(x) = \sqrt{x^2 - 4}$

8. $f(x) = \dfrac{1}{\sqrt{4 - x^2}}$, $g(x) = \sqrt[3]{x}$

In the exercises 9, 10 and 11, find the domain of the function.

9. $f(x) = \sqrt{4-x} + \sqrt{x-4}$ **10.** $f(x) = \sqrt{-x} + \dfrac{1}{\sqrt{x+2}}$

11. $g(x) = \dfrac{\sqrt{3-x} + \sqrt{x+2}}{x^2 - 9}$

In the exercises 12 through 16, find $f \circ g$, $g \circ f$, $f \circ f$ and $g \circ g$, with their respective domains.

12. $f(x) = x^2 - 1,\ g(x) = \sqrt{x}$

13. $f(x) = x^2,\ g(x) = \sqrt{x-4}$

14. $f(x) = x^2 - x,\ g(x) = \dfrac{1}{x}$

15. $f(x) = \dfrac{1}{1-x},\ g(x) = \sqrt[3]{x}$

16. $f(x) = \sqrt{x^2-1},\ g(x) = \sqrt{1-x}$

In the exercises 17 and 18, find $f \circ g \circ h$.

17. $f(x) = \sqrt{x}, \quad g(x) = \dfrac{1}{x}, \quad h(x) = x^2 - 1$

18. $f(x) = \sqrt[3]{x}, \quad g(x) = \dfrac{x}{1+x}, \quad h(x) = x^2 - x$

19. If $f(x) = \dfrac{1}{1-x}$, find $f \circ f \circ f$ with its domain.

In the exercises 20 through 23, find two functions f and g such that $F = f \circ g$.

20. $F(x) = \dfrac{1}{1+x}$

21. $F(x) = -3 + \sqrt{x}$

22. $F(x) = \sqrt[3]{(2x-1)^2}$

23. $F(x) = \dfrac{1}{\sqrt{x^2 - x + 1}}$

In the exercises 24 through 26, find f, g and h such that:

$$F = f \circ g \circ h$$

24. $F(x) = \frac{x^2}{1+x^2}$ **25.** $F(x) = \sqrt[3]{x^2 + |\, x \,| + 1}$ **26.** $F(x) = \sqrt[4]{\sqrt{x} - 1}$

27. If $f(x) = 2x + 3$ and $h(x) = 2x^2 - 4x + 5$, find a function g such that $f \circ g = h$.

28. If $f(x) = x - 3$ and $h(x) = \dfrac{1}{x-2}$, find a function g such that $g \circ f = h$.

SECCION 4.4

INVERSE FUNCTIONS

Let $f : A \to B$ be a function with domain A and range B. Function f assigns a unique element y from set B to each element x in set A. If possible, we would like to be able to invert function f, so that for each y in set B, it can be returned to the corresponding element x in set A from which it originated. This new function, with domain B and range A, is the **inverse function** of f, and is denoted by $\boldsymbol{f^{-1}}$.

Not all functions have inverse. From the two following functions, f and g, only f has inverse. The function g does not because the element 3 comes from two elements of A, a and c. The inverse function g would have to assign these two elements to 3, but this situation contradicts the definition of function.

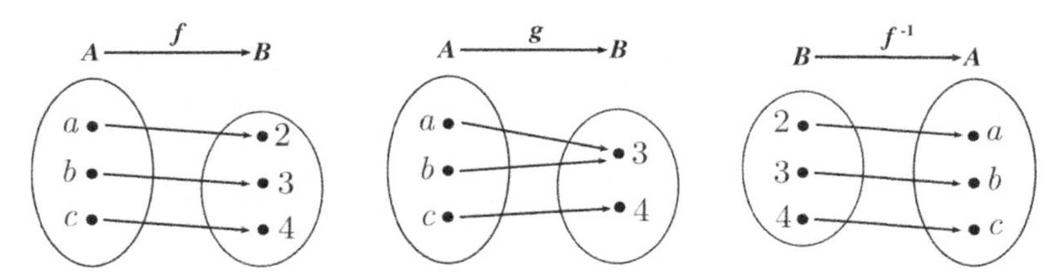

Functions like f, that assign different outputs to different inputs, are called **injective functions**.

Definition $f : A \to B$ is an injective or *one-to-one* function if:

$$\boldsymbol{x_1 \neq x_2 \Rightarrow f(x_1) \neq f(x_2)}$$

Thus, f is injective if different elements of the domain, are assigned to different elements of the range.

THE HORIZONTAL LINE TEST

To determine if a real function of real variable f is injective, we have the horizontal line test, which is similar to the vertical line test we used earlier to determine if a graph represents a function.

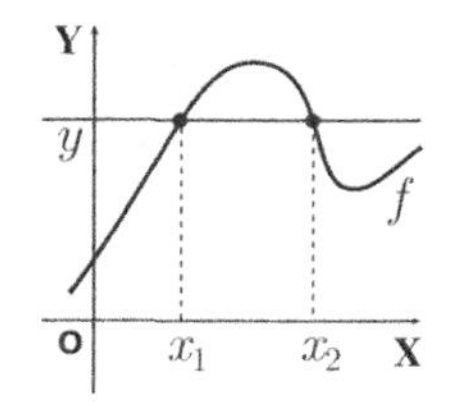

Assume that the graph of a function f is intersected by one horizontal line at two points. We have $x_1 \neq x_2$, but $y = f(x_1) = f(x_2)$, which contradicts the definition of injective function.

The next assertion clarifies this criterion further.

A real function of real variable f is injective
if and only if
every horizontal line intersects the graph of f at most at one point.

Example 4.4.1

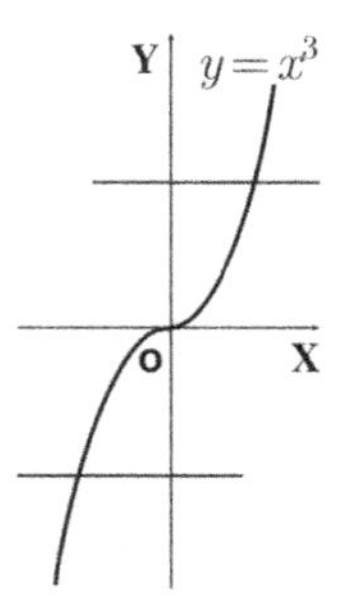

Show that the function $f(x) = x^3$ is injective.

Solution

We can see that every horizontal line intersects the graph of f exactly at one point. Hence, according to the horizontal line criterion, $f(x) = x^3$ is injective.

Example 4.4.2 Given the function $g(x) = x^2 + 2$:

a. show that $g(x)$ is not injective.

b. reduce the domain of g to obtain an injective function f that coincides with g on the domain of f.

Solution

a. Every horizontal line $y = c$, where $c > 2$, intersects the graph of $g(x)$ at two points. Hence g is not injective.

b. Let f be the restriction of g to $[0, +\infty)$. That is, $f(x) = x^2 + 2$, where $x \geq 0$. This function is injective, and $f(x) = g(x) = x^2 + 2$ on $[0, +\infty)$.

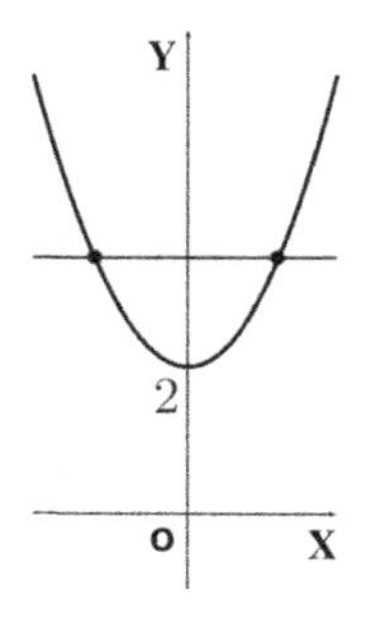

$g(x) = x^2 + 2$

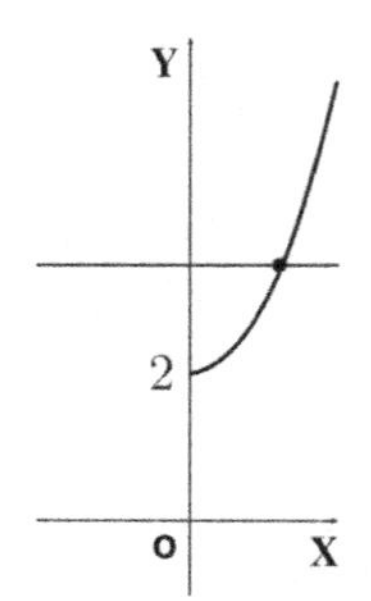

$f(x) = x^2 + 2, \; x \geq 0$

Example 4.4.3 Justify why a *monotone* function f is also *injective.*

If f is monotone, then f is either increasing or decreasing, therefore every horizontal line intersects the graph of f at most once. Hence, by the horizontal line test, f must be injective.

Definition Let f: $A \to B$ be a function with domain A, and range B.

If f is injective, the **inverse function** of f is:

$$\begin{aligned} \boldsymbol{f^{-1} : B \to A} \ \text{ such that} \\ \boldsymbol{x = f^{-1}(y) \Leftrightarrow y = f(x)} \end{aligned} \tag{1}$$

The expression (1) is equivalent to:

$$\boldsymbol{f^{-1}\left(f(x)\right) = x,\ \forall\ x \in A} \quad \text{and} \quad \boldsymbol{f\left(f^{-1}(y)\right) = y,\ \forall\ y \in B} \tag{2}$$

Indeed, if we replace y by $f(x)$ in $x = f^{-1}(y)$, we obtain:

$$x = f^{-1}\left(f(x)\right)$$

Similarly, if we replace x by $f^{-1}(y)$ in $y = f(x)$, we obtain:

$$y = f\left(f^{-1}(y)\right)$$

Remark

Do not confuse $f^{-1}(y)$ with the quotient y: $\frac{1}{f(x)}$. To avoid ambiguity, the quotient will be represented in this section as follows:

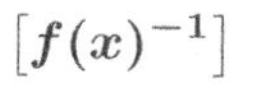

$$\left[\boldsymbol{f(x)^{-1}}\right]$$

STRATEGY TO FIND THE INVERSE OF A FUNCTION

Step 1. Solve the equation $y = f(x)$ for x in terms of y: $x = f^{-1}(y)$.

Step 2. In $x = f^{-1}(y)$, exchange x by y to obtain the function:

$$\boldsymbol{y = f^{-1}(x)}$$

GRAPH OF THE INVERSE FUNCTION

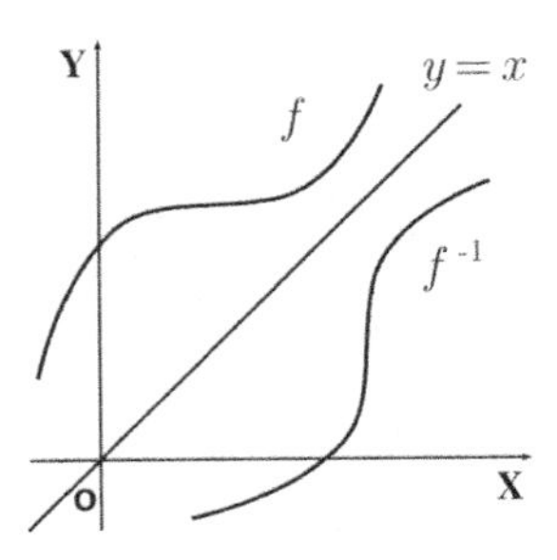

Considering the above step 2, where the variables x and y are exchanged, the graph of the inverse function can be obtained by reflecting the graph of $y = f(x)$ about the diagonal line $y = x$.

Example 4.4.4

Find the inverse function of $f(x) = x^2 + 2$, $x \geq 0$. Plot the graph.

Solution

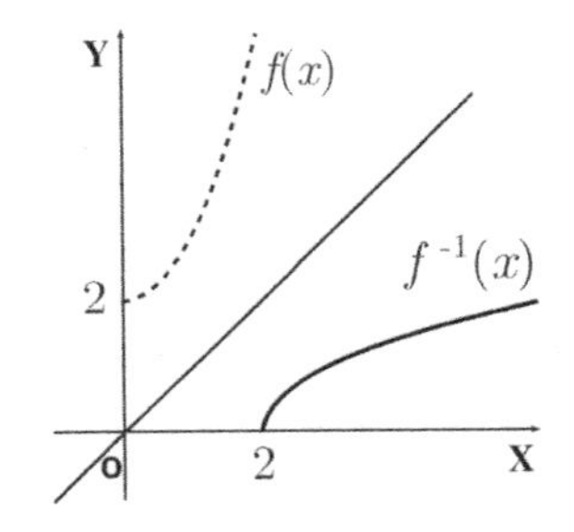

Step 1. $y = x^2 + 2 \Rightarrow x^2 = y - 2$

$$\Rightarrow x = \pm\sqrt{y-2}$$

Step 2. Exchange x by y in:

$$x = \sqrt{y-2}$$

We get: $f^{-1}(x) = \sqrt{x-2}$, $x \geq 2$

Example 4.4.5 Given the function $g(x) = \dfrac{4x+7}{2x+5}$

a. find the domain of g.

b. find the inverse function g^{-1}.

Solution

a. We must have that $2x + 5 \neq 0 \Rightarrow x \neq -\frac{5}{2}$. Hence:

$$\text{Dom}(g) = \{x \,/\, x \neq -\frac{5}{2}\}$$

b. Let's use the two-step strategy for finding inverse functions:

Step 1. $y = \dfrac{4x+7}{2x+5} \Rightarrow 2xy + 5y = 4x + 7 \Rightarrow 2xy - 4x = -5y + 7$

$$\Rightarrow x(2y-4) = -5y + 7 \Rightarrow x = \frac{-5y+7}{2y-4},\ y \neq 2$$

Step 2. Exchanging x by y:

$$g^{-1}(x) = \frac{-5x+7}{2x-4},\ x \neq 2$$

$$g(x) = \frac{4x+7}{2x+5} \qquad\qquad g^{-1}(x) = \frac{-5x+7}{2x-4}$$

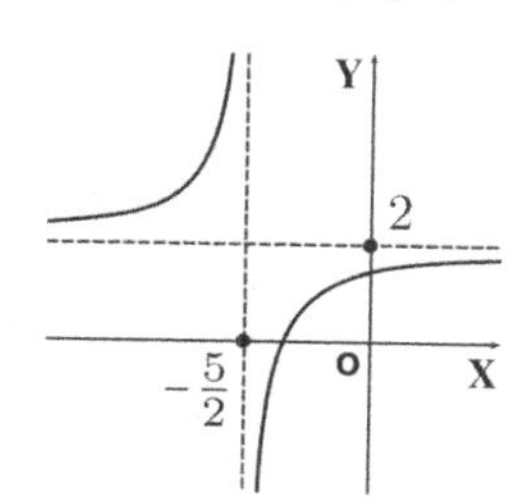

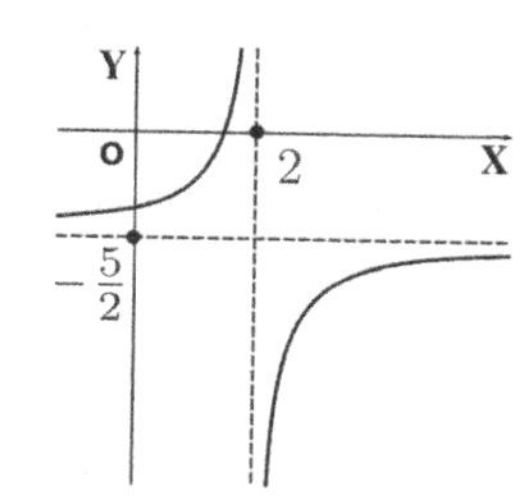

Since the graph of f^{-1} is obtained by reflecting the graph of f about the diagonal $y = x$, we infer that:

a. if f is **increasing**, then f^{-1} is **increasing**.

b. if f is **decreasing**, then f^{-1} is **decreasing**.

Jokes in the era of Science

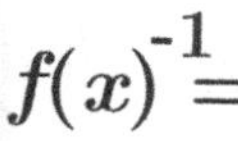

EXERCISES 4.4

In the exercises 1 through 6, find and graph the inverse.

1. $f(x) = 2x + 1$ **2.**$g(x) = x^2 - 1,\ x \geq 0$ **3.** $h(x) = x^3 + 2$

4. $k(x) = \frac{1}{x} - 1$ **5.**$f(x) = \sqrt{16 - 2x}$ **6.** $g(x) = \frac{5x-15}{3x+7}$

7. Formally prove that:

a. if f is increasing, then f^{-1} is increasing.

b. if f is decreasing, then f^{-1} is decreasing.

SECCION 4.5

INVERSE TRIGONOMETRIC FUNCTIONS

Trigonometric functions are not injective, however, we can restrict their domains so that they gain this property, which will allow us to obtain their inverse functions. These functions are presented below, preceded by their corresponding domain restriction.

INVERSE SINE FUNCTION OR ARCCOSINE

$$\mathbf{sin} : \left[-\frac{\pi}{2}, \frac{\pi}{2}\right] \to [-1,\ 1] \qquad \mathbf{sin}^{-1} : [-1,\ 1] \to \left[-\frac{\pi}{2}, \frac{\pi}{2}\right]$$

$$y = \sin^{-1}(x) \Leftrightarrow x = \sin y, \quad -\frac{\pi}{2} \leq y \leq \frac{\pi}{2}$$

$y = \sin x$ $\qquad$ $y = \sin^{-1} x$

INVERSE COSINE FUNCTION OR ARCCOSINE

$$\mathbf{cos} : [0,\ \pi] \to [-1,\ 1] \qquad \mathbf{cos}^{-1} : [-1,\ 1] \to [0,\ \pi]$$

$$y = \cos^{-1}(x) \Leftrightarrow x = \cos y, \quad 0 \leq y \leq \pi$$

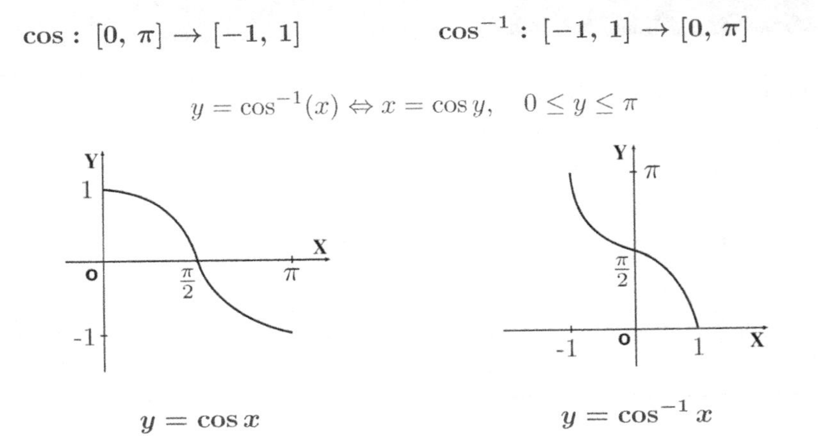

$y = \cos x$ $\qquad$ $y = \cos^{-1} x$

INVERSE TANGENT FUNCTION OR ARCTANGENT

$$\tan : \left(-\frac{\pi}{2}, \frac{\pi}{2}\right) \to \mathbb{R} \qquad \tan^{-1} : \mathbb{R} \to \left(-\frac{\pi}{2}, \frac{\pi}{2}\right)$$

$$y = \tan^{-1}(x) \Leftrightarrow x = \tan y, \quad -\frac{\pi}{2} < y < \frac{\pi}{2}$$

$y = \tan x$ $\qquad$ $y = \tan^{-1} x$

INVERSE COTANGENT FUNCTION OR ARCOTANGENT

$$\cot : (0, \pi) \to \mathbb{R} \qquad \cot^{-1} : \mathbb{R} \to (0, \pi)$$

$$y = \cot^{-1}(x) \Leftrightarrow x = \cot y, \quad 0 < y < \pi$$

$y = \cot x$ $\qquad$ $y = \cot^{-1} x$

Remark

We are about to introduce the inverse **secant** function. Some authors restrict the secant domain to the interval $\left[0, \frac{\pi}{2}\right) \cup \left(\frac{\pi}{2}, \pi\right]$, instead of $\left[0, \frac{\pi}{2}\right) \cup \left[\pi, \frac{3\pi}{2}\right)$ as we do. Our choice has the advantage of simplifying the formula for the derivative of the secant function, since it avoids the occurrence of an absolute value. This will be very convenient when we get to the Differential Calculus course that follows this book. Similar is the case with the cosecant function.

INVERSE SECANT FUNCTION OR ARCSECANT

$$\mathbf{sec}: \left[\mathbf{0},\ \frac{\pi}{\mathbf{2}}\right) \cup \left[\pi,\ \frac{\mathbf{3}\pi}{\mathbf{2}}\right) \to \mathbb{R} - (-\mathbf{1},\ \mathbf{1})$$

$$\mathbf{sec}^{-1}: \mathbb{R} - (-\mathbf{1},\ \mathbf{1}) \to \left[\mathbf{0},\ \frac{\pi}{\mathbf{2}}\right) \cup \left[\pi,\ \frac{\mathbf{3}\pi}{\mathbf{2}}\right)$$

$$y = \sec^{-1}(x) \Leftrightarrow x = \sec y, \quad 0 \leq y < \frac{\pi}{2} \quad \text{ó} \quad \pi \leq y < \frac{3\pi}{2}$$

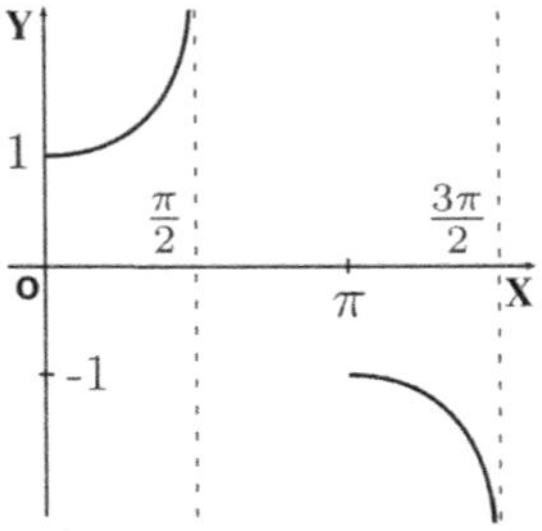

$\boldsymbol{y = \sec x}$

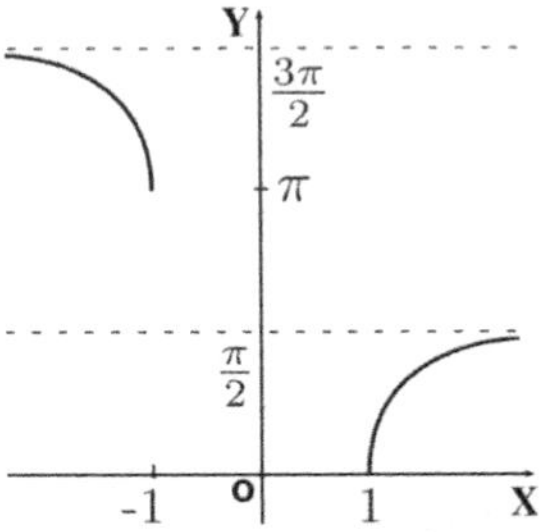

$\boldsymbol{y = \sec^{-1} x}$

INVERSE COSECANT FUNCTION OR ARCCOSECANT

$$\mathbf{csc}: \left(\mathbf{0},\ \frac{\pi}{\mathbf{2}}\right] \cup \left(\pi,\ \frac{\mathbf{3}\pi}{\mathbf{2}}\right] \to \mathbb{R} - (-\mathbf{1},\ \mathbf{1})$$

$$\mathbf{csc}^{-1}: \mathbb{R} - (-\mathbf{1},\ \mathbf{1}) \to \left(\mathbf{0},\ \frac{\pi}{\mathbf{2}}\right] \cup \left(\pi,\ \frac{\mathbf{3}\pi}{\mathbf{2}}\right]$$

$$y = \csc^{-1}(x) \Leftrightarrow x = \csc y, \quad 0 < y \leq \frac{\pi}{2} \quad \text{ó} \quad \pi < y \leq \frac{3\pi}{2}$$

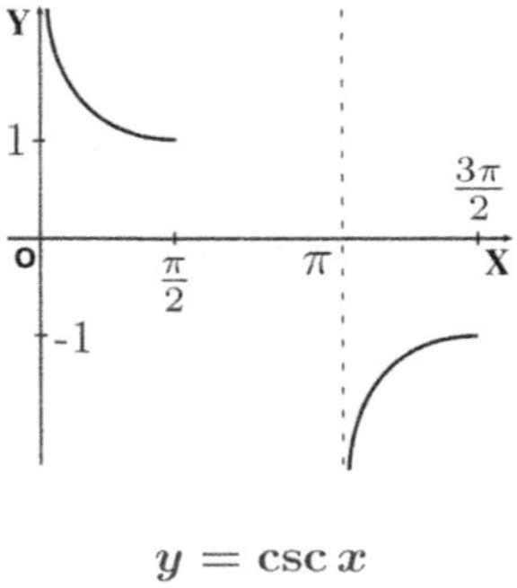

$\boldsymbol{y = \csc x}$

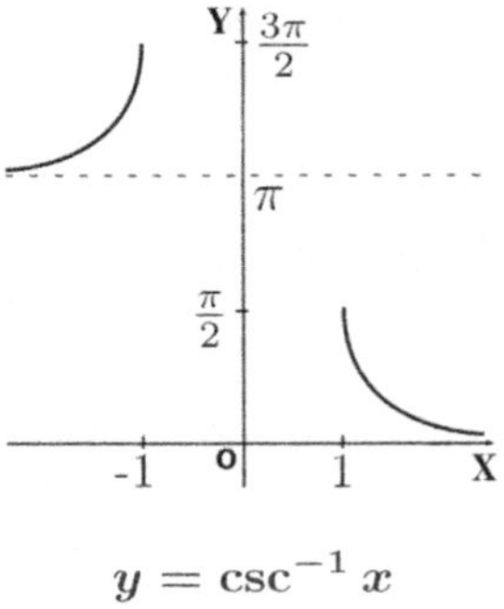

$\boldsymbol{y = \csc^{-1} x}$

Example 4.5.1 Find the value of:

a. $\sin^{-1}\left(\frac{1}{2}\right)$ b. $\cos^{-1}\left(-\frac{\sqrt{2}}{2}\right)$ c. $\tan^{-1}(-1)$

d. $\cot^{-1}\left(-\sqrt{3}\right)$ e. $\csc^{-1}(2)$

Solution

a. $\sin^{-1}\left(\frac{1}{2}\right)=\frac{\pi}{6}$, **since** $\sin\left(\frac{\pi}{6}\right)=\frac{1}{2}$ **and** $-\frac{\pi}{2}\leq\frac{\pi}{6}\leq\frac{\pi}{2}$

b. $\cos^{-1}\left(-\frac{\sqrt{2}}{2}\right)=\frac{3\pi}{4}$, **since** $\cos\left(\frac{3\pi}{4}\right)=-\frac{\sqrt{2}}{2}$ **and** $0\leq\frac{3\pi}{4}\leq\pi$

c. $\tan^{-1}(-1)=-\frac{\pi}{4}$, **since** $\tan\left(-\frac{\pi}{4}\right)=-1$ **and** $-\frac{\pi}{2}<-\frac{\pi}{4}<\frac{\pi}{2}$

d. $\cot^{-1}\left(-\sqrt{3}\right)=\frac{5\pi}{6}$, **since** $\cot\left(\frac{5\pi}{6}\right)=-\sqrt{3}$ **and** $\frac{\pi}{2}<\frac{5\pi}{6}<\pi$

e. $\csc^{-1}(2)=\frac{\pi}{6}$, **since** $\csc\left(\frac{\pi}{6}\right)=2$ **and** $0<\frac{\pi}{6}\leq\frac{\pi}{2}$

SOLVED PROBLEMS 4.5

Problem 4.5.1 Find the value of:

a. $\sin\left(\tan^{-1}\left(\frac{1}{2}\right)\right)$ b. $\tan\left(\sec^{-1}\left(-\frac{5}{3}\right)\right)$

Solution

a. Let $\alpha=\tan^{-1}\left(\frac{1}{2}\right)$. Then:

$$\tan\alpha=\frac{1}{2} \qquad \text{and} \qquad 0<\alpha<\frac{\pi}{2}$$

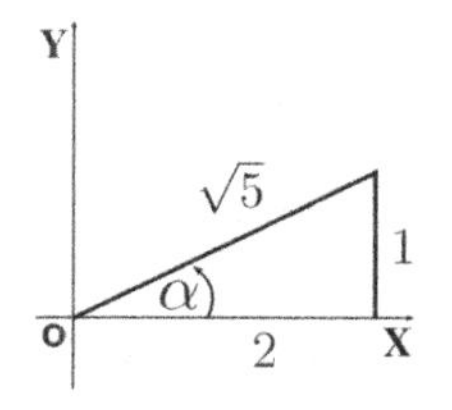

We have constructed a rectangle triangle with the above values considering the definition of $\tan\alpha$.

We can see that:

$$\sin\left(\tan^{-1}\left(\frac{1}{2}\right)\right) = \sin\alpha = \frac{1}{\sqrt{5}}$$

b. Let $\beta = \sec^{-1}\left(-\frac{5}{3}\right)$. Hence:

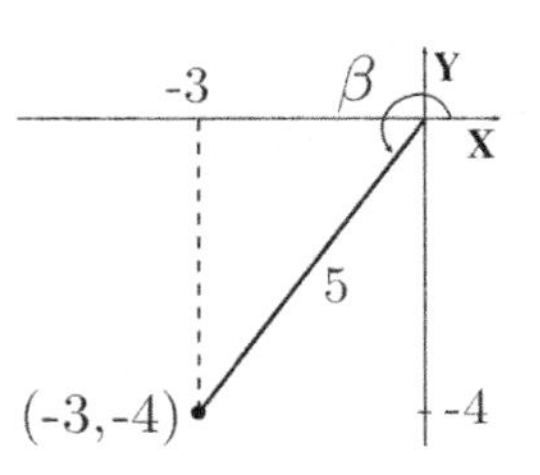

$$\sec\beta = -\frac{5}{3} \quad \text{and} \quad \pi \leq \beta < \frac{3\pi}{2}$$

Now, $\tan\left(\sec^{-1}\left(-\frac{5}{3}\right)\right) = \tan\beta = \frac{-4}{-3} = \frac{4}{3}$

Problem 4.5.2 If $-1 \leq x \leq 1$, express in terms of x:

a. $\cot(\sin^{-1} x)$ **b.** $\sec(\sin^{-1} x)$

Solution

Let $\alpha = \sin^{-1} x$. Then, $\sin\alpha = x$, where $-\frac{\pi}{2} \leq \alpha \leq \frac{\pi}{2}$.

Considering that $\sin\alpha = \frac{x}{1}$, we construct the first right triangle for the case $x > 0$, or the triangle for the case $x < 0$. Here, x is the opposite side and 1 is the hypotenuse.

The remaining side is $\pm\sqrt{1-x^2}$. From these two values, we take the positive one, since this root belongs to $\cos\alpha$, and $\cos\alpha > 0$ for $-\frac{\pi}{2} \leq \alpha \leq \frac{\pi}{2}$.

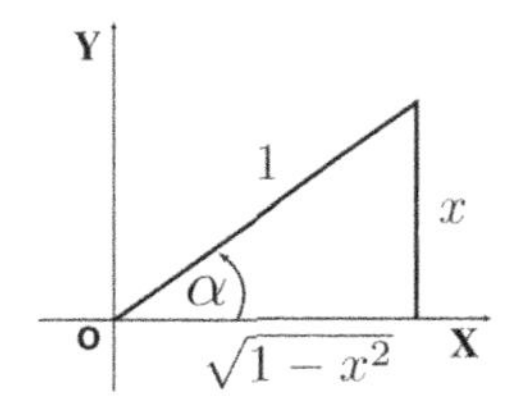

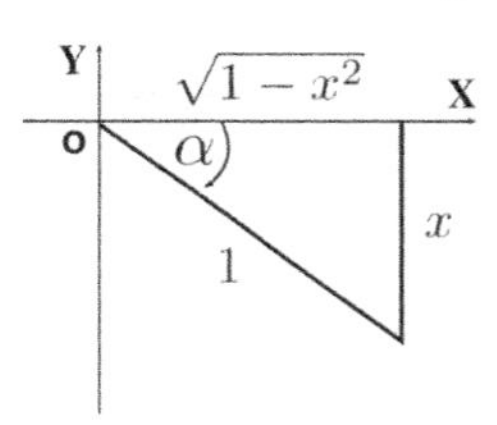

Now:

a. $\cot\left(\sin^{-1} x\right) = \cot\alpha = \dfrac{\sqrt{1-x^2}}{x}$, if $x \neq 0$

or

$$\cot\left(\sin^{-1} x\right) = \pm\infty \text{ if } x = 0$$

b. $\sec\left(\sin^{-1} x\right) = \sec\alpha = \dfrac{1}{\sqrt{1-x^2}}$

Problem 4.5.3 Without a calculator, find the value of:

$$\sin\left[\cot^{-1}\left(-\frac{5}{12}\right)-\cos^{-1}\left(\frac{3}{5}\right)\right]$$

Solution

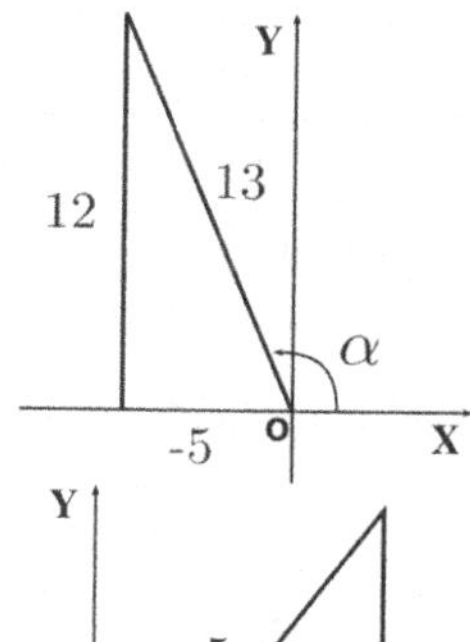

Let $\alpha=\cot^{-1}\left(-\frac{5}{12}\right)$. Then:

$$\cot\alpha=-\frac{5}{12}\quad\text{and}\quad\frac{\pi}{2}<\alpha<\pi$$

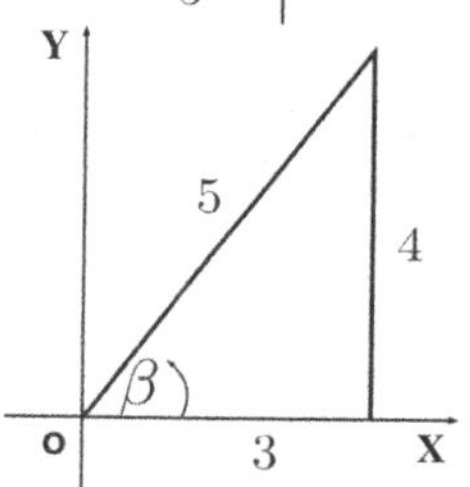

Let $\beta=\cos^{-1}\left(\frac{3}{5}\right)$. Then:

$$\cos\beta=\frac{3}{5}\quad\text{and}\quad 0<\beta<\frac{\pi}{2}$$

Now, we have:

$$\begin{aligned}\sin\left[\cot^{-1}\left(-\frac{5}{12}\right)-\cos^{-1}\left(\frac{3}{5}\right)\right]&=\sin(\alpha-\beta)\\&=\sin\alpha\cos\beta-\cos\alpha\sin\beta\\&=\frac{12}{13}\frac{3}{5}-\frac{-5}{13}\frac{4}{5}=\frac{56}{65}\end{aligned}$$

Problem 4.5.4 Solve the equation $\tan^{-1}(2x-3)=1$

Solution

$$\tan^{-1}(2x-3)=1\Leftrightarrow 2x-3=\tan(1)$$

Using a calculator, we find that $\tan(1)=1.5574077$. Then:

$$2x-3=1.5574077\Rightarrow x=\frac{1}{2}(1.5574077+3)=2.787038$$

EXERCISES 4.5

In the exercises 1 through 6, evaluate the given expressions without using a calculator.

1. $\sin^{-1}\left(\sqrt{3}/2\right)$ **2.** $\sec^{-1}\left(-\sqrt{2}\right)$ **3.** $\cos^{-1}(-1)$

4. $\tan^{-1}\left(-\sqrt{3}\right)$ **5.** $\cot^{-1}(-1)$ **6.** $\csc^{-1}(-2)$

7. Given $y = \sin^{-1}\left(\frac{1}{3}\right)$, find the precise value of:
a. $\cos y$ **b.** $\tan y$ **c.** $\cot y$ **d.** $\sec y$ **e.** $\csc y$

8. Given $y = \sec^{-1}\left(\frac{\sqrt{5}}{2}\right)$, find the precise value of:
a. $\sin y$ **b.** $\cos y$ **c.** $\tan y$ **d.** $\cot y$ **e.** $\csc y$

9. Given $y = \tan^{-1}(-3)$, find the precise value of:
a. $\sin y$ **b.** $\cos y$ **c.** $\cot y$ **d.** $\sec y$ **e.** $\csc y$

In the exercises 10 through 13, find the value of the expression.

10. $\cos^{-1}\left(\sqrt{\frac{3}{2}}\right)$ **11.** $\csc\left(\tan^{-1}(-2)\right)$

12. $\sin\left(\tan^{-1}\left(-\frac{3}{4}\right)\right)$ **13.** $\tan\left(\sin^{-1}\left(-\frac{3}{4}\right)\right)$

In the exercises 14 and 15, find the value of the expression.

14. $\sin^{-1}\left(\cos\left(-\frac{\pi}{6}\right)\right)$ **15.** $\tan^{-1}\left(\tan\left(\frac{4\pi}{3}\right)\right)$

In the exercises 16 through 19, find the value of the expression.

16. $\cos\left(\sin^{-1}\left(\frac{1}{3}\right) + \tan^{-1}\left(\frac{1}{3}\right)\right)$ **17.** $\sin\left(2\cos^{-1}\left(\frac{1}{3}\right)\right)$

18. $\tan\left(2\sin^{-1}\left(-\frac{\sqrt{3}}{2}\right)\right)$ **19.** $\cos\left(\left(\frac{1}{2}\right)\sin^{-1}\left(\frac{5}{13}\right)\right)$

In the exercises 20 through 23, find the algebraic expression.

20. $\sin\left(\tan^{-1}(x)\right)$ **21.** $\tan\left(\sin^{-1}(x)\right)$

22. $\sin\left(\cos^{-1}\left(\frac{x}{2}\right)\right)$ **23.** $\cos\left(\left(\frac{1}{2}\right)\cos^{-1}(x)\right)$

Solve the following equations:

24. $\sin^{-1}\left(\frac{x}{2}\right) = -\frac{1}{2}$ **25.** $\sin^{-1}\left(\sqrt{2x}\right) = \cos^{-1} x$

26. $\tan^2 x + 9\tan x - 12 = 0\,,\ -\frac{\pi}{2} < x < \frac{\pi}{2}$

SECCION 4.6

EXPONENTIAL FUNCTIONS

EXPONENT LAWS

As we said in section 1.2, the set of real numbers is the union of two disjoint sets, the set of rational numbers and the set of irrational numbers. A real number is rational if and only if its decimal expansion is periodic. On the other hand, a real number is irrational if and only if its decimal expansion is infinite and not periodic.

Now, we need to define $\boldsymbol{a^x}$, where $\boldsymbol{a}$ is a positive real number and x can be any real number, including irrationals. Let's briefly review how we defined a^x for a rational x in chapter 1:

- If $\boldsymbol{x = n}$, where $\boldsymbol{n}$ is a positive integer, then:

$$a^x = a^n = \underbrace{a\,a\ldots a}_{n}$$

- If $\boldsymbol{x = 0,\ a^0 = 1}$
- If $\boldsymbol{x = -n}$, and n is a positive integer, then:

$$a^{-n} = \frac{1}{a^n}$$

- If $\boldsymbol{x = \frac{m}{n}}$, where $\boldsymbol{m}$ and $\boldsymbol{n}$ are positive integers, then:

$$a^x = a^{m/n} = \sqrt[n]{a^m} = \left(\sqrt[n]{a}\right)^m$$

Example 4.6.1 Solve:

a. $4^3 = 4 \cdot 4 \cdot 4 = 64$ **b.** $4^0 = 1$

c. $4^{-3} = \dfrac{1}{4^3} = \dfrac{1}{64}$ **d.** $4^{\frac{5}{2}} = \left(4^{\frac{1}{2}}\right)^5 = \left(\sqrt{4}\right)^5 = (2)^5 = 32$

The difficulty arises when x is irrational. In this case, the concept of limit is required, but we will not study this concept until the next course. However, we can make an empiric description relying on the case 2^{π}, since π is the most famous irrational number. It first appeared when studying the circle.

As with any irrational number, Pi has an infinite decimal expansion. Its first 30 digits are the following:

$$\pi = 3.14159625358979323846264338327 9...$$

We can construct the next sequences of rational numbers using the above decimal expansion of pi:

1. 3.1 3.14 3.141 3.1415 ... and **2.** 3.2 3.15 3.142 3.1416

The terms of the first sequence are smaller than π, and they approach π from the left. Conversely, the terms of the second sequence are greater than π, and they approach π from the right.

Both sequences allow us to approach the value of π from both its right and left sides using the following rational powers:

$$\begin{array}{lllllllll} 3.1 & < & \pi & < & 3.2 & \Rightarrow & 2^{3.1} & < 2^{\pi} & < 2^{3.2} \\ 3.14 & < & \pi & < & 3.15 & \Rightarrow & 2^{3.14} & < 2^{\pi} & < 2^{3.15} \\ 3.141 & < & \pi & < & 3.142 & \Rightarrow & 2^{3.141} & < 2^{\pi} & < 2^{3.142} \\ 3.1415 & < & \pi & < & 3.1416 & \Rightarrow & 2^{3.1415} & < 2^{\pi} & < 2^{3.1416} \end{array}$$

This way, making use of the basic properties of the real numbers, we prove that there is only one real number that is greater than the following numbers:

$$2^{3.1} < 2^{3.14} < 2^{3.141} < 2^{3.1415} \ldots$$

and is smaller than:

$$\ldots 2^{3.1416} < 2^{3.142} < 2^{3.15} < 2^{3.2}$$

This unique real number is denoted by 2^{π}. Calculators give 2^{π} the value of:

$$2^{\pi} = 8.824977827$$

We can make use of this procedure to define $\boldsymbol{a}^{\boldsymbol{x}}$, where $\boldsymbol{a}$ is any real positive number, and x is an irrational number.

The next theorem provides the properties of the exponents. The proofs of these properties are not difficult to achieve for the case of rational exponents, however, we cannot claim the same for the case of irrational exponents. For this reason, this time, the proof of the theorem will be omitted.

Theorem 4.6.1 **Exponent Laws**

If a and b are positive real numbers and x and y are any real numbers, then we have that:

1. $a^0 = 1$
2. $a^1 = a$
3. $a^x a^y = a^{x+y}$
4. $\dfrac{a^x}{a^y} = a^{x-y}$
5. $(a^x)^y = a^{xy}$
6. $(ab)^x = a^x b^x$
7. $\left(\dfrac{a}{b}\right)^x = \dfrac{a^x}{b^x}$
8. $a^{-x} = \dfrac{1}{a^x}$

Example 4.6.2 Solve:

a. $\dfrac{3^{3/2}}{\sqrt{3}} = \dfrac{3^{3/2}}{3^{1/2}} = 3^{(3/2)-(1/2)} = 3^{2/2} = 3^1 = 3$

b. $\left(3^{2/3} \times 3^{1/6}\right)^6 = 3^{(2/3)6} \times 3^{(1/6)6} = 3^4 \times 3^1 = 3^{4+1} = 3^5 = 243$

THE EXPONENTIAL FUNCTIONS

Definition Let a be a real number, such that $a > 0$ and $a \neq 1$.

The **exponential function** with base a is the function:

$$f : \mathbb{R} \to \mathbb{R}^+, \quad f(x) = a^x$$

Example 4.6.3

Plot the graphs of the following functions:

1. $y = 2^x$
2. $y = 5^x$
3. $y = \left(\dfrac{1}{2}\right)^x = 2^{-x}$
4. $y = \left(\dfrac{1}{5}\right)^x = 5^{-x}$

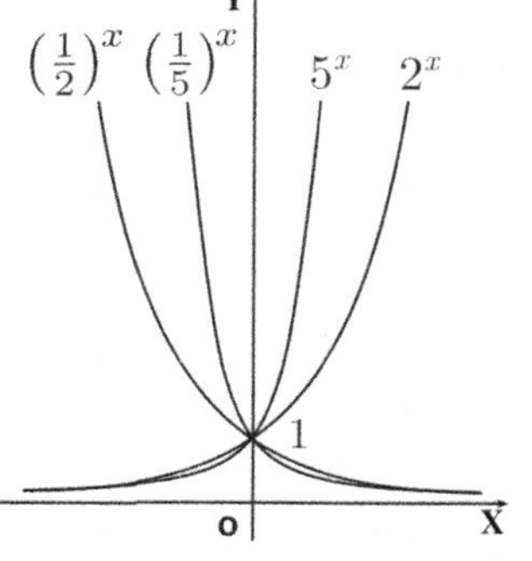

All of them pass through the point $(0, 1)$.

In the definition of the function $f(x) = a^x$, the base $a = 1$ was omitted because, in this case, $f(x) = 1^x = 1$ is the horizontal line $y = 1$, which has a very different performance with respect to the cases where $a \neq 1$.

PROPERTIES OF THE EXPONENTIAL FUNCTIONS

The exponential function $\boldsymbol{f(x) = a^x}$ has the next properties:

- If $\boldsymbol{a > 1}$, f is **increasing**. Conversely, if $\boldsymbol{0 < a < 1}$, f is **decreasing**.

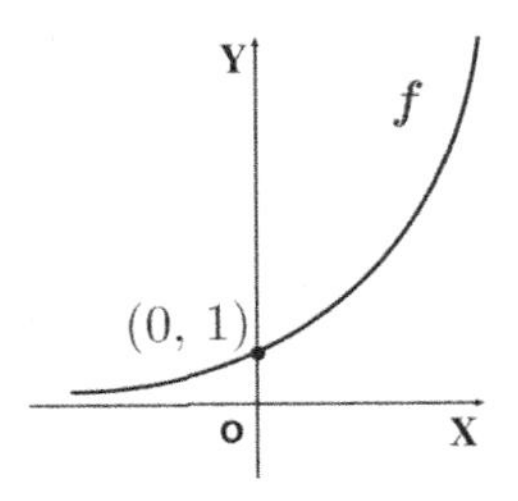

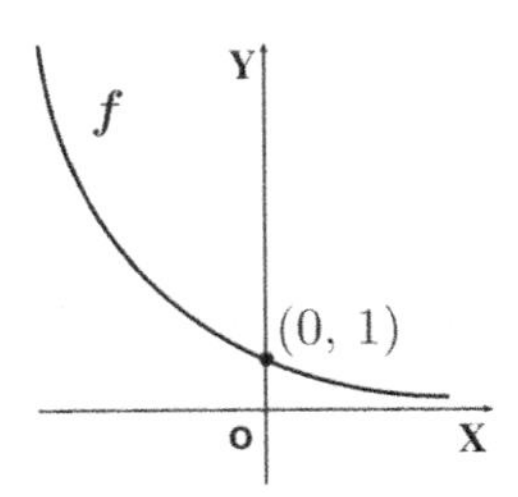

$\boldsymbol{f(x) = a^x}$ where $\boldsymbol{a > 1}$ $\quad$ $\boldsymbol{f(x) = a^x}$ where $\boldsymbol{0 < a < 1}$

- **Domain:** $\mathbb{R}$, **Range:** $\mathbb{R}^+ = \boldsymbol{(0, +\infty)}$.
- Is **injective**
- The graph of f intersects the Y-axis at $(0, 1)$, since $\boldsymbol{a^0 = 1}$.

Example 4.6.4

Considering the graph of $f(x) = 2^x$ (example 4.6.3) and making use of the translation and reflection techniques, sketch the graph of:

1. $g(x) = 2^x + 2$ $\qquad$ **2.** $h(x) = 2^{x-2}$ $\qquad$ **3.** $q(x) = -2^{-x}$

Solution

1. We have that $g(x) = 2^x + 2 = f(x) + 2$. Then, to obtain the graph of $g(x) = 2^x + 2$, we shift the graph of $f(x) = 2^x$ two units upward.
2. We have that $h(x) = 2^{x-2} = f(x-2)$. Then, to obtain the graph of $h(x) = 2^{x-2}$ we shift the graph of $f(x) = 2^x$ two units to the right.
3. We have that $q(x) = -2^{-x} = -f(-x)$. Then, we obtain the graph of $q(x)$ in two steps. Firstly, reflect the graph of f about the Y-axis to get the graph of $y = f(-x) = 2^{-x}$. Next, reflect the graph of $y = f(-x)$ about the X-axis to get the graph of $y = -f(-x) = -2^{-x} = q(x)$.

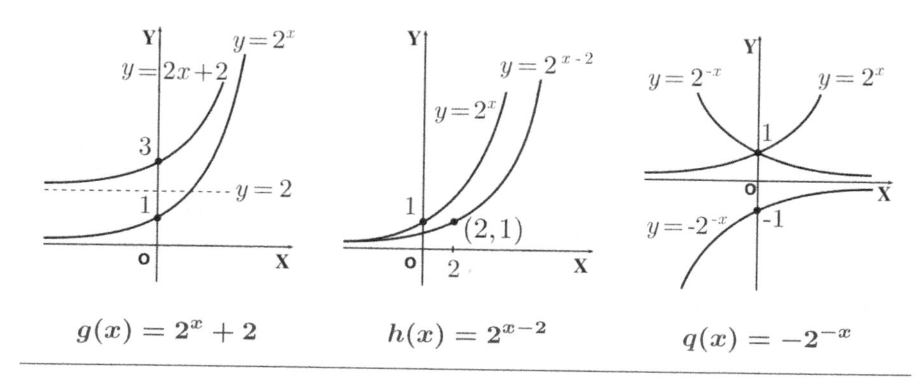

$g(x) = 2^x + 2$ $\qquad$ $h(x) = 2^{x-2}$ $\qquad$ $q(x) = -2^{-x}$

THE NUMBER e

The number **e** is an irrational number that plays a very important roll in Calculus. We cannot give a precise definition of this number without relying on Limits, the first topic of the Calculus course. However, for now, we will only say that it is an irrational number of which the first 21 digits of its non-periodic decimal expansion are:

$$e \approx \mathbf{2.71828182845904523536\ldots}$$

The name **e** for this number was given by **Leonardo Euler**. It is uncertain whether this was by the word *exponential* or by his last name *Euler*.

THE NATURAL EXPONENTIAL FUNCTION

Definition

The **natural** function is the exponential function with base e. That is:

$$f : \mathbb{R} \to \mathbb{R}^+, \; f(x) = e^x$$

Since $e > 1$, we can tell that the natural function is increasing.

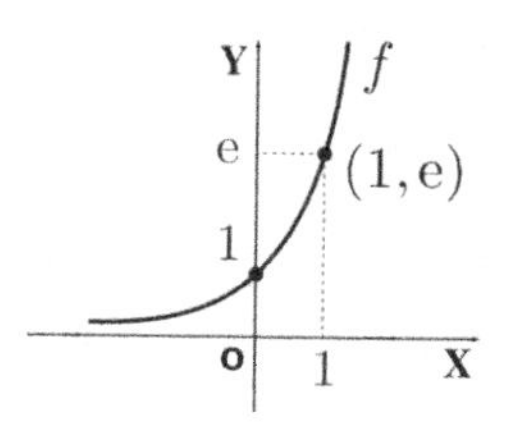

Did you know this?

Number **e** *arises spontaneously when performing operations with exponential functions. An illustration of this scenario is the next story starring Roberto.*

Roberto's Financial Adventure

Roberto has \$1 and he intends to invest it in a bank financial product to earn some profits. The bank offers Roberto an investment product with an interest rate of 100% per year. More precisely, his dollar will produce another dollar of profit in one year. That is:

Seed capital ($)	***Yearly compounding periods***	***Earned money in a year*** ($)	***Year-end balance*** ($)
1	1	1	2

The investment will double in one year, which makes Roberto eager to take a little more risk, so he asks his banker about the possibility of better returns.

The banker offers him a more lucrative product by increasing the annual compounding periods. The bank's condition is that the interest rate be divided by the number of annual compounding periods.

In everyday words, this means that if he opts for a six-month compounding, he will have 2 compounding periods in a year, so the interest rate will be:

$$\frac{100}{2}\% = 50\%, \quad \textit{each semester}$$

Roberto's dollar will increase by 50% *at the end of the first semester, that is:* $\$1 \times 1.5 = \$1.5$. *This will be the seed capital for the second semester, therefore, by the end of the year he will have:* $\$1.5 \times 1.5 = \$2.25$.

Let's compare the benefits of the two products the banker offered to Roberto:

Seed capital ($)	***Yearly compounding periods***	***Earned money in a year*** ($)	***Year-end balance*** ($)
1	1	1	2
1	2	1.25	2.25

In financial terms, this system is called ***compound interest***.

Roberto is happy to have made the decision to increase the number of compounding periods to 2, since his profit increased by $0.25 *in the same time span, so he is enthusiastic to ask the banker to further increase the number of periods. Moreover, The bank gave Roberto the possibility to choose any number of periods he liked.*

The banker prepared the following table to show him the amount of money he will have in his bank account by the end of the year if he increases the annual compounding periods from one (yearly) to 525, 960, *i.e., by minute.*

Compounding period	***Year-end balance***
Yearly	$2
Half-yearly	$2.25
Monthly	$2.6130...
Daily	$2.71456...
By minute	$2.718279...

As you can see, the value to which the balance in the account approaches, as the compounding periods increase, is the **e** *number.*

SOLVED PROBLEMS 4.6

Problem 4.6.1 Simplify the following expressions:

a. $\dfrac{e^{3/2}}{\sqrt{e}}$ b. $\left[\dfrac{1}{8}\left(8^{2/3}\right)\right]^3$ c. $\dfrac{\left(9^{4/5}\right)^{5/8}}{\left(\frac{8}{27}\right)^{2/3}}$

Solution

a. $\dfrac{e^{3/2}}{\sqrt{e}} = \dfrac{e^{3/2}}{e^{1/2}} = e^{3/2-1/2} = e^{2/2} = e$

b. $\left[\dfrac{1}{8}\left(8^{2/3}\right)\right]^3 = \left(\dfrac{1}{8}\right)^3\left(8^{2/3}\right)^3 = \left(\dfrac{1^3}{8^3}\right)\left(8^2\right) = \dfrac{8^2}{8^3} = \dfrac{1}{8}$

c. $\dfrac{\left(9^{4/5}\right)^{5/8}}{\left(\dfrac{8}{27}\right)^{2/3}} = \dfrac{9^{20/40}}{\left(\dfrac{2^3}{3^3}\right)^{2/3}} = \dfrac{9^{1/2}}{\dfrac{2^{(3)(2/3)}}{3^{(3)(2/3)}}}$

$$= \frac{3}{\frac{2^2}{3^2}} = \frac{3\left(3^2\right)}{2^2} = \frac{27}{4}$$

Problem 4.6.2 If $h(x) = 3^{5x}$, find x such that $h(x) = 81$.

Solution

Since $81 = 3^4$, we must find x such that $3^{5x} = 3^4$. Matching exponents:

$$5x = 4 \Rightarrow x = \frac{4}{5}$$

Problem 4.6.3 If $f(x) = e^{kx}$ and $f(1) = 3$, find $f(5)$

Solution

If $f(1) = 3$, then $e^k = 3$.

Hence:

$$f(5) = e^{k(5)} = \left(e^k\right)^5 = 3^5 = 243$$

Problem 4.6.4

A company is offering a job for exactly 18 days. You have to choose between the two following ways of payment:

- 2.500 dollars by the end of the 18 days.
- 1 cent of dollar for the first day, 2 cents for the second, 4 cents for the third and so forth. In general, 2^{n-1} cents for the nth day.

Which of the two ways of payment will be more profitable?

Solution

I wouldn't blame you if you opted for the first choice, but you must know that the second choice is more profitable. Indeed, the first day you will receive 1 cent, and the last day ($n = 18$), $2^{18-1} = 2^{17}$ cents. If S is the sum of all cents, then you will receive:

$$S = 1 + 2 + 2^2 + 2^3 + \ldots + 2^{17} \tag{1}$$

Multiplying the previous equality by 2:

$$2S = 2 + 2^2 + 2^3 + 2^4 + \ldots + 2^{18} \tag{2}$$

Subtracting (1) from (2):

$$S = 2^{18} - 1 = 262,143 \text{ cents} = 2,621.43 \text{ dollars.}$$

EXERCISES 4.6

In the exercises 1 through 7, find the value of the expression:

1. $(81)^{1/4}$ **2.** $8^{4/3}$ **3.** $(25)^{3/2}$ **4.** $(25)^{-3/2}$

5. $\left(\frac{1}{8}\right)^{-2/3}$ **6.** $\left(\frac{27}{16}\right)^{-1/2}$ **7.** $(0.01)^{-1}$

In the exercises 8 through 13, simplify the expression:

8. $\left(\frac{e^7}{e^3}\right)^{-1}$ **9.** $\frac{3^3 3^5}{(3^4)^3}$ **10.** $\frac{5^{1/2}\left(5^{1/2}\right)^5}{5^4}$

11. $\frac{2^{-3}2^5}{(2^4)^{-3}}$ **12.** $\frac{\left(2^4\right)^{1/3}}{16\left(2^{7/3}\right)}$ **13.** $\frac{\left(2^{1/3}3^{2/3}\right)^3}{3^{5/2}3^{-1/2}}$

In the exercises 14 through 19, solve the equation.

14. $2^{2x-1} = 8$ **15.** $\left(\frac{1}{3}\right)^{x+1} = 27$ **16.** $8\sqrt[3]{2} = 4^x$

17. $\left(3^{2x}3^2\right)^4 = 3$ **18.** $e^{-6x+1} = e^3$ **19.** $e^{x^2-2x} = e^3$

In exercises 20 through 28, sketch the graph of the functions using translation and reflection techniques in all of them, except for exercises 25 and 27.

20. $y = e^{x+2}$ **21.** $y = -2e^x + 1$ **22.** $y = e^{-x}$

23. $y = e^{-x} + 2$ **24.** $y = 2 - e^{-x}$ **25.** $y = 3^x$

26. $y = 3^{-x+2}$ **27.** $y = 4^x$ **28.** $y = -4^{-x-1}$

29. If $g(x) = Ae^{-kx}$, $g(0) = 9$ and $g(2) = 5$, find $g(6)$.

30. If $h(x) = 30 - Pe^{-kx}$, $h(0) = 10$ and $h(3) = -30$, find $h(12)$.

SECCION 4.7

LOGARITHMIC FUNCTIONS

Definition Let a be a real number such that $\boldsymbol{a > 0}$ and $\boldsymbol{a \neq 1}$.

The **logarithmic function** with base a, denoted by a $\mathbf{log}_a$, is the inverse of the exponential function:

$$f : \mathbb{R} \to \mathbb{R}^+, \quad f(x) = a^x$$

$$\text{That is,} \quad \log_a : \mathbb{R}^+ \to \mathbb{R}, \quad \log_a = f^{-1}$$

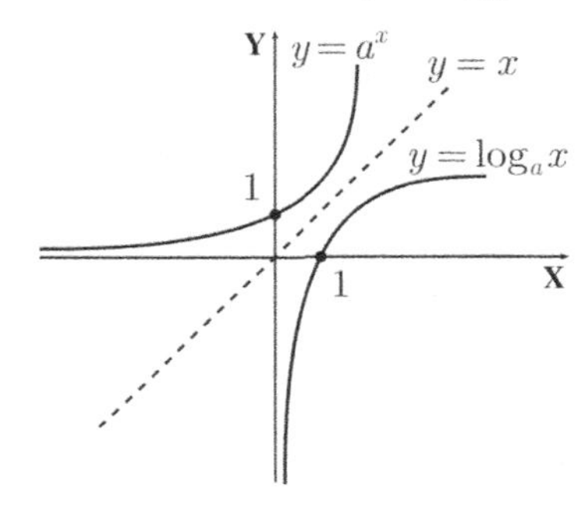

$y = \log_a(x), \ a > 1$

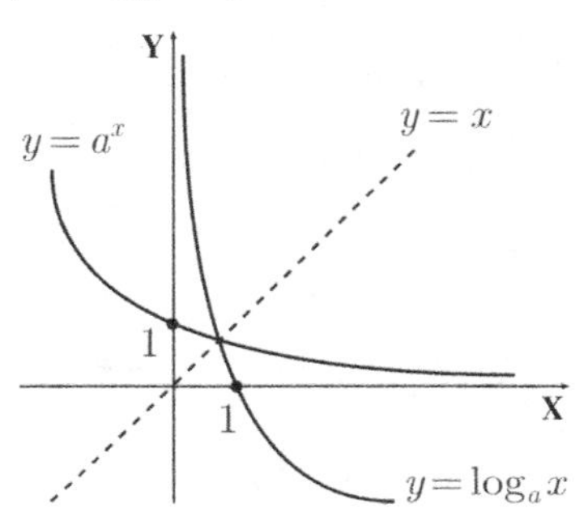

$y = \log_a(x), \ 0 < a < 1$

Since $y = \log_a(x)$ is the inverse function of $y = a^x$, we have:

$$(1) \qquad a^{\log_a(x)} = x \qquad \text{and} \qquad (2) \qquad \log_a(a^x) = x$$

The properties (1) and (2) are equivalent to the following proposition:

$$\log_a(x) = y \Leftrightarrow a^y = x \tag{3}$$

This last equivalence indicates that $\mathbf{log}_a(\boldsymbol{x})$ is the exponent to which the base a must be raised in order to obtain the number x.

Since $a^1 = a$ and $a^0 = 1$, then, according to (3) we get:

$$(4) \qquad \log_a(a) = 1 \qquad \text{y} \qquad (5) \qquad \log_a(1) = 0$$

We will often write $y = \log_a x$ (without parenthesis) instead of $\log_a(x)$.

Example 4.7.1 Solve:

a. $\log_4 64 = \log_4 (4^3) = 3$

b. $\log_7 \sqrt{7} = \log_7 \left(7^{1/2}\right) = \dfrac{1}{2}$

c. $\log_5 \left(\dfrac{1}{5}\right) = \log_5 (5^{-1}) = -1$

d. $\log_{10} 0.001 = \log_{10} \dfrac{1}{1,000} = \log_{10} 10^{-3} = -3$

PROPERTIES OF THE LOGARITHMIC FUNCTION

The function $y = \log_a x$ has the next properties:

- Is **increasing** if $a > 1$. Conversely, is **decreasing** if $0 < a < 1$.
- **Domain** $= \mathbb{R}^+$, **Range** $= \mathbb{R}$.
- Is **one-to-one.**
- The graph of $y = \log_a x$ intersects the X-axis at $(1, 0)$. It does not intersect the Y-axis.

Theorem 4.7.1 **LAWS OF LOGARITHMS**

If $a > 0$, $a \neq 1$, $u > 0$, $v > 0$ and n is a real number, then:

1. $\log_a(uv) = \log_a u + \log_a v$ (Product Rule)

2. $\log_a\left(\dfrac{u}{v}\right) = \log_a u - \log_a v$ (Quotient Rule)

3. $\log_a u^n = n\log_a u$ (Power Rule)

Proof

1. If $x = \log_a u$ and $y = \log_a v$, then:

$$u = a^x,\ v = a^y \text{ and } uv = a^x a^y = a^{x+y}$$

Applying $\log_a$ to the last equation, and making use of the property (2) of the logarithmic function definition, we have:

$$\log_a(uv) = \log_a\left(a^{x+y}\right) = x + y = \log_a u + \log_a v$$

Proofs 2 and 3 follow the same procedure as 1, so we leave both as an exercise for the reader.

Example 4.7.2 Let x, y and z be positive real numbers.

Express the following expressions in terms of the logarithm of x, y and z:

i. $\log_a\left(\dfrac{x^4\sqrt{z}}{y^3}\right)$ **ii.** $\log_a\sqrt[7]{\dfrac{x^2}{y^3z^4}}$

Solution

i. $$\log_a\left(\frac{x^4\sqrt{z}}{y^3}\right) = \log_a\left(\frac{x^4z^{1/2}}{y^3}\right) = \log_a\left(x^4z^{1/2}\right) - \log_a y^3 \qquad \text{(Quotient Rule)}$$

$$= \log_a x^4 + \log_a z^{1/2} - \log_a y^3 \qquad \text{(Product Rule)}$$

$$= 4\log_a x + \frac{1}{2}\log_a z - 3\log_a y \qquad \text{(Power Rule)}$$

ii. $$\log_a \sqrt[7]{\frac{x^2}{y^3z^4}} = \log_a\left(\frac{x^2}{y^3z^4}\right)^{1/7} = \frac{1}{7}\log_a\left(\frac{x^2}{y^3z^4}\right) \qquad \text{(Power Rule)}$$

$$= \frac{1}{7}\left[\log_a x^2 - \log_a\left(y^3z^4\right)\right] \qquad \text{(Quotient Rule)}$$

$$= \frac{1}{7}\left[\log_a x^2 - \log_a y^3 - \log_a z^4\right] \qquad \text{(Product Rule)}$$

$$= \frac{2}{7}\log_a x - \frac{3}{7}\log_a y - \frac{4}{7}\log_a z \qquad \text{(Power Rule)}$$

Example 4.7.3 Solve the equations::

a. $2^{8x-1} = 64$ **b.** $2\log_9(4x) = 1$

Solution

a. Applying $\log_2$ to both sides:

$$\log_2\left(2^{8x-1}\right) = \log_2 64 \Rightarrow \log_2\left(2^{8x-1}\right) = \log_2\left(2^6\right)$$

$$\Rightarrow (8x-1)\log_2 2 = 6\log_2 2 \Rightarrow 8x - 1 = 6 \Rightarrow x = \frac{7}{8}$$

b. $2\log_9(4x) = 1 \Rightarrow \log_9(4x) = \dfrac{1}{2} \Rightarrow 4x = 9^{1/2} \Rightarrow 4x = 3 \Rightarrow x = \dfrac{3}{4}$

THE NATURAL LOGARITHMIC FUNCTION

The **natural logarithmic** function is the logarithmic function with base **e**. This function is the denoted by $\boldsymbol{y = \ln x}$. Thus:

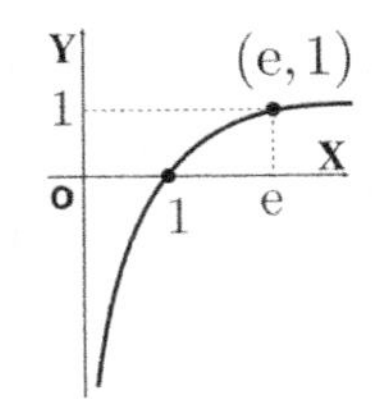

$$\ln x = \log_e x$$

This function is the inverse of the exponential function $y = e^x$. Therefore:

$$(1) \quad \boldsymbol{e^{\ln x} = x} \qquad \text{y} \qquad (2) \quad \boldsymbol{\ln e^x = x}$$

or, equivalently,

$$\boldsymbol{y = \ln x \Leftrightarrow e^y = x} \tag{3}$$

Since $e^1 = e$, we have that $\boldsymbol{\ln e = 1}$.

Example 4.7.4 Solve the equation $3^{2x+1} = 5^{3x-1}$

Solution

We apply natural logarithm to both sides of the equation:

$$\begin{aligned}
\ln 3^{2x+1} = \ln 5^{3x-1} &\Rightarrow (2x+1)\ln 3 = (3x-1)\ln 5 \\
&\Rightarrow 2x\ln 3 + \ln 3 = 3x\ln 5 - \ln 5 \\
&\Rightarrow 2x\ln 3 - 3x\ln 5 = -\ln 5 - \ln 3 \\
&\Rightarrow x(2\ln 3 - 3\ln 5) = -(\ln 5 + \ln 3) \\
&\Rightarrow x = -\frac{\ln 5 + \ln 3}{2\ln 3 - 3\ln 5} \approx 1.03
\end{aligned}$$

Remark

The most widely used logarithms are the naturals and the decimals (with base 10). In the notation of decimal logarithms, the base is omitted and we just write $\boldsymbol{\log x}$ instead of $\boldsymbol{\log_{10} x}$.

CHANGE THE LOGARITHMIC AND EXPONENTIAL BASE

The next equality expresses a logarithmic function of any base in terms of the natural logarithmic function.

Theorem 4.7.2 **Change of the logarithmic base.**

If $x > 0$, then:

$$\boxed{\log_a x = \frac{\ln x}{\ln a}}$$

Proof

$$y = \log_a x \Rightarrow a^y = x \Rightarrow \ln a^y = \ln x \Rightarrow y \ln a = \ln x$$

$$\Rightarrow y = \frac{\ln x}{\ln a} \Rightarrow \log_a x = \frac{\ln x}{\ln a}$$

Corolary

$$\boldsymbol{\log_a \mathrm{e} = \frac{1}{\ln a}}$$

Proof

Just take $x = \mathrm{e}$ in the formula of theorem 4.7.2. Consider that $\ln \mathrm{e} = 1$.

Example 4.7.5 Find the value of:

a. $\log_5 \mathrm{e}$ **b.** $\log_4 19$

Solution

a. According to the previous corollary:

$$\log_5 \mathrm{e} = \frac{1}{\ln 5} = \frac{1}{1.6094379} = 0.609437912$$

b. According to the theorem 4.7.2:

$$\log_4 19 = \frac{\ln 19}{\ln 4} = \frac{2.944438979}{1.38629361} = 2.123963757$$

Theorem 4.7.3 **Change of the exponential base.**

If $a > 0$ and $a \neq 1$, then:

$$\boldsymbol{a^x = \mathrm{e}^{x \ln a}}$$

Proof

We already know that $a = \mathrm{e}^{\ln a}$. Then:

$$a^x = \left(\mathrm{e}^{\ln a}\right)^x = \mathrm{e}^{x \ln a}$$

Did you know this?

Johann Bernoulli

Johann Bernoulli *(1667-1748), also known as the Archimedes of his time, was one of the famous mathematician who studied the exponential functions. He set himself the problem of calculating the area under the curve* $y = x^x$*, from* $x = 0$ *to* $x = 1$*.*

By using the identity $x^x = e^{x \ln x}$*, he finally discovered that this area can be expressed by the series:*

$$\frac{1}{1^1} - \frac{1}{2^2} + \frac{1}{3^3} - \frac{1}{4^4} + \ldots + (-1)^{n+1}\frac{1}{n^n} \cdots$$

As a curious fact, the Bernoulli family is recognized as the only mathematical dynasty in history, since there are almost a dozen brilliant mathematicians in their genealogical tree.

SOLVED PROBLEMS 4.7

Problem 4.7.1 Solve the following equations:

a. $\log_{27} 4x = \dfrac{2}{3}$ **b.** $3^{2x-1} = 81$

Solution

a. $\log_{27} 4x = \dfrac{2}{3} \Rightarrow 4x = 27^{\frac{2}{3}} \Rightarrow 4x = \left(\sqrt[3]{27}\right)^2 = 3^2 = 9 \Rightarrow x = \dfrac{9}{4}$

b. Applying $\log_3$ to both sides of the equation:

$$\log_3 3^{2x-1} = \log_3 81 \Rightarrow 2x - 1 = \log_3(3^4) \Rightarrow 2x - 1 = 4 \Rightarrow x = \frac{5}{2}$$

Problem 4.7.2 Graph the function $y = \ln |\, x \,|$.

Solution

$$y = \ln |\, x \,| = \begin{cases} \ln x, & \text{if } x > 0 \\ \ln -x, & \text{if } x < 0 \end{cases}$$

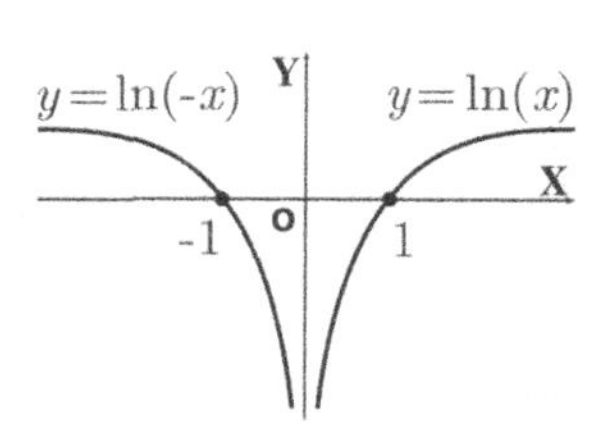

Hence, $y = \ln |\, x \,|$ consists of two graphs:

(1) $y = \ln x,\ x > 0$ **(2)** $y = \ln(-x),\ x < 0$

We obtain **(2)** by reflecting **(1)** (already known) on the Y-axis.

EXERCISES 4.7

In the exercises 1 through 8, find the value of the expression without using of tables or a calculator.

1. $\log_2\left(\frac{1}{64}\right)$ **2.**$\log_{1/2}\left(\frac{1}{16}\right)$ **3.** $\log_{1/3}(81)$

4. $\log_{100}(0.1)$ **5.**$e^{\ln 3}$ **6.** $e^{2\ln 3}$

7. $e^{(\ln 3)/2}$ **8.** $e^{3\ln 2-2\ln 3}$

In the exercises 9 through 19, solve the given equation.

9. $\log_x(25)=\frac{1}{2}$ **10.** $\log_4\left(x^2-6x\right)=2$

11. $\log x+\log(2x-8)=1$ **12.** $-3\ln x=a$ **13.** $\frac{k}{20}-\ln x=1$

14. $4\ln x=\frac{1}{2}\ln x+7$ **15.** $3\ln(\ln x)=-12$ **16.** $3e^{-1.2x}=14$

17. $3^{x-1}=e^3$ **18.** $3^x2^{3x}=64$ **19.** $(3^x)^2=16\sqrt{2^x}$

In the exercises 20 through 27, use translation and reflection techniques to sketch the graph of the given functions.

20. $y=\ln(x-2)$ **21.** $y=\ln(-x)$ **22.** $y=\ln(x+3)$

23. $y=4-\ln x$ **24.** $y=4-\ln(x+3)$ **25.** $y=2-\ln|x|$

26. $y=3+\log x$ **27.** $y=3+\log(x+3)$

In the exercises 28 through 31, write the expression in terms of the logarithms of a, b and c.

28. $\log\dfrac{a^2b}{c}$ **29.** $\log\dfrac{\sqrt{b}}{a^2c^3}$ **30.** $\ln\left(\dfrac{1}{a}\sqrt{\dfrac{c^3}{b}}\right)$ **31.** $\ln\sqrt[5]{\dfrac{a^2}{bc^4}}$

In the exercises 32, 33 and 34, rewrite the expression using only one logarithm of coefficient 1.

32. $3\ln x+\ln y-2\ln z$ **33.** $2\log a+\log b-3(\log z+\log x)$

34. $\frac{3}{4}\ln a+3\ln b-\frac{3}{2}\ln c$

35. Express each of the following functions with the form $y=Ae^{kt}$:

a. $y=(5)3^{0.5t}$ **b.** $y=6(1.04)^t$

SECCION 4.8

FUNCTION APPLICATIONS

Some phenomena of natural, social and economic sciences can be modeled using exponential or logarithmic functions. In this last section we will discuss a few simple cases, such as the population growth and the radioactive decay.

EXPONENTIAL GROWTH MODELS

Let $f(t)$ be a function in which the independent variable t represents time. Mathematical models for exponential growth are given by the formula:

$$f(t) = Aa^{kt},$$

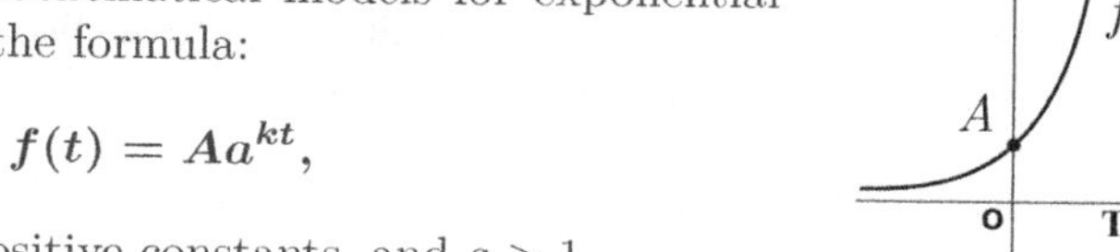

where A and k are positive constants, and $a > 1$.

Note that the function f is **increasing**, and $f(0) = A$.

Example 4.8.1

A bacteria culture triples its population each minute. If the initial culture starts with 50 bacteria:

a. find a formula for the number of bacteria after t minutes.

b. how many bacteria are there after 15 minutes?

Solution

a. Let $f(t)$ be the number of bacteria after t minutes.

The initial number of bacteria is $f(0) = 50$.

after 1 minute , there are $f(1) = 50(3)$

after 2 minutes , there are $f(2) = 50(3)(3) = 50(3^2)$

after 3 minutes , there are $f(3) = 50(3^2)(3) = 50(3^3)$

In general, after t minutes, there are:

$$\boldsymbol{f(t) = 50(3^t)} \text{ bacteria}$$

b. After 15 minutes, there are:

$$f(15) = 50(3^{15}) \approx 717,445,350 \text{ bacteria.}$$

EXPONENTIAL DECAY MODELS

Mathematical models for exponential decay are given by the formula:

$$f(t) = Aa^{-kt},$$

where A and k are positive constants, and $a > 1$.

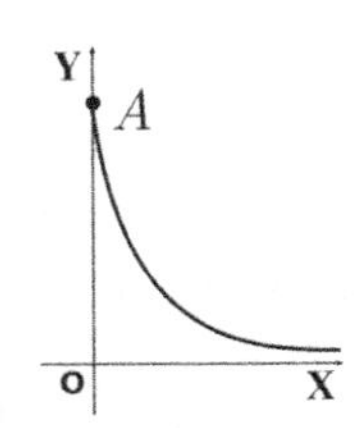

Note that f is **decreasing** and $f(0) = A$.

One of the most common examples of this model is the decay of the radioactive substances. This substances have a property by which some of their atoms, over a period of time, disintegrate to become another element; thus, the amount of unchanged atoms decreases(decay) with time.

If $N(t)$ is the number of atoms of the radioactive substance at time t, then:

$$N(t) = N_0 e^{-kt} \qquad (1)$$

where $N_0 = N(0)$ is the initial number of atoms at $t = 0$, and k is a positive constant that depends only of the radioactive substance. If k is big, the material decays rapidly. If k is small (close to 0), the material decays slowly.

Example 4.8.2

The amount $Q(t)$ of a radioactive substance after t years is given by:

$$Q(t) = Ae^{-0.0004t}$$

After 2,000 years, 300 grams of the substance remain. How many grams were there at the beginning?

Solution

We have:

$$300 = Q(2,000) = Ae^{-0.0004(2,000)} = Ae^{-0.8} \Rightarrow A = \frac{300}{e^{-0.8}}$$
$$= 300e^{0.8} \approx 667.66 \text{ grams}$$

EXPONENTIAL DECAY AND HALF-LIFE

The **half-life** of a radioactive substance is the time required for half of the mass of the substance to disintegrate. For example, it is known that the half-life of the Polonium 210 (isotope of the polonium) is 140 days. This means that, after 140 days, we have only half of the initial quantity.

The half-lives of some important radioactive elements are shown bellow:

Uranium (U^{238})	4,510,000,000 years
Plutonium (Pu^{230})	24,360 years
Carbon 14 (C^{14})	5,730 years
Radium (Ra^{226})	1,620 years
Polonium (Po^{210})	140 days.

Let's see what the relationship is between the half-life and the constant k of the exponential decay of a radioactive substance.

If λ is the half-life of the radioactive material, then, after this time λ, we should have only half of the initial atoms. Thus, $N(\lambda) = \frac{1}{2}N_0$. Therefore:

$$\begin{aligned} N_0 e^{-k\lambda} = \frac{1}{2}N_0 \Rightarrow e^{-k\lambda} &= \frac{1}{2} \\ &\Rightarrow -k\lambda = \ln\left(\frac{1}{2}\right) \\ &\Rightarrow -k\lambda = \ln 1 - \ln 2 \\ &\Rightarrow -k\lambda = -\ln 2 \\ &\Rightarrow k\lambda = \ln 2 \\ &\Rightarrow \lambda = \frac{\ln 2}{k} \end{aligned}$$

Hence:

$$(2) \quad \lambda = \frac{\ln 2}{k} \qquad \text{or} \qquad (3) \quad k = \frac{\ln 2}{\lambda}$$

Replacing (3) in (1), we get:

$$N(t) = N_0 e^{-\left(\frac{\ln 2}{\lambda}\right)t} \qquad (4)$$

Example 4.8.3 Find the half-life of the potassium ^{42}K.

The exponential decay formula for this element is:

$$Q(t) = Q_0 e^{-0.0555t}, \quad \text{where } t \text{ is given in hours.}$$

Solution

We have $k = 0.0555$. Hence, the half-life of potassium ^{42}K is:

$$\lambda = \frac{\ln 2}{k} = \frac{0.693147}{0.0555} \approx 12.489 \text{ hours}$$

CARBON-14 DATING

The carbon-14(^{14}C) is a radioactive isotope of the carbon-12(^{12}C), which is not radioactive. The archaeologists use carbon-14 to determine the age of fossils and organic remains. The half-life of the carbon-14 is 5,730 years. According to (4), its exponential decay formula is:

$$N(t) = N_0\, e^{-\left(\frac{\ln 2}{5,730}\right)t} \tag{5}$$

The proportion of carbon-14 in our atmosphere has remained constant since the genesis of the planet. When a living being breathes, he absorbs this element from the atmosphere, so its body gets the same carbon-14 proportion as the atmosphere. When a living being dies, he stops absorbing this element, and the carbon in his organism starts the process of disintegration; meaning that the time of death could be determined by calculating the proportion of carbon-14 of the mortal remains.

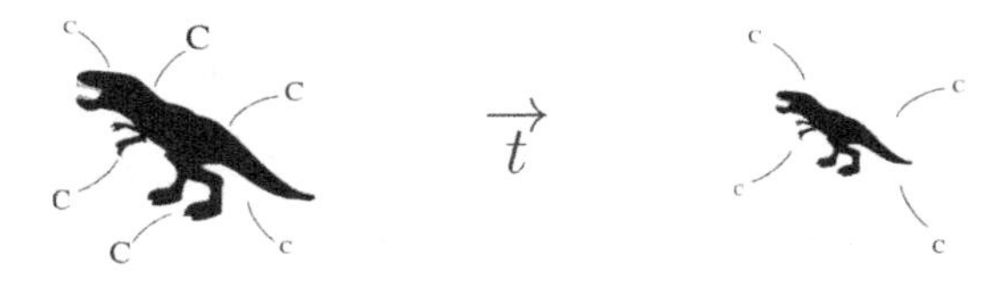

Example 4.8.4 **The rock paintings in the Cave of Altamira, Spain.**

These paintings are some of the most famous monuments left by prehistoric European man. An analysis of an organic material used in these paintings revealed that they only have 29% of carbon-14, relative to the same organic material in the present time. Find the age of these paintings.

Solution

Let t be the age of the paintings. For practical results, t can be also considered as the elapsed time since the death of the organism whose materials were used in the paintings. According to equation (4):

$$N(t) = N_0\, e^{-\left(\frac{\ln 2}{5,730}\right)t}$$

On the other hand, N_0 is the amount of carbon-14 the organic material had when the organism died, which is the same amount that the present-day organic material has.

Hence:

$$N(t) = 0.29N_0 \Rightarrow N_0\,e^{-\left(\frac{\ln 2}{5,730}\right)t} = 0.29N_0$$
$$\Rightarrow e^{-\left(\frac{\ln 2}{5,730}\right)t} = 0.29$$
$$\Rightarrow -\frac{\ln 2}{5,730}t = \ln 0.29$$
$$\Rightarrow t = -5,730\frac{\ln 0.29}{\ln 2}$$
$$\Rightarrow t \approx 10,233 \text{ years}$$

THE AGE OF THE UNIVERSE

According to the Big Bang Theory, in the genesis of the universe, the total quantity of both, uranium ^{235}U and uranium ^{238}U isotopes, were the same in the whole universe. Since that moment, the ratio between these quantities has changed, because the half-life of the ^{235}U isotope is shorter than the half-life of the ^{238}U isotope.

Example 4.8.5 **Find the age of the universe.**

A recent investigation determined that, for each atom of uranium ^{235}U, there are 78.374 atoms of uranium ^{238}U. The half-life of the ^{238}U is 4.51 billion years, and the half-life of the ^{235}U is 0.71 billion years. Calculate the age of the universe considering that the total quantity of both elements was the same at the genesis of the universe.

Solution

Let $N_8(t)$ and $N_5(t)$ be the number of atoms of ^{238}U and ^{235}U, respectively, t billion years after the Big Bang. By (3), we have:

$$N_8(t) = N_0\,e^{-kt} \qquad \text{and} \qquad N_5(t) = N_0\,e^{-rt}$$

where N_0 is the number of atoms, as much of ^{238}U as of ^{238}U, when $t = 0$.

Moreover:

$$k = \frac{\ln 2}{4.51} \qquad \text{and} \qquad r = \frac{\ln 2}{0.71}$$

Since there are 78.374 atoms of uranium ^{238}U for each atom of uranium ^{235}U at present time, we have:

$$78,374 = \frac{N_8(t)}{N_5(t)} = \frac{N_0\,\mathrm{e}^{-kt}}{N_0\,\mathrm{e}^{-rt}} = \frac{\mathrm{e}^{-kt}}{\mathrm{e}^{-rt}} = \mathrm{e}^{(r-k)t} \Rightarrow \mathrm{e}^{(r-k)t} = 78,374$$

$$\Rightarrow (r-k)t = \ln 78,374$$

$$\Rightarrow t = \frac{\ln 78,374}{r-k}$$

$$\Rightarrow t = \frac{\ln 78,374}{\frac{\ln 2}{4.51} - \frac{\ln 2}{0.71}} \approx 13,700 \text{ billion years}$$

Hence, the age of the universe is 13.700 billion years.

SIMPLE INTEREST

A capital invested in **simple interest** remains constant during the total operation. Interest earned does not bear any further interest. We can easily infer that:

> *A capital* $\boldsymbol{P}$, *called the* ***principal***, *invested during t years at an annual simple interest rate of* $\boldsymbol{100r\%}$, *produces the following amount of money:*
>
> $$\boldsymbol{M(t) = P(1+rt)} \qquad (1)$$

COMPOUND INTEREST

In **compound interest**, the interest earned becomes part of the principal by the end of each time period, so it will earn interest in the next period.

Assume that a given amount of money (principal) $\boldsymbol{P}$ is invested at an annual rate of $\boldsymbol{100r\%}$, compounded once per year. By the end of year, the interest earned is Pr, and the accumulated amount of money is:

$$A(1) = P + Pr = P(1+r)$$

The new principal for the second year is $P(1+r)$, and the accumulated amount of money by the end of the second year is:

$$A(2) = P(1+r)(1+r) = P(1+r)^2$$

In general terms, after t years, the accumulated amount of money is:

$$A(1) = P(1+r)^t$$

If the interest is compounded n times per year, then the interest rate in each time period is $\mathbf{100\frac{r}{n}\%}$, meaning that there are $\boldsymbol{nt}$ **periods** in t years.

Hence, the accumulated amount of money will be:

$$A(t) = P\left(1+\frac{r}{n}\right)^{nt} \qquad (2)$$

CONTINUOUSLY COMPOUNDED INTEREST

Continuously compound interest arises when the number n, of time periods, increases without limit, that is $n \to +\infty$.

If a principal $\boldsymbol{P}$ is invested $\boldsymbol{t}$ years at a continuously compounded annual rate of $\mathbf{100}\boldsymbol{r}\mathbf{\%}$, then the accumulated amount of money will be:

$$A(t) = P\,\mathrm{e}^{rt} \qquad (3)$$

We can get the previous formula by taking **limits**, a concept to be discussed in our book **Differential Calculus**.

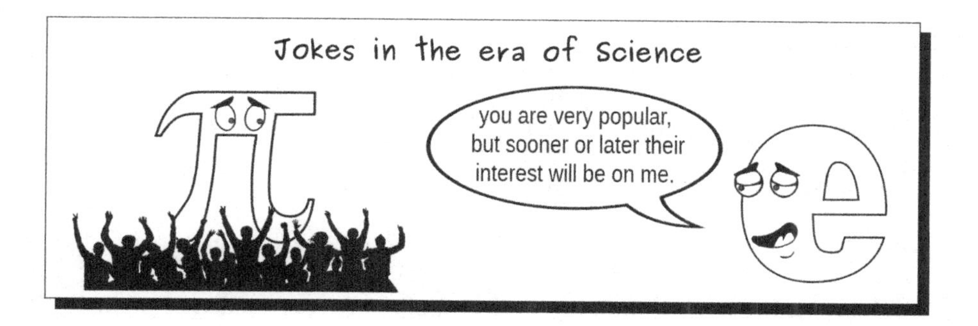

Example 4.8.6 An investment of $\$1,000$ is placed on a financial product.

The corresponding rate is 25% per year. Find the total amount of money in the account after the end of the second year if:

a. the interest is simple.

b. the interest is compounding monthly.

c. the interest is compounding continuously.

Solution

a. We have: $P = 1,000,000, \quad r = 0.25, \quad \text{and} \quad t = 2.$

Replacing these values in the formula (1):

$$M(2) = 1,000,000(1 + 0.25(2)) = \$\,1,500,000$$

b. We have: $P = 1,000,000, \quad r = 0.25, \quad n = 12, \quad t = 2.$

Replacing these values in the formula (2):

$$M(2) = 1,000,000\left(1 + \frac{0.25}{12}\right)^{24} = \$\,1,640,273.33$$

c. We have: $P = 1,000,000, \quad r = 0.25 \quad \text{and} \quad t = 2$. Replacing these values in the formula (3):

$$M(2) = 1,000,000\,\mathrm{e}^{0.25(2)} = \$\,1,648,721.27$$

Example 4.8.7

An investment is made at an interest rate of 20% per year. Find how many years will it take to double the money if the interest is compounded:

a. quarterly? (every 3 moths) **b.** continuously?

Solution

Let P be the invested capital, and λ the number of years needed to double P.

a. Applying the formula (2), with $n = 4$, $r = 0.2$ and $t = \lambda$, we get:

$$A(\lambda) = P\left(1 + \frac{0.2}{4}\right)^{4\lambda} = P(1.05)^{4\lambda}$$

Since $A(\lambda)$ is $2P$ after λ years, we have:

$$\begin{aligned} P(1.05)^{4\lambda} = 2P &\Rightarrow (1.05)^{4\lambda} = 2 \\ &\Rightarrow 4\lambda \ln(1.05) = \ln 2 \\ &\Rightarrow \lambda = \frac{\ln 2}{4\ln(1.05)} \approx 3.552 \approx \begin{array}{l}\text{3 years, 6 months} \\ \text{and 19 days}\end{array} \end{aligned}$$

b. Applying the formula (3) with $n = 4$, $r = 0.2$ and $t = \lambda$, we have:

$$\begin{aligned} P\,\mathrm{e}^{0.2\lambda} = 2P &\Rightarrow \mathrm{e}^{0.2\lambda} = 2 \\ &\Rightarrow 0.2\lambda = \ln 2 \\ &\Rightarrow \lambda = \frac{\ln 2}{0.2} \approx 3.466 \text{ years} \approx \begin{array}{c}\text{3 years, 5 months} \\ \text{and 18 days.}\end{array} \end{aligned}$$

EXERCISES 4.8

1. **(Population growth).** The population of a city, t years after 2000, is:

$$P(t) = 60,000\,\mathrm{e}^{0.05t} \text{ inhabitants}$$

   a. Compute the population of the city at the end of the year 2015.

   b. Find the annual percentage of growth of the population.

2. **(Depreciation).** The value of a machine, t years after it was bought, is:

$$V(t) = A\,\mathrm{e}^{-0.25t}$$

   The machine was bought 9 years ago for \$150,000.

   a. How much is it worth today?

   b. Find the annual percentage of depreciation of its value.

3. **(Population growth).** The population of a country in t years will be:

$$P(t) = 18\,\mathrm{e}^{0.02t} \text{ million of inhabitants.}$$

   a. What is the current population of the country?

   b. Find the population after 15 years.

   c. Find the annual percentage of growth of the population.

4. **(Bacterial population growth).** An experiment to study a bacterial population growth started with 4,000 bacteria. 10 minutes later, they were 12,000. If the growth is given by the function $f(t) = A\,\mathrm{e}^{kt}$, find the number of bacteria after 30 minutes?

5. **(Profits growth).** The profits of a company increase exponentially according to the function $f(t) = A\,\mathrm{e}^{kt}$. In 1995 they reached the value of 3 millions of dollars, and 4.5 million dollars by the year 2000. Find the profits by the year 2005.

6. **(Radioactive Decay).** The quantity $Q(t)$ of a radioactive substance that remains after t years is given by:

$$Q(t) = A\,\mathrm{e}^{-0.00015t} \text{ grams}$$

If there were 3,000 grams left after 5000 years, how many grams were there originally?

7. **(Radioactive decay).** A radioactive substance decays according to the function $f(t) = A\,\mathrm{e}^{-kt}$. Originally, they were 450 grams; 60 years later, there were 400 grams. Find the amount, in grams, after 240 years.

8. **(National product).** The national product (N.P.) of a certain country, t years after 1995, is $f(t)$ million dollars, where:

$$f(t) = P(10)^{kt}\text{ ,}P \text{ and } k \text{ are constants}$$

In 1995 the N.P. was 8,000 million dollars, and it was 16,000 million dollars by the year 2000. Find the N.P. by the year 2010.

9. **(Atmospheric pressure).** Atmospheric pressure is $P(h)$ pounds per square feet at an altitude of h feet above sea level, where:

$$P(h) = M\,\mathrm{e}^{-0.00003h},\ M \text{ is a constant}$$

If the atmospheric pressure at sea level is 2,116 pounds per square feet, find the atmospheric pressure outside a plane flying at an altitude of 12,000 feet.

10. **(Light bulb life).** A light bulb manufacturer discovers that the share $f(t)$ of bulbs that still work after t months of use is given by:

$$f(t) = \mathrm{e}^{-0.2t}$$

   a. What percentage of light bulbs last at least 1 month?

   b. What percentage of light bulbs last at least 2 months?

   c. What percentage of light bulbs fail during the second month?

11. **(Product sales).** A transnational company knows that if they give away x thousand of free products to influencers, the sales will be given by:

$$V(x) = 30 - 18\,\mathrm{e}^{-0.3x} \text{ thousand of products sold}$$

   a. Find the number of products sold if they don't distribute any free product to influencers.

   b. Find the number of products sold if they distribute 800 free products to influencers.

12. (Depreciation). The value of a machine after t years of use is:

$$V(t) = 520\,\mathrm{e}^{-0.15t} + 460 \text{ thousand dollars}$$

a. Sketch the graph of the function $V(t)$.

b. Find the value of the machine when it was brand new.

c. Find the value of the machine after 20 years of use.

13. (Radioactive decay). Q_0 is the initial amount of a radioactive substance, disintegrating according to $Q(t) = Q_0\,\mathrm{e}^{-kt}$. The half-life of the substance is λ time units (years, months, hours, etc.). Prove that $Q(t)$, the amount that remains after t time units, is:

$$Q(t) = Q_0\,\mathrm{e}^{-\left(\frac{\ln 2}{\lambda}\right)t}$$

14. (Radioactive decay). The radium is a radioactive element with a half-life of 1,690 years. How long will it take for 200 grams of radium to be reduced to 40 grams?.
Hint: See the previous problem.

15. (Blood alcohol level). After consuming whiskey, the blood alcohol level of a bus-driver is 0.4 milligrams per milliliter (mg/ml). The blood alcohol level decreases according to the function:

$$f(t) = (0.4)\left(\frac{1}{2}\right)^t,$$

where t is the number of hours elapsed since he reached the above level. The legal limit to drive a vehicle is 0.08 mg/ml. How long will the bus-driver have to wait for driving without breaking the law?

16. (Estimation of the amount). An amount of 12 million dollars is invested at interest rate of 14% per year, compounding continuously. Find the time needed to obtain 21 million.

17. (Subscribers). Two Youtube channels compete for subscribers from a specific audience. One of them has 500,000 subscribers and is growing at a monthly rate of 1.5%. The other one has 900,000 subscribers and is decreasing at a monthly rate of 0.5%. How long will it take for both channels to have the same number of subscribers?

18. (Book sales). A new Data Science book will be in the market soon. It is expected that if x thousands of copies are delivered to the teachers, as presents, the sales in the first year will be $f(x) = 12 - 5\,\mathrm{e}^{-0.2x}$ thousands of copies. How many copies will have to be given as presents to sell 9,000 copies in the first year?

19. (**National product**). The national product (N.P.) of a country grows exponentially. In 1995 it was 60,000 million, and it was 70,000 million by the year 2000. Find the N.P. of 2005.

20. (**World population forecast**). The world population was 4,917 million in 1986, and it grows at a rate of 1.65% annually. If the rate keeps constant, how many years will it take for the world population to reach 8,000 millions?

21. (**Age of a fossil**). An archaeologist estimated that the amount of ^{14}C in a fossilized tree trunk represents a quarter of the amount of ^{14}C in present-day trees. Find the age of the fossilized tree trunk.

22. (**Estimation of the amount**). An investment of $\$7,500,000$ is made at a annual rate of 28%. Find the balance in the account after 2 years, if the interest:

- **a.** is simple.
- **b.** is compounding annually.
- **c.** is compounding quarterly (every 3 months).
- **d.** is compounding monthly.
- **e.** is compounded continuously.

23. (**Estimation of the principal**). How much money invested will produce $\$2,500,000$ in 5 years if the rate is 16% annually, and is compounded:

a. quarterly?. **b.** continuously?.

24. (**Estimation of the amount**). In 1626, the Dutch colonial governor, Peter Minuit, bought the Manhattan Island (New York) from the Native Americans, for a mere 24 dollars. Assume that the natives invested those 24 dollars in a bank at a annual rate of 5% compounding continuously. How much money would they have had by the year 2000?

25. (**Time to double an investment**). How long will it take for an investment to double in value if the interest rate is 15% per year, compounding:

a. semiannually?. **b.** continuously?.

26. (**Time to triple an investment**) How long will it take for an investment to triple in value if the interest rate is 15% per year, compounding:

a. semiannually?. **b.** continuously?.

HELP TABLES

ALGEBRA

EXPONENTS AND RADICALS

1. $a^0 = 1,\ a \neq 0$ **2.** $(ab)^x = a^x b^x$ **3.** $a^x a^y = a^{x+y}$

4. $\frac{a^x}{a^y} = a^{x-y}$ **5.** $(a^x)^y = a^{xy}$ **6.** $a^{-x} = \frac{1}{a^x}$

7. $\left(\frac{a}{b}\right)^x = \frac{a^x}{b^x}$ **8.** $a^{\frac{1}{n}} = \sqrt[n]{a}$ **9.** $a^{\frac{m}{n}} = \sqrt[n]{a^m} = \left(\sqrt[n]{a}\right)^m$

10. $\sqrt[n]{ab} = \sqrt[n]{a}\,\sqrt[n]{b}$ **11.** $\sqrt[n]{\frac{a}{b}} = \frac{\sqrt[n]{a}}{\sqrt[n]{b}}$

THE BINOMIAL THEOREM

13. $(a \pm b)^2 = a^2 \pm 2ab + b^2$ **14.** $(a \pm b)^3 = a^3 \pm 3a^2 b + 3ab^2 \pm b^3$

15. $(a+b)^n = a^n + na^{n-1}b + \frac{n(n-1)}{2}a^{n-2}b^2 + \cdots + \binom{n}{k} a^{n-k}b^k + \cdots + na^{n-1}b + b^n$

16. $(a-b)^n = a^n - na^{n-1}b + \frac{n(n-1)}{2}a^{n-2}b^2 + \cdots + (-1)^k \binom{n}{k} a^{n-k}b^k + \cdots - na^{n-1}b + (-1)^n b^n$, where $\binom{n}{k} = \frac{n(n-1)(n-2)\ldots(n-k+1)}{k!}$

GEOMETRIC PROGRESSIONS

17. $a_1 = a,\ a_2 = ar,\ a_3 = ar^2,\ a_4 = ar^3, \ldots,\ a_n = ar^{n-1}$

$$S_n = \sum_{k=1}^{n} a_k = a\frac{1-r^n}{1-r}$$

FACTORING FORMULAS

18. $a^2 - b^2 = (a+b)(a-b)$ **19.** $a^2 \pm 2ab + b^2 = (a \pm b)^2$

20. $a^3 + b^3 = (a+b)\left(a^2 - ab + b^2\right)$ **21.** $a^3 - b^3 = (a-b)\left(a^2 + ab + b^2\right)$

INEQUALITIES AND ABSOLUTE VALUE

22. $a < b \Rightarrow a + c < b + c$ **23.** $a < b$ y $c > 0 \Rightarrow ac < bc$

24. $a < b$ y $c < 0 \Rightarrow ac > bc$ **25.** $|x| = a \Leftrightarrow x = a$ ó $x = -a$

26. $|x| < a \Leftrightarrow -a < x < a$ **27.** $|x| > a \Leftrightarrow -a < x$ ó $x > a$

GEOMETRY

h = Height, A = Area, AL = Lateral Area, V = Volume

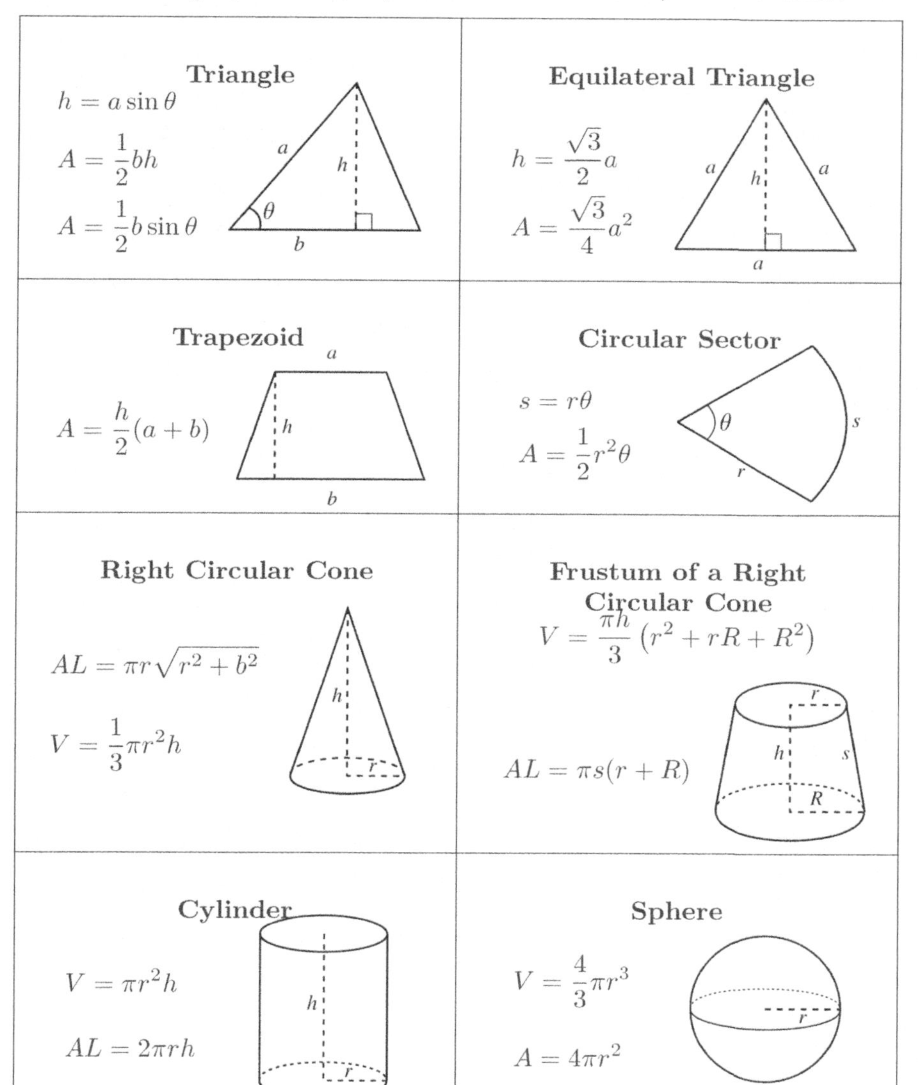

TRIGONOMETRY

TRIGONOMETRIC RATIOS

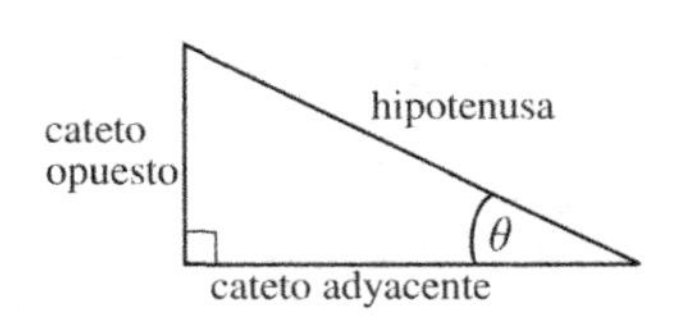

$$\sin\theta = \frac{\text{opposite side}}{\text{hypotenuse}}$$
$$\cos\theta = \frac{\text{adjacent side}}{\text{hypotenuse}}$$
$$\tan\theta = \frac{\text{opposite side}}{\text{adjacent side}}$$

Fundamental Identities

1. $\sec x = \dfrac{1}{\cos x}$ **2.** $\csc x = \dfrac{1}{\sin x}$ **3.** $\tan x = \dfrac{\sin x}{\cos x}$

4. $\cot x = \dfrac{\cos x}{\sin x}$ **5.** $\sin^2 x + \cos^2 x = 1$ **6.** $1 + \tan^2 x = \sec^2 x$

7. $1 + \cot^2 x = \csc^2 x$ **8.** $\sin(-x) = -\sin x$ **9.** $\cos(-x) = \cos x$

10. $\tan(-x) = -\tan x$

Cofunction and Reduction Identities

11. $\sin\left(\frac{\pi}{2} - x\right) = \cos x$ **12.** $\cos\left(\frac{\pi}{2} - x\right) = \sin x$

13. $\tan\left(\frac{\pi}{2} - x\right) = \cot x$ **14.** $\cot\left(\frac{\pi}{2} - x\right) = \tan x$

15. $\sec\left(\frac{\pi}{2} - x\right) = \csc x$ **16.** $\csc\left(\frac{\pi}{2} - x\right) = \sec x$

17. $\sin\left(\frac{\pi}{2} + x\right) = \cos x$ **18.** $\cos\left(\frac{\pi}{2} + x\right) = -\sin x$

19. $\tan\left(\frac{\pi}{2} + x\right) = -\cot x$ **20.** $\cos(x + \pi) = -\cos x$

21. $\sin(x + \pi) = -\sin x$ **22.** $\tan(x + \pi) = \tan x$

Sum and Difference Identities

23. $\sin(x \pm y) = \sin x \cos y \pm \cos x \sin y$

24. $\cos(x \pm y) = \cos x \cos y \mp \sin x \sin y$

25. $\tan(x \pm y) = \dfrac{\tan x \pm \tan y}{1 \mp \tan x \tan y}$ **26.** $\cot(x \pm y) = \dfrac{\cot x \cot y \mp 1}{\cot y \pm \cot x}$

Double-Angle and Triple-Angle Identities

27. $\sin 2x = 2\sin x \cos x$

28. $\cos 2x = \cos^2 x - \sin^2 x = 1 - 2\sin^2 x = 2\cos^2 x - 1$

29. $\sin 3x = 3\sin x - 4\sin^3 x$ **30.** $\cos 3x = 4\cos^3 x - 3\cos x$

31. $\tan 2x = \dfrac{2\tan x}{1 - \tan x}$

Power-Reducing Identities

32. $\sin^2 x = \frac{1-\cos 2x}{2}$ **33.** $\cos^2 x = \frac{1+\cos 2x}{2}$ **34.** $\tan^2 x = \frac{1-\cos 2x}{1+\cos 2x}$

Half-Angle Identities

35. $\sin \frac{x}{2} = \pm\sqrt{\dfrac{1-\cos x}{2}}$ **36.** $\cos \frac{x}{2} = \pm\sqrt{\dfrac{1+\cos x}{2}}$

Product-to-Sum Identities

37. $\sin x \cos y = \dfrac{1}{2}[\sin(x+y) + \sin(x-y)]$

38. $\cos x \cos y = \dfrac{1}{2}[\cos(x+y) + \cos(x-y)]$

39. $\sin x \sin y = \dfrac{1}{2}[\cos(x-y) - \cos(x+y)]$

Sum-Product Identities

40. $\sin x + \sin y = 2\sin \frac{x+y}{2} \cos \frac{x-y}{2}$

41. $\sin x - \sin y = 2\cos \frac{x+y}{2} \sin \frac{x-y}{2}$

42. $\cos x + \cos y = 2\cos \frac{x+y}{2} \cos \frac{x-y}{2}$

43. $\cos x - \cos y = -2\sin \frac{x+y}{2} \sin \frac{x-y}{2}$

Law of Sines

44. $\dfrac{\sin A}{a} = \dfrac{\sin B}{b} = \dfrac{\sin C}{c}$

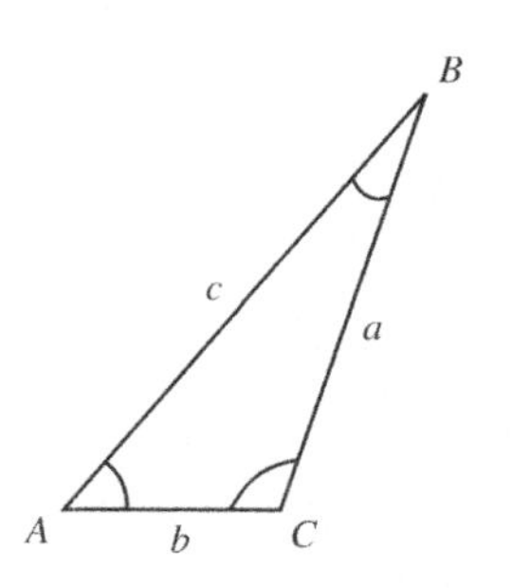

Law of Cosines

45. $a^2 = b^2 + c^2 - 2bc\cos A$

46. $b^2 = a^2 + c^2 - 2ac\cos B$

47. $c^2 = a^2 + b^2 - 2ab\cos C$

SPECIAL VALUES OF THE TRIGONOMETRIC FUNCTIONS

Degrees	Radians	$\sin\theta$	$\cos\theta$	$\tan\theta$	$\cot\theta$	$\sec\theta$	$\csc\theta$
$0°$	0	0	1	0	$\mp\infty$	1	$\mp\infty$
$30°$	$\frac{\pi}{6}$	$\frac{1}{2}$	$\frac{\sqrt{3}}{2}$	$\frac{\sqrt{3}}{3}$	$\sqrt{3}$	$\frac{2\sqrt{3}}{3}$	2
$45°$	$\frac{\pi}{4}$	$\frac{\sqrt{2}}{2}$	$\frac{\sqrt{2}}{2}$	1	1	$\sqrt{2}$	$\sqrt{2}$
$60°$	$\frac{\pi}{3}$	$\frac{\sqrt{3}}{2}$	$\frac{1}{2}$	$\sqrt{3}$	$\frac{\sqrt{3}}{3}$	2	$\frac{2\sqrt{3}}{3}$
$90°$	$\frac{\pi}{2}$	1	0	$\pm\infty$	0	$\pm\infty$	1
$120°$	$\frac{2\pi}{3}$	$\frac{\sqrt{3}}{2}$	$-\frac{1}{2}$	$-\sqrt{3}$	$-\frac{\sqrt{3}}{3}$	-2	$\frac{2\sqrt{3}}{3}$
$135°$	$\frac{3\pi}{4}$	$\frac{\sqrt{2}}{2}$	$-\frac{\sqrt{2}}{2}$	-1	-1	$-\sqrt{2}$	$\sqrt{2}$
$150°$	$\frac{5\pi}{6}$	$\frac{1}{2}$	$-\frac{\sqrt{3}}{2}$	$\frac{\sqrt{3}}{3}$	$-\sqrt{3}$	$-\frac{2\sqrt{3}}{3}$	2
$180°$	π	0	-1	0	$\mp\infty$	-1	$\pm\infty$
$210°$	$\frac{7\pi}{6}$	$-\frac{1}{2}$	$-\frac{\sqrt{3}}{2}$	$\frac{\sqrt{3}}{3}$	$\sqrt{3}$	$-\frac{2\sqrt{3}}{3}$	-2
$225°$	$\frac{5\pi}{4}$	$-\frac{\sqrt{2}}{2}$	$-\frac{\sqrt{2}}{2}$	1	1	$-\sqrt{2}$	$-\sqrt{2}$
$240°$	$\frac{4\pi}{3}$	$-\frac{\sqrt{3}}{2}$	$-\frac{1}{2}$	$\sqrt{3}$	$\frac{\sqrt{3}}{3}$	-2	$-\frac{2\sqrt{3}}{3}$
$270°$	$\frac{3\pi}{2}$	-1	0	$\pm\infty$	0	$\mp\infty$	-1
$300°$	$\frac{5\pi}{3}$	$-\frac{\sqrt{3}}{2}$	$\frac{1}{2}$	$-\sqrt{3}$	$-\frac{\sqrt{3}}{3}$	2	$-\frac{2\sqrt{3}}{3}$
$315°$	$\frac{7\pi}{4}$	$-\frac{\sqrt{2}}{2}$	$\frac{\sqrt{2}}{2}$	-1	-1	$\sqrt{2}$	$-\sqrt{2}$
$330°$	$\frac{11\pi}{6}$	$-\frac{1}{2}$	$\frac{\sqrt{3}}{2}$	$-\frac{\sqrt{3}}{3}$	$-\sqrt{3}$	$\frac{2\sqrt{3}}{3}$	-2
$360°$	2π	0	1	0	$\mp\infty$	1	$\mp\infty$

ANSWERS

Chapter 1

SECTION 1.1

1. **a.** $\{1,9\}$ **b.** $A=\{2,4,6,8\}$ **c.** $\{2,5,7\}$ **d.** $\{3,4,5,6,7\}$
2. $A=\{0,5,7,8,9\}$, $B=\{0,1,2,3,4,5,8\}$
3. $A=\{0,3,4,8,9\}$, $B=\{1,3,5,6,9\}$
4. $A=\{0,2,3,6\}$, $B=\{0,1,2,6,8,9\}$, $C=\{0,1,3,5,6,9\}$, $U=\{0,1,3,4,5,6,8,9\}$

SECTION 1.2

1. $-x^2+8x-3$ **2.** $2a^2-18a$ **3.** $1+\frac{3}{a}$ **4.** $1-\frac{4}{b}$
5. $\frac{1}{a}-\frac{1}{b}$ **6.** $-\frac{2}{b}+\frac{5}{a}$ **7.** $\frac{4}{5}$ **8.** $\frac{1}{2}$
9. $6b^2$ **10.** $\frac{6a}{5b}$ **11.** $-\frac{5x}{24y}$ **12.** $\frac{5x+6}{10x^2}$
13. $\frac{x(b+1)}{ab}$ **14.** $-\frac{7a}{b}$ **15.** $\frac{1}{3}$ **16.** $\frac{17}{24}$
17. $\frac{2}{35}$ **18.** $-\frac{3}{4}$ **19.** $-\frac{1}{90}$ **20.** $-\frac{1}{12}$
21. -7 **22.** $\frac{19}{10}$ **23.** 1 **24.** $-\frac{1}{5}$
25. $\frac{3}{2}$ **26.** $\frac{4}{9}$ **27.** $\frac{7b}{5a}$ **28.** $-\frac{5x}{18y}$
29. $2^{10}=1.034$ **30.** 1 **31.** $\frac{4}{3}$ **32.** $\frac{5}{6^2}$
33. $\frac{3}{2^4}=\frac{3}{16}$ **34.** $\frac{2^6}{3^6}=\frac{64}{729}$ **35.** $\frac{4}{5}+1=\frac{9}{5}$ **36.** $3\times 2^3=24$
37. $\frac{15}{4}$ **38.** $3\times 2^4=48$ **39.** $2\times 5^6=31.250$ **40.** $\frac{1}{3ab^7}$
41. $\frac{16}{x^2y^5}$ **42.** $-\frac{2^7y^{12}}{x^3}=-128\frac{y^{12}}{x^3}$ **43.** $\frac{3^2a^8}{b^6}=9\frac{a^8}{b^6}$
44. $\frac{y^{12}}{2^3x^6}=\frac{y^{12}}{8x^6}$ **45.** $\frac{1}{4}$ **46.** $\frac{a^2b^2}{b^2-a^2}$
47. $\frac{9x^3-2x}{21}$ **48.** $\frac{3}{4}x^2y$ **49.** $\frac{1}{2}$ **50.** $-\frac{9}{5x}$
51. **a.** $9.44\times 10^{12}\ km$ **b.** $4\times 10^{-13}\ cm$ **c.** 6.251×10^9 inhabitants **d.** $1.67\times 10^{-22}\ kg$
52. **a.** $462,400\ km$ **b.** $0.0000000000492\ m$

SECTION 1.3

1. 5 **2.** -0.3 **3.** $\frac{1}{0.4}=\frac{5}{2}$ **4.** $\frac{1}{2^2}=\frac{1}{4}$ **5.** $-\frac{3}{2}$
6. 125 **7.** 5 **8.** $\frac{1}{75}$ **9.** $\frac{2}{3}$ **10.** $\frac{108}{b}$
11. $\frac{81}{4y^4}$ **12.** $\frac{y^{10}}{x^{15}}$ **13.** $-\frac{2a}{3}$ **14.** $\frac{x^2}{y}$ **15.** $3\sqrt{5}$
16. $2\sqrt{7}-\sqrt{3}$ **17.** $-\sqrt{3}$ **18.** $\frac{1}{9}$ **19.** $3\sqrt[3]{5}$ **20.** $13\sqrt{3}$
21. $-3\sqrt{7}$ **22.** $7\sqrt{3}$ **23.** $-\frac{3}{4}\sqrt{6}$ **24.** $\frac{\sqrt{3}}{3}$ **25.** $\frac{5}{12}\sqrt[3]{2}$
26. $\frac{1}{4}$ **27.** $2^n\times 5^{3n}=250^n$ **28.** $n=\frac{13}{6}$
29. $n=\frac{1}{10}$ **30.** $n=3$

SECTION 1.4

1. $4x^2-5$ **2.** $4x-y$ **3.** $9x^4-16y^6$
4. h **5.** $x-\frac{1}{y^2}$ **6.** $a^2+b^2-c^2+2ab$

7. $16x^2+40x+25$ **8.** $4x^2-20xy+25y^2$ **9.** $x^2-2+\frac{1}{x^2}$
10. $x^6-2+\frac{1}{x^6}$ **11.** $64x^3+48x^2y+12xy^2+y^3$ **12.** $a^6+3a^4b^2+3a^2b^4+b^6$
13. $x^6-3x^4y+3x^2y^2-y^3$ **14.** $x+3\sqrt[3]{x^2y}+3\sqrt[3]{xy^2}+y$
15. x^4-50x^2+625 **16.** $16x^4-y^4$ **17.** $7x^2(x-9)$
18. $4xy^2z^2\left(2xz-6y-x^2y^2z\right)$ **19.** $(x-2)^2(x+2)$ **20.** $4(y+4)(y+3x)$
21. $(x-1)\left(xy^2+y^2-4\right)$ **22.** $(2x-5y)\left(a^2-3b\right)$ **23.** $(x+8)(x-4)$
24. $(x-5)(x+1)$ **25.** $(xy+29)(y-1)$ **26.** $(x+24)(x-9)$
27. $\left(x^2-10\right)\left(x^2+8\right)$ **28.** $(ab+4)(ab-3)$ **29.** $(3x+4)(x+1)$
30. $5(y+5)(y-3)$ **31.** $(ax+2)(5ax-6)$ **32.** $(3x-10)(3x+5)$
33. $y^2(x+2)(4x+3)$ **34.** $\left(5x^2-1\right)^2$ **35.** $\left(5x+6y^2\right)\left(5x-6y^2\right)$
36. $7x^2(3x+1)(3x-1)$ **37.** $5x^2(3y+x)(3y-x)$ **38.** $\left(\frac{x}{6}+\frac{y}{5}\right)\left(\frac{x}{6}-\frac{y}{5}\right)$
39. $\left(4x^n+\frac{1}{7}\right)\left(4x^n-\frac{1}{7}\right)$ **40.** $(a-b+3)(a-b-3)$ **41.** $4ab$
42. $(x+y-3)(x-y+1)$ **43.** $(x+y+3)(x-y-3)$ **44.** $(5a-b)(a-5b)$
45. $\left(a^2-1\right)^2$ **46.** $(4x-3y)^2$ **47.** $\left(20x^2+1\right)^2$
48. $\left(\frac{x}{3}+1\right)^2$ **49.** $\left(\frac{2x}{5}-\frac{1}{4}\right)^2$ **50.** $(2x-y)\left(4x^2+2xy+y^2\right)$
51. $(3a+4b)\left(9a^2-12ab+16b^2\right)$ **52.** $5(xy+1)\left(x^2y^2-xy+1\right)$
53. $x^2(x-5)\left(x^2+5x+25\right)$ **54.** $(x+y-1)\left(x^2+2xy+y^2+x+y+1\right)$
55. $(x-y-2)\left(x^2-2xy+y^2+2x-2y+4\right)$ **56.** $9\left(x^2-x+1\right)$
57. $4ab-3$ **58.** $-x$ **59.** $a-1$
60. $\frac{x-5}{x-2}$ **61.** $2x+4$ **62.** $\frac{x-1}{2x+2}$
63. $\frac{x-y}{x+y}$ **64.** $\frac{x-2y}{x^2+2xy+4y^2}$ **65.** $\frac{3-a}{9+3a+a^2}$
66. $\frac{1}{x-1}$ **67.** $\frac{4y+1}{y^2+6y}$ **68.** $\frac{x+y}{6+x}$
69. $-2-2\sqrt{2}$ **70.** $\sqrt{3+h}+\sqrt{3}$ **71.** $a\sqrt{a+1}+a\sqrt{a-1}$
72. $-\frac{21+9\sqrt{6}}{5}$ **73.** $\frac{x-\sqrt{ax}-2a}{x-4a}$ **74.** $\frac{\sqrt{x-3}+\sqrt{x-13}}{2}$
75. $\frac{\sqrt[3]{49}-\sqrt[3]{14}+\sqrt[3]{4}}{3}$ **76.** $8\sqrt[3]{x^2}+4\sqrt[3]{x}+2$
77. $8\sqrt[3]{(x-1)^2}-12\sqrt[3]{x^2-x}+18\sqrt[3]{x^2}$ **78.** $3\sqrt[3]{x}-3\sqrt[3]{3y}$
79. $\left(\sqrt{2-\sqrt[3]{x}}\right)\left(4+2\sqrt[3]{x}+\sqrt[3]{x^2}\right)$ **80.** $\sqrt{2\sqrt[3]{x^2}+\sqrt{2}x}-\sqrt{4\sqrt{x}+\sqrt{8}}$
81. $\frac{1}{3-\sqrt{5}}$ **82.** $\frac{1}{\sqrt{a+2}+\sqrt{a}}$ **83.** $\frac{1}{\sqrt{a-1+h}+\sqrt{a-1}}$
84. $\frac{5a^2-a}{a^2-1}$ **85.** $\frac{4xy}{x^2-y^2}$ **86.** $\frac{x+1}{x+3}$
87. $\frac{x-3}{x^2-1}$ **88.** $\frac{3x}{x^2-1}$ **89.** $\frac{3x^2+3x-24}{x^3-3x^2-9x-5}$
90. $\frac{x+2}{x^2+8x+7}$ **91.** $\frac{x^2y-x^3}{y^3-x^2y}$ **92.** $\frac{3x^2+2x}{x-4}$
93. $\frac{x-2}{a-1}$ **94.** $\frac{x^3+8y^3-3yx^2-6xy^2}{x^2-2xy-8y^2}$ **95.** $\frac{a^3-a^2b-6ab^2}{a^2b-4b^3}$
96. $\frac{x^3+x^2+x}{x+2}$ **97.** $\frac{5x^2+x}{2x+3}$ **98.** $\frac{x-1}{x}$
99. $\frac{3x-9}{x^2+2x}$ **100.** $\frac{b^2+ab+a^2}{b}$ **101.** x^2+6x
102. $\frac{y}{x}$ **103.** $\frac{x-1}{x^2+1}$ **104.** $\frac{a}{a^2+2}$

105. x^2+x+1 **106.** $\frac{a^2+ab+b^2}{a+b}$ **107.** $\frac{a^3}{a^2+b^2}$
108. x^2 **109.** $\frac{a+1}{a^2+5a-14}$

SECTION 1.5

1. $x=36$ **2.** $y=2$ **3.** $x=-\frac{5}{8}$ **4.** $x=2$
5. $x=13$ **6.** $z=-4$ **7.** $x=-2$ **8.** $x=3$
9. $x=-5$ **10.** $x=-7$ **11.** $x=2$ **12.** $x=-4$
13. $x=\frac{1}{2}$ **14.** $x=\frac{4}{5}$ **15.** $x=\frac{a}{a+5}$ **16.** $x=a$
17. $x=\frac{b-1}{2}$ **18.** $x=2a$ **19.** $x=a+b$ **20.** $x=2m$
21. $x=2$ **22.** $x=3b$ **23.** $s=\frac{A+\pi r^2}{\pi r}$ **24.** $a=\frac{S(I-r)}{1-r^n}$
25. $h=\frac{HS-f}{S}$ **26.** $x=\frac{ay}{y-a}$ **27.** $-2,\ 6$ **28.** 3
29. $-3,\ -8$ **30.** $1,\ \frac{1}{2}$ **31.** $2,\ -\frac{1}{9}$ **32.** $5,\ -\frac{1}{3}$
33. $-2,\ -\frac{3}{2}$ **34.** $3,\ -\frac{5}{6}$ **35.** $\frac{1}{4},\ \frac{1}{6}$ **36.** $8,-\frac{19}{4}$
37. $-1,\ 1,\ -4,\ 4$ **38.** $-\frac{1}{2},\ \frac{1}{2}$ **39.** $-27,\ 8$ **40.** $\frac{1}{8},\ -8$
41. $1-\frac{1}{3}\sqrt{5},\ 1+\frac{1}{3}\sqrt{5}$ **42.** $\frac{1}{2}\sqrt{3}$ **43.** $\frac{3}{4}-\frac{\sqrt{5}}{4},\ \frac{3}{4}+\frac{\sqrt{5}}{4}$ **44.** $-3\sqrt{5},\ 3\sqrt{5}$
45. $-a,\ a+2$ **46.** $a,\ 2$ **47.** $x=3$ **48.** $x=0$
49. $x=0$ **50.** $x=\frac{3}{8}$ **51.** 2 **52.** $1-\sqrt{2},\ 1+\sqrt{2}$
53. $2-\frac{1}{3}\sqrt{42},\ 2+\frac{1}{3}\sqrt{42}$ **54.** $\frac{5}{2}$ **55.** $1-\sqrt{2},\ 1+\sqrt{2}$ **56.** $-3-\sqrt{2},\ -3+\sqrt{2}$
57. $\frac{1}{3},\ -\frac{1}{5}$ **58.** $3,\ \frac{2}{5}$ **59.** $-1,\ \frac{5}{2}$ **60.** -1
61. 11 **62.** -10 **63.** 10 **64.** $y=7$
65. $x=3$ **66.** $z=9$ **67.** $x=2$ **68.** $\frac{1}{4}$
69. 2 **70.** 2 **71.** 4 **72.** 4
73. 1 **74.** 2 **75.** $\frac{9}{16}$ **76.** 2
77. $-4,\ -\frac{2}{5}$ **78.** $4,\ -\frac{11}{13}$ **79.** -4 **80.** -60
81. Roots: $1,\ -2,\ -1$; $(x-1)(x+2)(x+1)$
82. Roots: $1,\ 1+\sqrt{3},\ 1-\sqrt{3}$; $(x-1)\left(x-1-\sqrt{3}\right)\left(x-1+\sqrt{3}\right)$
83. Roots: $1,\ -\frac{3}{2},\ \frac{1}{2}$; $4(x-1)\left(x+\frac{3}{2}\right)\left(x-\frac{1}{2}\right)$
84. Roots: $-2,\ \frac{3}{2}+\frac{\sqrt{7}}{2},\ \frac{3}{2}-\frac{\sqrt{7}}{2}$; $2(x+2)\left(x-\frac{3}{2}+\frac{\sqrt{7}}{2}\right)\left(x-\frac{3}{2}-\frac{\sqrt{7}}{2}\right)$
85. Roots: $-1,\ 2,\ \sqrt{3},\ -\sqrt{3}$; $(x+1)(x-2)\left(x-\sqrt{3}\right)\left(x+\sqrt{3}\right)$
86. Roots: $1,\ -1,\ -2,\ \frac{1}{3}$; $3(x-1)(x+1)(x+2)\left(x-\frac{1}{3}\right)$
87. Roots: $-1,\ -2,\ 1,\ 2,\ 3$; $(x+1)(x+2)(x-1)(x-2)(x-3)$
88. Roots: $-1,\ -2,\ -3,\ 3$; $(x+1)^2(x+2)(x+3)(x-3)$

SECTION 1.6

1. $(-\infty,\ 4)$ **2.** $\left(-\infty,\ -\frac{32}{3}\right)$ **3.** $\left(\frac{17}{2},\ +\infty\right)$ **4.** $\left(-\infty,\ -\frac{43}{37}\right]$
5. $\left(\frac{17}{5},\ 19\right]$ **6.** $(-19,\ -9)$ **7.** $(-2,\ 3)$ **8.** $(-1,\ 1)$
9. $\left(-\infty,\ -1-\sqrt{21}\right]\cup\left[-1+\sqrt{21},\ +\infty\right)$ **10.** $(-\infty,\ -3)\cup\left(\frac{1}{2},\ +\infty\right)$

11. $\left(-\infty, \frac{1}{3}\right) \cup \left(\frac{2}{3}, +\infty\right)$ **12.** $(3, 4)$ **13.** $[-3, -2] \cup [1, +\infty)$
14. $(-2, 2]$ **15.** $\left[-\frac{10}{3}, 0\right)$ **16.** $\left[\frac{1}{3}, 1\right)$ **17.** $(-\infty, -2] \cup (0, 2]$
18. $\left(-\infty, -1-\sqrt{3}\right] \cup \left(-1, -1+\sqrt{3}\right]$ **19.** $(-3, -1] \cup (0, +\infty)$
20. $(-\infty, -2) \cup (1, +\infty)$ **21.** $\left(2-2\sqrt{3}, 0\right) \cup \left(3, 2+2\sqrt{3}\right)$
22. $41 \leq F \leq 68$ **23.** $15 \leq C \leq 35$ **24.** $6\ cm$

SECTION 1.7

1. $9, 1$ **2.** $-\frac{4}{3}, 2$ **3.** $\frac{7}{2}$ **4.** $\frac{11}{4}$ **5.** -1
6. $\frac{5}{3}, 3$ **7.** $-6, 2$ **8.** $\frac{1}{4}, 1$ **9.** $-2, \frac{8}{3}$ **10.** $(1, 7)$
11. $\left(-\frac{16}{3}, \frac{14}{3}\right)$ **12.** $\left(-\frac{3}{2}, \frac{9}{2}\right)$ **13.** $\left[-2, \frac{2}{3}\right]$ **14.** $\left(-\infty, -\frac{3}{5}\right] \cup \left[-\frac{1}{5}, +\infty\right)$
15. $(-\infty, -1) \cup \left(-\frac{1}{2}, +\infty\right)$ **16.** $\left(-\infty, -\frac{5}{2}\right] \cup \left[\frac{25}{2} + \infty\right)$
17. $[-\infty, -3] \cup [-1, 1] \cup [3, +\infty)$ **18.** $[-4, -1) \cup (1, 4]$ **19.** $(2, 4) - \{3\}$
20. $\left(\frac{1}{2}, +\infty\right)$ **21.** $\left[\frac{2}{3}, 4\right]$ **22.** $[-1, 2] - \left\{\frac{1}{2}\right\}$ **23.** $(-\infty, 1) \cup (2, +\infty)$
24. $[-2, 2]$ **25.** $(-1, 0) \cup (0, +\infty)$ **26.** $(-\infty, -7] \cup \left[\frac{1}{3}, +\infty\right)$
27. $M = 43$ **28.** $M = 9$ **29.** $M = 10$

Chapter 2

SECTION 2.1

1. $\sqrt{5}$, $\left(\frac{1}{2}, 1\right)$ **2.** $2\sqrt{2}$, $(2, 4)$ **3.** $\sqrt{7-2\sqrt{2}}$, $\left(0, \frac{1+\sqrt{2}}{2}\right)$
5. $B = (3, 9)$ **6.** $A = (-1, 18)$ **13.** $(2, 2)$ y $(-4, 2)$
14. $(1, 13)$ and $(1, -11)$ **15.** $5x + 2y - 3 = 0$ **16.** $x^2 + y^2 = 9$
17. $(1, -3)$, $(3, 1)$, $(-5, 7)$ **18.** $(-2, -5)$, $(0, -9)$ **19.** $\left(\frac{9}{2}, 1\right)$

SECTION 2.2

1. Y-axis
2. Origin
3. X-axis, Y-axis and Origin
4. X-axis, Y-axis and Origin
5. X-axis
6. X-axis
7. X-axis, Y-axis and Origin
8. $(x-2)^2 + (y+1)^2 = 25$
9. $(x+3)^2 + (y-2)^2 = 5$
10. $x^2 + y^2 = 25$
11. $(x-1)^2 + (y+1)^2 = 50$
12. $(x-1)^2 + (y+3)^2 = 9$
13. $(x+4)^2 + (y-1)^2 = 16$
14. $(x-3)^2 + (y-1)^2 = 10$
15. $(x-1)^2 + y^2 = 1$
16. $(x-3)^2 + (y-4)^2 = 25$
17. Center $(1, 0)$, $r = 2$
18. Center $(0, -2)$, $r = 2\sqrt{2}$
19. Center $\left(0, -\frac{1}{2}\right)$, $r = \frac{1}{2}$
20. Center $(1, -2)$, $r = 3$
21. Center $\left(\frac{1}{4}, -\frac{1}{4}\right)$, $r = \frac{\sqrt{10}}{4}$
22. Center $\left(\frac{3}{2}, \frac{1}{2}\right)$, $r = \frac{9}{4}$

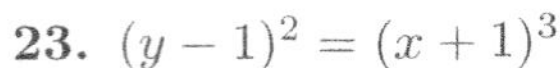

23. $(y-1)^2 = (x+1)^3$

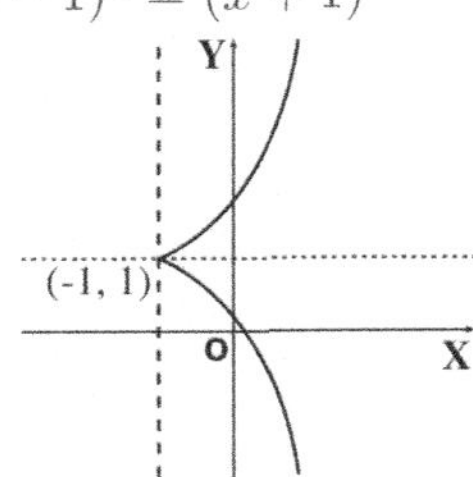

24. $(x-1)^2 = (y+1)^3$

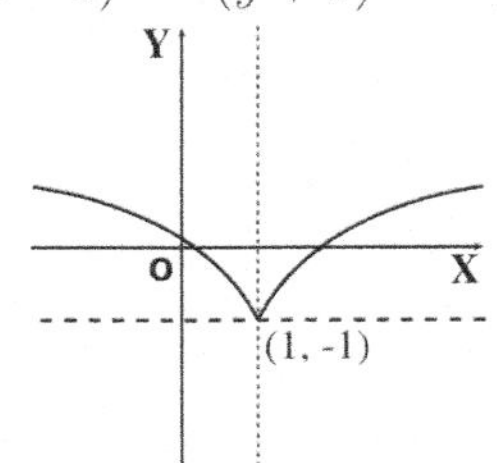

25. $(y+1)^2 = (x-1)^3$

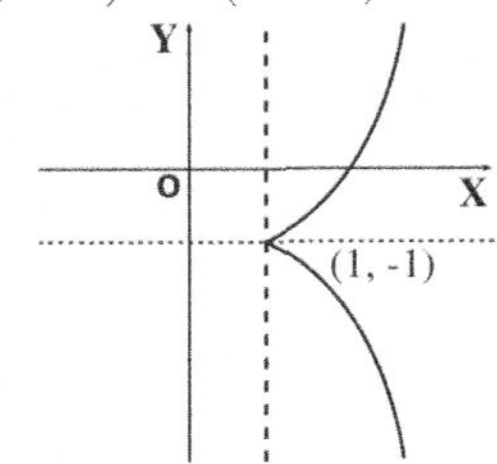

26. $(x-3)^2(y-2) = 4\,(2-(y-2))$

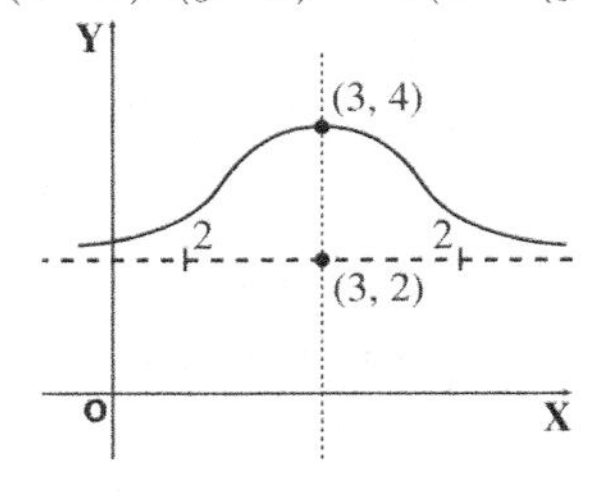

27. $(y-3)^2(x-2) = 4\,(2-(x-2))$

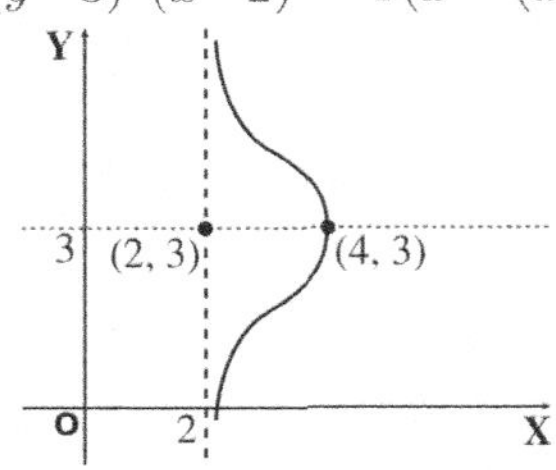

28. $(x+3)^2(y+2) = 4\,(2-(y+2))$

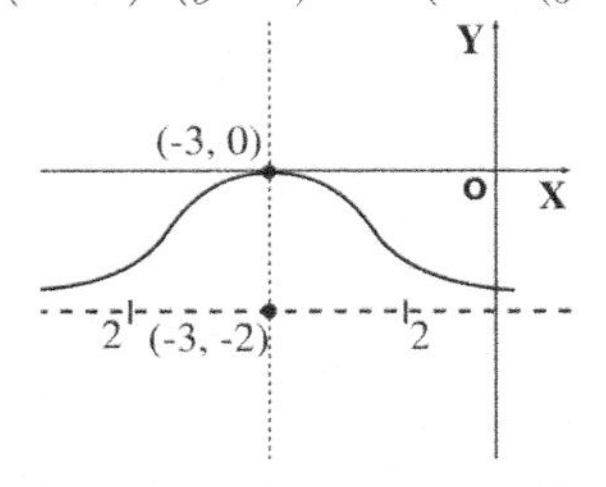

SECTION 2.3

2. $y = 5x - 2$ **3.** $y = -3x$ **4.** $y = 2x - 1$ **5.** $y = -\frac{2}{5}x + 2$

6. $y = -\frac{3}{5}x + \frac{18}{5}$ **7.** $y = \frac{x}{5} + \frac{11}{5}$ **8.** $y = -2x + \frac{41}{23}$ **9.** $x + y = 2$; $x - y = 14$

10. **a.** $y = -\frac{x}{2} + \frac{3}{2}$
b. $\frac{9\sqrt{5}}{10}$

11. 5

12. L_2 is parallel to L_5;
L_3 is perpendicular to L_1;
L_4 is perpendicular to L_6

13. **a.** $x - 3y - 6 = 0$
b. $x + 2y - 13 = 0$
c. $y = 1$

14. $y + 3x - 25 = 0$ **15.** 3 **16.** 2

17. $\frac{2}{\sqrt{10}}$ **18.** 2 **19.** $\frac{4\sqrt{10}}{5}$ **20.** $\frac{28}{5}$

21. $C = -7$ ó $C = \frac{59}{3}$ **22.** $5x + 12y + 40 = 0$; $5x + 12y - 64 = 0$

23. $3x - 4y + 7 = 0$ **24.** $5x - 3y - 34 = 0$; $3x + 5y + 34 = 0$

25. $(5, -3)$ y $(-3, -5)$ **26.** $x - y - 3\sqrt{2} = 0$; $x - y + 3\sqrt{2} = 0$

27. $3x + 4y - 14 = 0$ **28.** $(x-1)^2 + (y+1)^2 = 9$ **29.** $x^2 + y^2 = 16$

30. $(x-2)^2 + (y-4)^2 = 10$ **31.** $(x+2)^2 + (y+1)^2 = 20$

32. $3x - 2y - 12 = 0$; $3x - 8y + 24 = 0$

33. **a.** $k \neq 3$, any n **b.** $k = -\frac{4}{3}$, any n **c.** $k = 3$, $n \neq 6$
d. $k = 3$, $n = 6$

34. **a.** $k = -4$ and $n \neq 2$ or $k = 4$ and $n \neq -2$ **c.** $k = 0$ and any n
b. $k = -4$ and $n = 2$ or $k = 4$ and $n = -2$

35. $x - 2y - 18 = 0$; $2x + y + 14 = 0$; $2x + y - 16 = 0$

38. $A = \left(0, \frac{14}{5}\right)$, $B = \left(\frac{7}{4}, 0\right)$

Chapter 3

SECTION 3.2

1. $F = (0, 1)$, $y = -1$, $L = 4$

2. $F = \left(0, -\frac{1}{3}\right)$, $y = \frac{1}{3}$, $L = \frac{4}{3}$

3. $F = \left(\frac{3}{2}, 0\right)$, $x = -\frac{3}{2}$, $L = 6$

4. $F = (-5, 0)$, $x = 5$, $L = 20$

5. $F = \left(-\frac{1}{16}, 0\right)$, $x = \frac{1}{16}$, $L = \frac{1}{4}$

6. $V = \left(1, \frac{11}{8}\right)$, $x = 1$, $F = \left(1, \frac{27}{8}\right)$, $y = -\frac{5}{8}$, $L = 8$

7. $V = (1, -5)$, $y = -5$, $F = \left(\frac{5}{4}, -5\right)$, $x = \frac{3}{4}$, $L = 1$

8. $V = (-4, 2)$, $y = 2$, $F = \left(-\frac{7}{2}, 2\right)$, $x = -\frac{9}{2}$, $L = 2$

9. $V = \left(-\frac{1}{2}, 0\right)$, $x = -\frac{1}{2}$, $F = \left(-\frac{1}{2}, -\frac{1}{4}\right)$, $y = \frac{1}{4}$, $L = 1$

10. $V = \left(-\frac{4}{3}, -1\right)$, $x = -\frac{4}{3}$, $F = \left(-\frac{4}{3}, -3\right)$, $y = 1$, $L = 8$

11. $y^2 = -24x$

12. $x^2 = 16y$

13. $(x-2)^2 = 12(y-2)$

14. $2(y+2)^2 = x + 1$

15. $(y-2)^2 = -16(x+2)$

16. $(x+2)^2 = 16(y-2)$

17. $(x-3)^2 = 16(y-1)$

18. $2x^2 = -9y$

19. $(y-2)^2 = 9(x-1)$

20. $(x-1)^2 = 6(y+2)$ or $(x-1)^2 = -6(y+2)$

21. $(y-1)^2 = 8x$ or $(y-1)^2 = -8(x+4)$

22. $(x-4)^2 = 6\left(y + \frac{1}{2}\right)$

23. $x^2 = -8y$

24. **a.** $x^2 = -25y$ **b.** $40\,m$

25. $4.5\ cm$

26. $25\ cm$

27. **a.** $x^2 = 375(y-8)$ **b.** $17.6\ m$

28. **a.** $x^2 = -200(y-50)$ **b.** 45.5 feet

29. 15 millions of Km

30. $r = 1{,}303.5\ km$

31. $(y-1)^2 = 4(x-3)$

32. $\left(x - \frac{3}{4}\right)^2 = \frac{1}{2}\left(y - \frac{1}{8}\right)$

SECTION 3.3

1. $\frac{x^2}{36} + \frac{y^2}{32} = 1$

2. $\frac{x^2}{39} + \frac{y^2}{64} = 1$

3. $\frac{(x-4)^2}{4} + \frac{(y-2)^2}{3} = 1$

4. $\frac{(x+4)^2}{16} + \frac{(y-3)^2}{25} = 1$

5. $(x-3)^2 + \frac{(y-1)^2}{4} = 1$

6. $\frac{x^2}{25} + \frac{y^2}{9} = 1$

7. $\frac{(x+1)^2}{4} + \frac{y^2}{9} = 1$

8. $\frac{(x-2)^2}{\frac{1600}{91}} + \frac{y^2}{100} = 1$

9. $\frac{x^2}{9} + \frac{y^2}{5} = 1$

10. $\frac{(x+1)^2}{8} + \frac{(y+4)^2}{9} = 1$

11. $\frac{x^2}{36} + \frac{(y+1)^2}{27} = 1$

13. a. $\frac{(x-3)^2}{4} + \frac{(y+2)^2}{1} = 1$
b. Vertices: $(1, -2)$, $(5, -2)$. Foci: $\left(3-\sqrt{3}, -2\right), \left(3+\sqrt{3}, -2\right)$

14. a. $\frac{(x-1)^2}{4} + \frac{(y+3)^2}{9} = 1$
b. Vertices: $(1, -6)$, $(1, 0)$. Foci: $\left(1, -3-\sqrt{5}\right), \left(1, -3+\sqrt{5}\right)$

15. a. $\frac{(x+2)^2}{16} + \frac{(y-3)^2}{25} = 1$
b. Vertices: $(-2, -2)$, $(-2, 8)$. Foci: $(-2, 0)$, $(-2, 6)$

16. Yes. The tunnel height when $x = 9$ is 8, and $7.5 < 8$

17. $\frac{x^2}{(240)^2} + \frac{y^2}{(140)^2} = 1$ **18.** $\frac{x^2}{16} + \frac{y^2}{12} = 1$. Ellipse **19.** $\frac{x^2}{9} + \frac{y^2}{25} = 1$. Ellipse

20. a. $e = \frac{8}{17}$ **b.** $\frac{x^2}{18{,}062{,}500} + \frac{y^2}{14{,}062{,}500} = 1$

SECTION 3.4

1. $\frac{x^2}{25} - \frac{y^2}{24} = 1$ **2.** $\frac{x^2}{25} - \frac{y^2}{144} = 1$ **3.** $\frac{y^2}{4} - \frac{x^2}{32} = 1$ **4.** $\frac{y^2}{16} - \frac{x^2}{209} = 1$

5. $\frac{(x-3)^2}{9} - \frac{(y-2)^2}{16} = 1$ **6.** $\frac{(y+3)^2}{9} - \frac{(x+3)^2}{27} = 1$ **7.** $\frac{(x-2)^2}{4} - \frac{(y-2)^2}{5} = 1$

8. $\frac{x^2}{\frac{9}{5}} - \frac{y^2}{\frac{36}{5}} = 1$ **9.** $\frac{y^2}{50} - \frac{x^2}{8} = 1$ **10.** $\frac{y^2}{4} - \frac{x^2}{12} = 1$

11. $\frac{(x-4)^2}{2} - \frac{(y-2)^2}{2} = 1$ **12.** $\frac{(y-2)^2}{3} - \frac{\left(x-\frac{1}{2}\right)^2}{\frac{3}{4}} = 1$ **13.** $\frac{(y+2)^2}{9} - \frac{(x-3)^2}{36} = 1$

14. $\frac{(x-1)^2}{4} - \frac{(y-3)^2}{5} = 1$ **15.** $\frac{(y-1)^2}{9} - \frac{(x+2)^2}{3} = 1$

16. a. $\frac{(x-3)^2}{16} - \frac{(y-2)^2}{9} = 1$ **b.** $(-1, 2)$, $(7, 2)$ **c.** $(-2, 2)$, $(8, 2)$
d. $3x - 4y - 1 = 0$; $3x + 4y - 17 = 0$

17. a. $\frac{(y-2)^2}{4} - \frac{(x+4)^2}{9} = 1$ **b.** $(-4, 0)$, $(-4, 4)$
c. $\left(-4, 2-\sqrt{13}\right), \left(-4, 2+\sqrt{13}\right)$ **d.** $3y-2x-14 = 0$; $3y+2x+2 = 0$

18. a. $\frac{(x-1)^2}{4} - \frac{(y+3)^2}{64} = 1$ **b.** $(-1, -3)$, $(3, -3)$
c. $\left(1-2\sqrt{17}, -3\right), \left(1+2\sqrt{17}, -3\right)$ **d.** $y-4x+7 = 0$; $y+4x-1 = 0$

19. a. $\frac{(x-2)^2}{9} - \frac{(y-3)^2}{4} = 1$ **b.** $(-1, 3)$, $(5, 3)$
c. $\left(2-\sqrt{13}, 3\right), \left(2+\sqrt{13}, 3\right)$ **d.** $2x-3y+5 = 0$; $2x+3y-13 = 0$

20. a. $\frac{x^2}{3{,}600} - \frac{y^2}{6{,}400} = 1$ **b.** At 40 km from the station B. **c.** 0.0002 seg.

21. $\frac{x^2}{28{,}900} - \frac{y^2}{11{,}100} = 1$ **22.** $\frac{x^2}{3} - \frac{(y-1)^2}{1} = 1$

SECTION 3.5

1. $\left(-1, -\sqrt{3}\right)$ **2.** $\left(2\sqrt{2}, 4\sqrt{2}\right)$ **3.** $\left(-1, 3\sqrt{3}\right)$

4. $(4, -2)$ **5.** $\left(3, -3\sqrt{2}\right)$ **6.** $y'^2 - x'^2 = 1$, hyperbola

7. $\frac{y'^2}{10} - \frac{x'^2}{6} = 1$, hyperbola **8.** $\frac{x'^2}{2} + \frac{y'^2}{10} = 1$, Ellipse **9.** $y' = x'^2$, Parabola

10. a. $\frac{x'^2}{9} + \frac{y'^2}{3} = 1$ **b.** In X′Y′: $V_1 = (-3,\, 0)$, $V_2 = (3,\, 0)$.

In XY: $V_1 = \left(-\frac{3}{\sqrt{5}},\, -\frac{6}{\sqrt{5}}\right)$, $V_2 = \left(\frac{3}{\sqrt{5}},\, \frac{6}{\sqrt{5}}\right)$

c. In X′Y′: $F_1 = \left(-\sqrt{6},\, 0\right)$, $F_2 = \left(\sqrt{6},\, 0\right)$.

In XY: $F_1 = \left(-\sqrt{\frac{6}{5}},\, -2\sqrt{\frac{6}{5}}\right)$, $F_2 = \left(\sqrt{\frac{6}{5}},\, 2\sqrt{\frac{6}{5}}\right)$

d. $2x - y = 0$ **e.** $x + 2y = 0$

11. a. $\frac{(x'-1)^2}{4} + \frac{(y'-2)^2}{1} = 1$

b. In X′Y′: $C = (1,\, 2)$, $V_1 = (-1,\, 2)$, $V_2 = (3,\, 2)$.

In XY: $C = \left(-\frac{2}{5},\, \frac{11}{5}\right)$, $V_1 = (-2,\, 1)$, $V_2 = \left(\frac{6}{5},\, \frac{17}{5}\right)$

c. In X′Y′: $F_1 = \left(1 - \sqrt{5},\, 2\right)$, $F_2 = \left(1 + \sqrt{5},\, 2\right)$

In XY: $F_1 = \left(-\frac{2+4\sqrt{5}}{5},\, \frac{11-3\sqrt{5}}{5}\right)$, $F_2 = \left(-\frac{2-4\sqrt{5}}{5},\, \frac{11+3\sqrt{5}}{5}\right)$

Chapter 4

SECTION 4.1

1. a. $\frac{3}{4}$ **b.** $\frac{1+\sqrt{2}}{2+\sqrt{2}}$ **c.** $\frac{h}{3(h+3)}$ **d.** $\frac{h}{(a+1)(a+h+1)}$

2. a. 2 **b.** $\frac{1}{4}a^2 + a + 2$ **c.** $\frac{h^2+2ah}{4}$

3. $\text{Dom}(f) = [9,\, +\infty)$, $\text{Rang}(f) = [0,\, +\infty)$

4. $\text{Dom}(g) = [-4,\, 4]$, $\text{Rang}(g) = \left[0,\, \frac{4}{3}\right]$

5. $\text{Dom}(h) = (-\infty,\, 2] \cup [2,\, +\infty)$, $\text{Rang}(h) = [0,\, +\infty)$

6. $\text{Dom}(u) = \text{Rang}(u) = \mathbb{R}$

7. $\text{Dom}(f) = \mathbb{R} - \{0\}$, $\text{Rang}(f) = \mathbb{R}$

8. $\text{Dom}(y) = (-\infty,\, 0] \cup [2,\, +\infty)$, $\text{Rang}(y) = [0,\, +\infty)$

9. $\text{Dom}(g) = (-\infty,\, 9] - \{5\}$

10. $\text{Dom}(y) = (-\infty,\, -2] \cup [2,\, +\infty) - \{-2\sqrt{2},\, 2\sqrt{2}\}$

11. $\text{Dom}(y) = (-\infty,\, 0) \cup \left[\frac{1}{4},\, +\infty\right)$

12. $\text{Dom}(y) = (-\infty,\, 1] - \{-15\}$

13. $\text{Dom}(y) = [-1,\, 2)$

14. $\text{Dom}(y) = (-\infty,\, 5] \cup (3,\, +\infty)$

15. $\text{Dom}(y) = \mathbb{R}$,
$\text{Rang}(y) = [0,\, 1]$

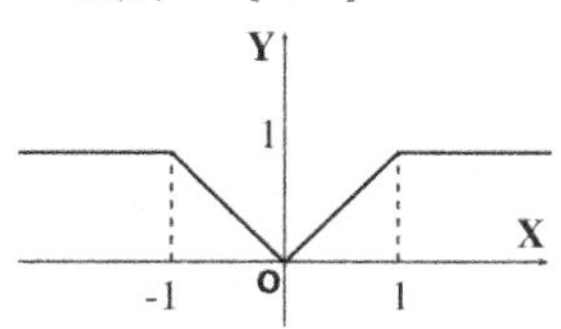

16. $\text{Dom}(y) = \mathbb{R}$,
$\text{Rang}(y) = [0,\, +\infty)$

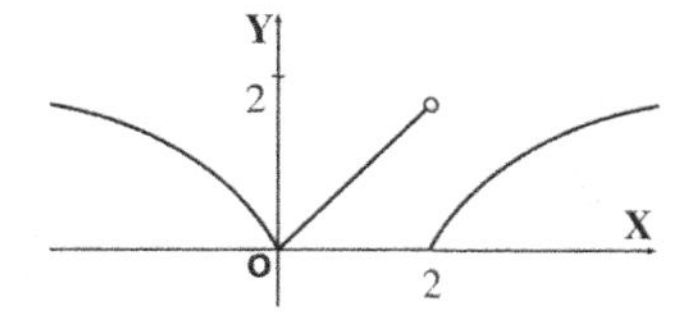

18. $f(x-1) = (x-5)^2$ **19.** $f(x) = \frac{1}{2}x^2 + \frac{1}{2}x$ **20.** $U(x) = 226x - 5x^2$

21. $G(x) = \begin{cases} 4,000x, & \text{si } 0 \le x \le 1,000 \\ 4,000,000 + (x - 1,000)(14,000 - 10x), & \text{si } x > 1,000 \end{cases}$

22. $P(x) = 1,760x - 10x^2$ **23.** $V(x) = x^2(150 - 2x)$

24. $A(r) = \pi r^2 + \frac{1}{4}(6 - \pi r)^2$ **25.** $A(x) = 6(18 - x)\sqrt{x - 9}$

26. $A(x) = \frac{x}{8}(28 - 4x - \pi x)$ **27.** $V(x) = 4x(40 - x)(25 - x)$

28. $A(x) = \frac{1}{x}(x + 4)(252 + 6x)$

SECTION 4.2

1. a. $-\frac{\sqrt{3}}{3}$ **b.** $-\frac{1}{2}$ **c.** $-\sqrt{3}$ **d.** $-\frac{2\sqrt{3}}{3}$ **e.** -2

2. a. $\alpha = n\pi,\ n \in \mathbb{Z}$ **b.** $\alpha = \frac{\pi}{2} + n\pi,\ n \in \mathbb{Z}$ **c.** none **d.** none **e.** $\alpha = \frac{4}{3}\pi + 2n\pi$ ó $\frac{5}{3}\pi + 2n\pi,\ n \in \mathbb{Z}$

6. -1

7. a. $-\sin\alpha$ **b.** 0

8. a. $\frac{2\pi}{\lambda}$ **b.** $\frac{\pi}{2}$

9. a. $\frac{1}{3}\,rad.$ **b.** $\frac{1}{10}\,rad$ **c.** $\frac{\pi}{3}\,rad$

10. a. $4.71\,cm$ **b.** $35.34\,cm$ **c.** $7.85\,cm$

11. a. $111.13\,km$ **b.** $3,333.76\,km$ **c.** $5,000.64\,km$ **d.** $8,973.37\,km$

12. $1,852\,km$ **13.** $\frac{3}{2}\pi\,rad$ **14.** $61.35°$ **15.** $22.5°$

16. $\left(-\sqrt{3},\,-1\right)$ **17.** $P = \left(-\frac{3}{2},\,\frac{3}{2}\sqrt{3}\right)$ **18.** 18

19. a. $\frac{\sqrt{3}}{3}$ **b.** $\frac{\sqrt{3}}{2}$ **20.** $\frac{\sqrt{3}}{12}$ **21.** $2r\sin\frac{\pi}{n}$

22. $\frac{2,500}{\pi} \approx 795.78\,revol/min$ **23.** $49\,revol./seg$

24. $P(\theta) = 20\left[\cos\frac{\theta}{2} + \cos\frac{\theta}{2}\sin\frac{\theta}{2}\right]$ **25.** $V(\theta) = \frac{125}{3\pi^2}\theta^2\sqrt{4\pi^2 - \theta^2}$

26. $y - x + 4\sqrt{2} = 0$ **27.** $\frac{\pi}{4}$ **28.** $x - 5y + 3 = 0;\ 5x + y - 11 = 0$

29. $3x - 4y + 15 = 0;\ 4x + 3y - 30 = 0;\ 3x - 4y - 10 = 0;\ 4x + 3y - 5 = 0$

SECTION 4.3

1. a. $y = x^3 - 3$ **b.** $y = (x - 1)^3$ **c.** $y = -x^3 + 1$ **d.** $-y = (x-1)^3 + 1$

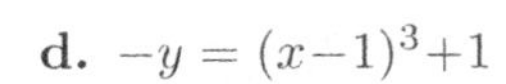

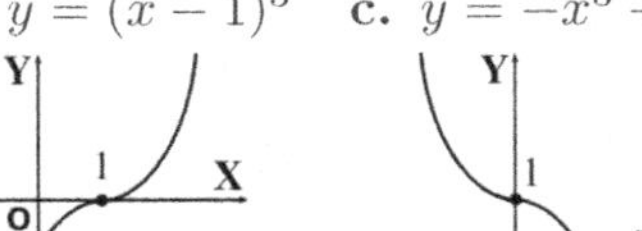

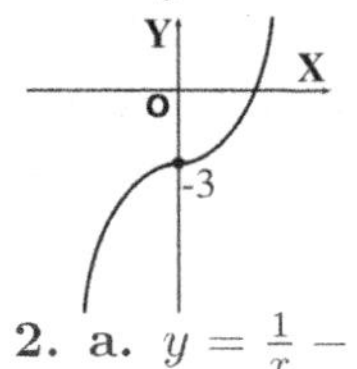

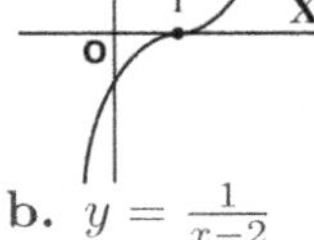

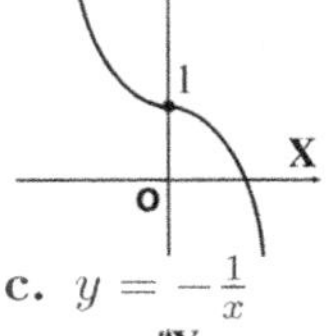

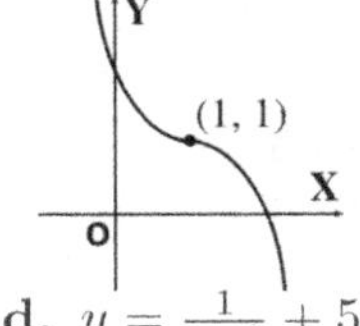

2. a. $y = \frac{1}{x} - 2$ **b.** $y = \frac{1}{x-2}$ **c.** $y = -\frac{1}{x}$ **d.** $y = \frac{1}{x-2} + 5$

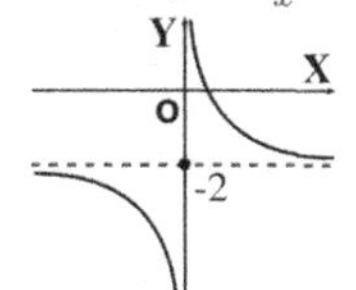

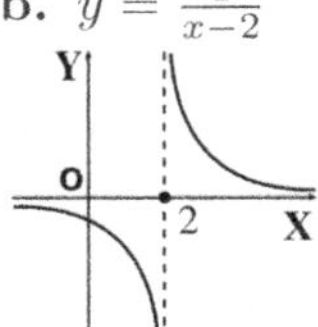

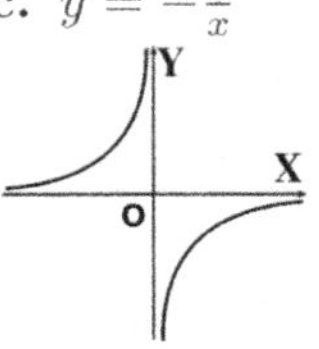

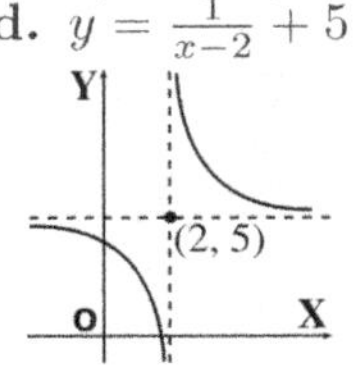

3. **a.** $y = -\lfloor x \rfloor$

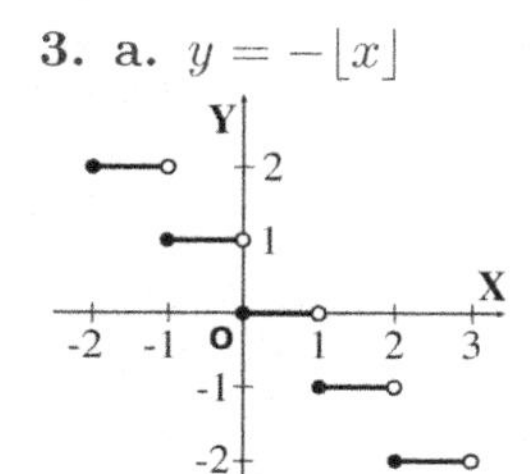

b. $y = \lfloor 2x \rfloor$

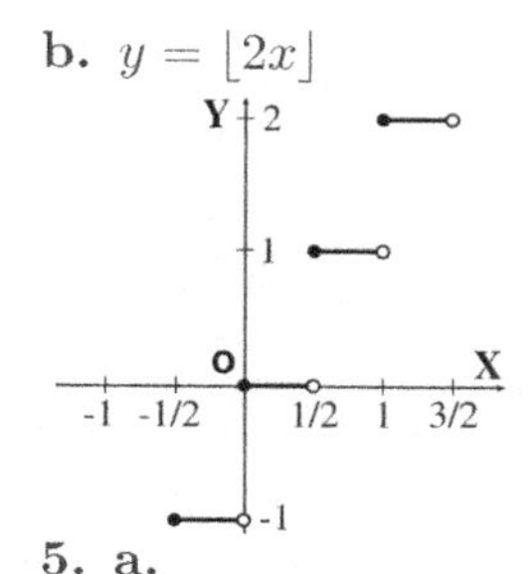

c. $y = \frac{1}{2}\lfloor x \rfloor$

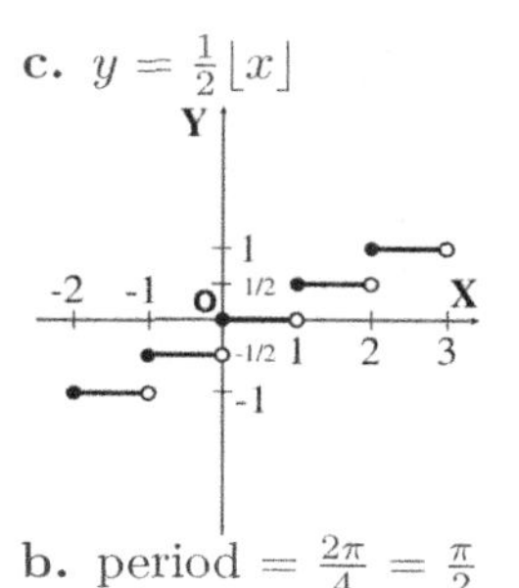

4.

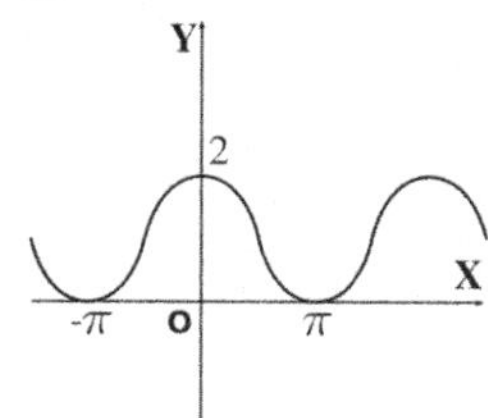

5. **a.**

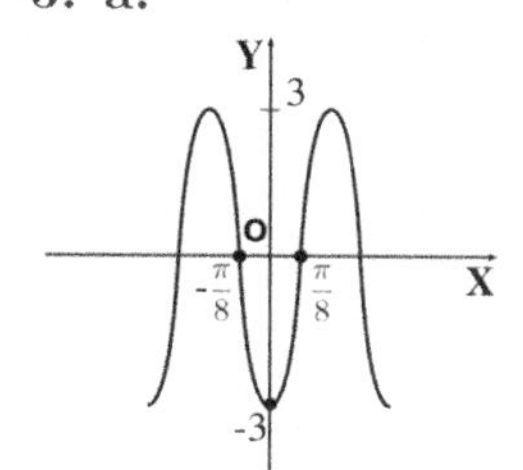

b. period $= \frac{2\pi}{4} = \frac{\pi}{2}$

6. $\text{Dom}(f+g) = \text{Dom}(f-g) = \text{Dom}(fg) = (-\infty,\ 1) \cup (1,\ 2]$
$\text{Dom}\left(\frac{f}{g}\right) = (-\infty,\ 1) \cup (1,\ 2)$

7. $\text{Dom}(f+g) = \text{Dom}(f-g) = \text{Dom}(fg) = [-4,\ -2] \cup [2,\ 4]$,
$\text{Dom}\left(\frac{f}{g}\right) = [-4,\ -2) \cup (2,\ 4]$

8. $\text{Dom}(f+g) = \text{Dom}(f-g) = \text{Dom}(fg) = (-2,\ 2)$,
$\text{Dom}\left(\frac{f}{g}\right) = (-2,\ 2) - \{0\}$

9. $\text{Dom}(f) = 4$ **10.** $\text{Dom}(f) = (-2,\ 0]$ **11.** $\text{Dom}(g) = [-2,\ 3)$

12. $(f \circ g)(x) = x - 1$, $\text{Dom}(f \circ g) = [0,\ +\infty)$
$(g \circ f)(x) = \sqrt{x^2 - 1}$, $\text{Dom}(g \circ f) = (-\infty,\ -1] \cup [1,\ +\infty)$
$(f \circ f)(x) = x^4 - 2x^2$, $\text{Dom}(f \circ f) = \mathbb{R}$
$(g \circ g)(x) = \sqrt[4]{x}$, $\text{Dom}(g \circ g) = [0,\ +\infty)$

13. $(f \circ g)(x) = x - 4$, $\text{Dom}(f \circ g) = [4,\ +\infty)$
$(g \circ f)(x) = \sqrt{x^2 - 4}$, $\text{Dom}(g \circ f) = (-\infty,\ -2] \cup [2,\ +\infty)$
$(f \circ f)(x) = x^4$, $\text{Dom}(f \circ f) = \mathbb{R}$
$(g \circ g)(x) = \sqrt{\sqrt{x - 4} - 4}$, $\text{Dom}(g \circ g) = [20,\ +\infty)$

14. $(f \circ g)(x) = \frac{1}{x^2} - \frac{1}{x}$, $\text{Dom}(f \circ g) = \mathbb{R} - \{0\}$
$(g \circ f)(x) = \frac{1}{x^2 - x}$, $\text{Dom}(g \circ f) = \mathbb{R} - \{0,\ 1\}$
$(f \circ f)(x) = x^4 - 2x^3 + x$, $\text{Dom}(f \circ f) = \mathbb{R}$
$(g \circ g)(x) = x$, $\text{Dom}(g \circ g) = \mathbb{R} - \{0\}$

15. $(f \circ g)(x) = \frac{1}{1 - \sqrt[3]{x}}$, $\text{Dom}(f \circ g) = \mathbb{R} - \{1\}$
$(g \circ f)(x) = \frac{1}{\sqrt[3]{1 - x}}$, $\text{Dom}(g \circ f) = \mathbb{R} - \{1\}$

$(f \circ f)(x) = \frac{x-1}{x}$, $\mathrm{Dom}(f \circ f) = \mathbb{R} - \{0,\, 1\}$
$(g \circ g)(x) = \sqrt[9]{x}$, $\mathrm{Dom}(g \circ g) = \mathbb{R}$

16. $(f \circ g)(x) = \sqrt{-x}$, $\mathrm{Dom}(f \circ g) = (-\infty,\, 0]$
$(g \circ f)(x) = \sqrt{1 - \sqrt{x^2 - 1}}$, $\mathrm{Dom}(g \circ f) = \left[-\sqrt{2},\, -1\right] \cup \left[1,\, \sqrt{2}\right]$
$(f \circ f)(x) = \sqrt{x^2 - 2}$, $\mathrm{Dom}(f \circ f) = \left(-\infty,\, -\sqrt{2}\right] \cup \left[\sqrt{2},\, +\infty\right)$
$(g \circ g)(x) = \sqrt{1 - \sqrt{1 - x}}$, $\mathrm{Dom}(g \circ g) = [0,\, 1]$

17. $(f \circ g \circ h)(x) = \sqrt{\frac{1}{x^2-1}}$

18. $(f \circ g \circ h)(x) = \sqrt[3]{\frac{x^2-x}{x^2-x+1}}$

19. $(f \circ f \circ f)(x) = x$,
$\mathrm{Dom}(f \circ f \circ f) = \mathbb{R} - \{0,\, 1\}$

20. $f(x) = \frac{1}{x}$, $g(x) = 1 + x$

21. $f(x) = x - 3$, $g(x) = \sqrt{x}$

22. $f(x) = \sqrt[3]{x}$, $g(x) = (2x - 1)^2$

23. $f(x) = \frac{1}{x}$, $g(x) = \sqrt{x^2 - x + 1}$

24. $f(x) = \frac{1}{x+1}$, $g(x) = \frac{1}{x}$,
$h(x) = x^2$

25. $f(x) = \sqrt[3]{x}$, $g(x) = x + 1$,
$h(x) = x^2 + |\, x\,|$

26. $f(x) = \sqrt[4]{x}$, $g(x) = x - 1$,
$h(x) = \sqrt{x}$

27. $g(x) = x^2 - 2x + 1$

28. $g(x) = \frac{1}{x+1}$

SECTION 4.4

1. $f^{-1}(x) = \frac{1}{2}x - \frac{1}{2}$

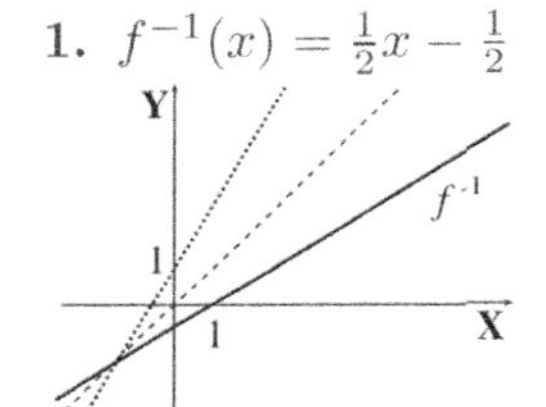

2. $g^{-1}(x) = \sqrt{x + 1}$

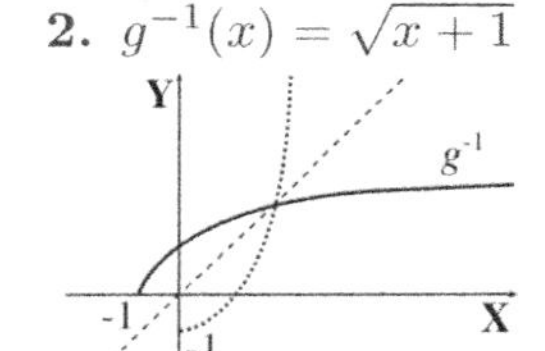

3. $h^{-1}(x) = \sqrt[3]{x - 2}$

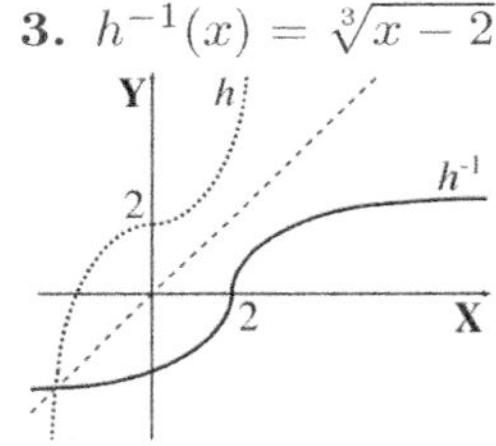

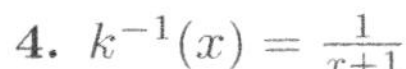

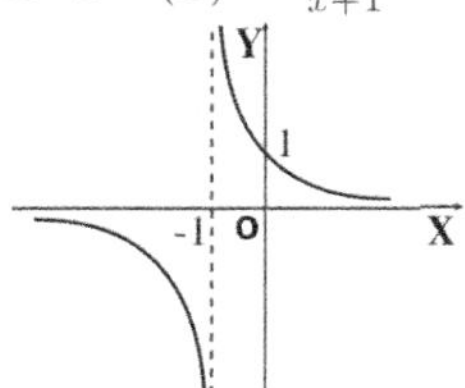

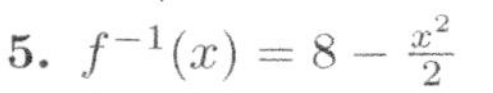

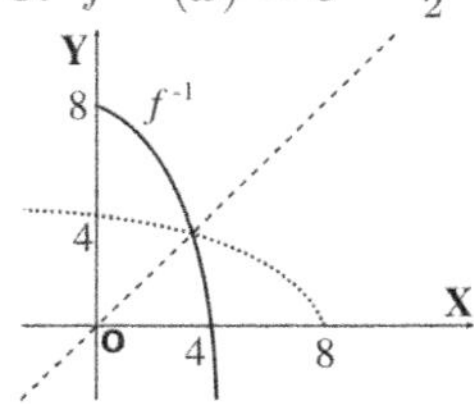

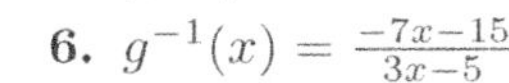

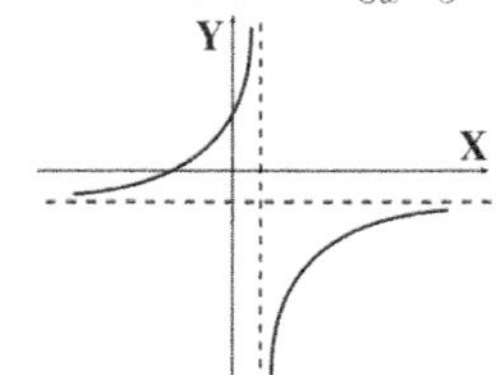

SECTION 4.5

1. $\frac{\pi}{3}$ **2.** $\frac{5}{4}\pi$ **3.** π **4.** $-\frac{\pi}{3}$ **5.** $\frac{3\pi}{4}$ **6.** $\frac{7\pi}{6}$

7. a. $\frac{2}{3}\sqrt{2}$ **b.** $\frac{1}{4}\sqrt{2}$ **c.** $2\sqrt{2}$ **d.** $\frac{3}{4}\sqrt{2}$ **e.** 3

8. a. $\frac{1}{5}\sqrt{5}$ **b.** $\frac{2}{5}\sqrt{5}$ **c.** $\frac{1}{2}$ **d.** 2 **e.** $\sqrt{5}$

9. a. $-\frac{3\sqrt{10}}{10}$ **b.** $\frac{1}{10}\sqrt{10}$ **c.** $-\frac{1}{3}$ **d.** $\sqrt{10}$ **e.** $-\frac{\sqrt{10}}{3}$

10. $\frac{1}{2}$ **11.** $-\frac{\sqrt{5}}{2}$ **12.** $-\frac{3}{5}$ **13.** $-\frac{3\sqrt{7}}{7}$ **14.** $\frac{\pi}{3}$ **15.** $\frac{\pi}{3}$

16. $\frac{2\sqrt{5}}{5} - \frac{\sqrt{10}}{30}$ **17.** $\frac{4}{9}\sqrt{2}$ **18.** $\sqrt{3}$ **19.** $\frac{5\sqrt{26}}{26}$

20. $\frac{x}{\sqrt{1+x^2}}$ **21.** $\frac{x}{\sqrt{1-x^2}}$ **22.** $\frac{\sqrt{4-x^2}}{2}$ **23.** $\sqrt{\frac{1+x}{2}}$

24. $x = 2\sin(-0.5) \approx -0.958851077$ **25.** $x = \sqrt{2} - 1$

26. $x \approx 0.8673$ or $x \approx -1.4728682$

SECTION 4.6

1. 3 **2.** 16 **3.** 125 **4.** $\frac{1}{125}$ **5.** 4 **6.** $\frac{4}{3\sqrt{3}}$

7. 100 **8.** $e^{-4} = \frac{1}{e^4}$ **9.** $\frac{1}{81}$ **10.** $\frac{1}{5}$ **11.** 2^{14} **12.** $\frac{1}{32}$

13. 2 **14.** 2 **15.** -4 **16.** $\frac{5}{3}$ **17.** $-\frac{7}{8}$ **18.** $-\frac{1}{3}$

19. -1 ó 3

20. $y = e^{x+2}$

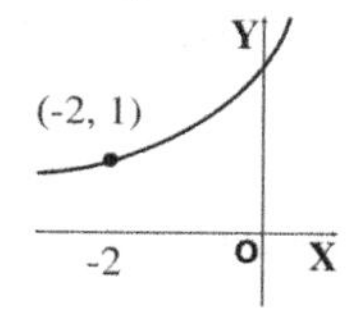

21. $y = -2e^x + 1$

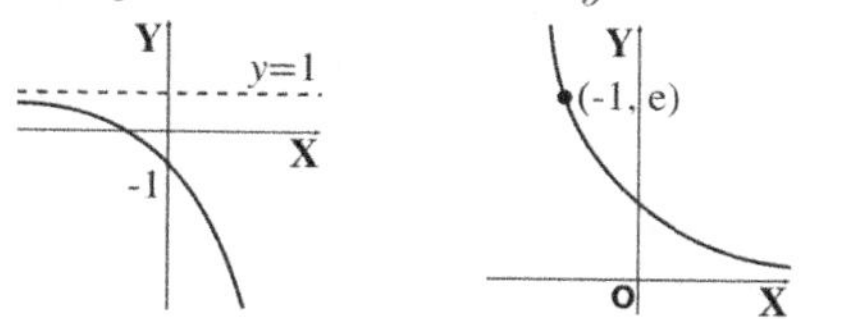

22. $y = e^{-x}$

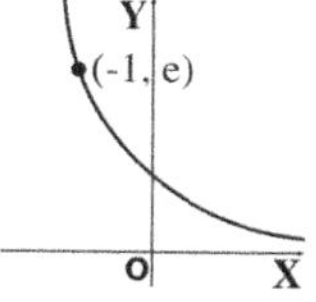

23. $y = e^{-x} + 2$

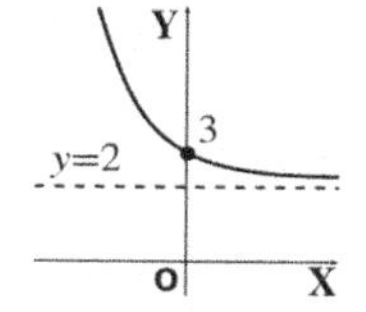

24. $y = 2 - e^{-x}$

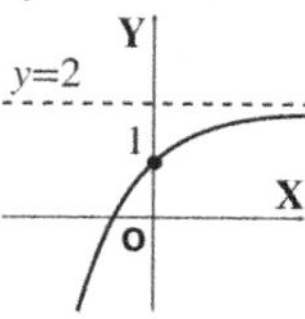

26. $y = 3^{-x+2}$

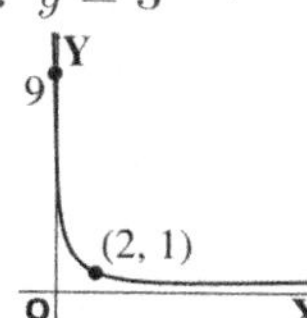

28. $y = -4^{-x-1}$

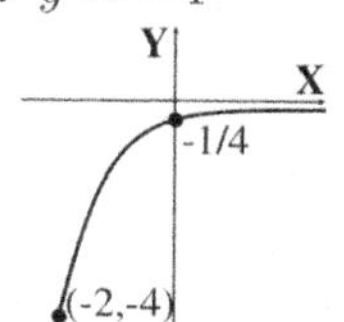

29. $\frac{125}{81}$ **30.** $-1,590$

SECTION 4.7

1. -6 **2.** 4 **3.** -4 **4.** $-\frac{1}{2}$ **5.** 3 **6.** 9

7. $\sqrt{3}$ **8.** $\frac{8}{9}$ **9.** 625 **10.** 8, -2 **11.** 5 **12.** $e^{-\frac{a}{3}}$

13. $e^{-1+\frac{k}{20}}$ **14.** e^2 **15.** $e^{e^{-4}}$ **16.** $\frac{\ln\left(\frac{14}{3}\right)}{-1.2} \approx 1.2837$

17. $1 + \frac{3}{\ln 3} \approx 3.73$ **18.** $\frac{6}{(3\log_2 3)} \approx 1.3086$ **19.** $\frac{8}{(4\log_2 3-1)} \approx 1.498$

20. $y = \ln(x-2)$

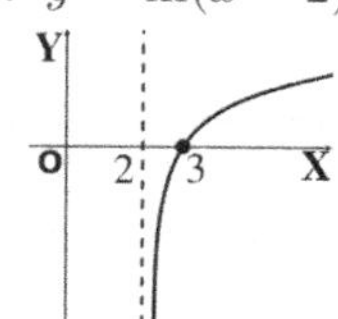

21. $y = \ln(-x)$

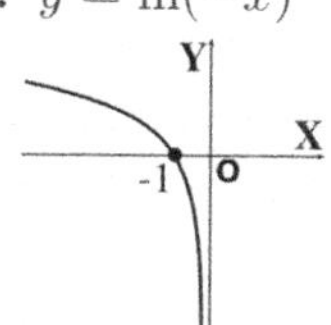

22. $y = \ln(x+3)$

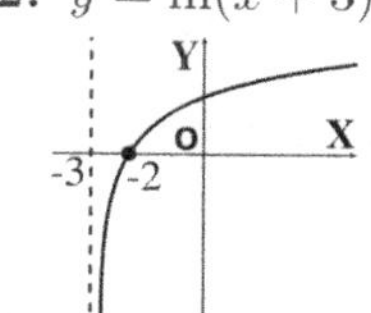

23. $y = 4 - \ln x$

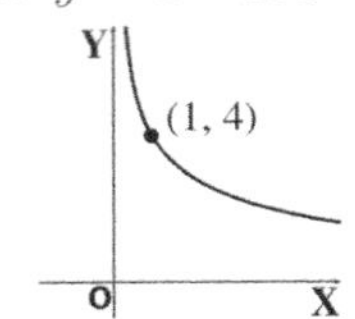

24. $y = 4 - \ln(x + 3)$

25. $y = 2 - \ln \mid x \mid$

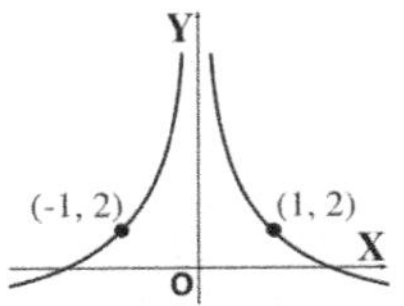

26. $y = 3 + \log x$

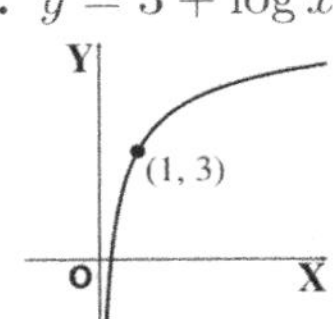

27. $y = 3 + \log(x + 3)$

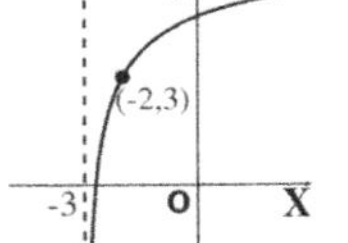

28. $2\log a + \log b - \log c$

29. $\frac{1}{2}\log b - 2\log a - 3\log c$

30. $-\ln a + \frac{3}{2}\ln c - \frac{1}{2}\ln b$

31. $\frac{1}{5}(2\ln a - \ln b - 4\ln c)$

32. $\ln \frac{x^3 y}{z^2}$

33. $\log \frac{a^2 b}{(zx)^3}$

34. $\ln \frac{\sqrt[4]{a^3}b^3}{\sqrt{c^3}}$

35. **a.** $y = 5e^{(0.5\ln 3)t}$ **b.** $y = 6e^{(\ln(1.04))t}$

SECTION 4.8

1. **a.** 127,020
b. 5,127%

2. **a.** \$15,809.88
b. 22.12%

3. **a.** 18 million
b. 24.3 million
c. 2.02%

4. 108,000

5. 6.75 million

6. 6,351 *gr*

7. 280.93 *gr*

8. 64,000 million

9. 1,476.28 $pound/feet^2$

10. **a.** 81.87%
b. 67.03%
c. 14.84%

11. **a.** 12,000
b. 15,841

12. **b.** 980,000
c. \$485,889.27

14. 3,924 years

15. 2.32 hours

16. 4 years

17. 29.54 months

18. 2,554 books

19. 81,666,666 million

20. 29.5 years

21. 11,460 years

22. **a.** 11,700,000
b. 12,288,000
c. 12,886,396
d. 13,045,843.42
e. 13,130,043

23. **a.** 1,140,967.37
b. 1,123,322.4

24. \$3,173,350,575

25. **a.** 4,792 years
b. 4,621 years

26. **a.** 7,595 years
b. 7,324 years

A PERSONAL INVITATION FROM ONE SOUL TO ANOTHER

Are you ready to start your own past life journey?

I would be honored to guide you on your explorations via ZOOM in the privacy of your own home anywhere in the world.

For details, put "past life" in the subject line and email me at

John.Koenig.Hypnotist@gmail.com

Or visit my website:

https://possibilities.nu

If you enjoyed reading *My Autobiographies,* please consider posting a review on amazon.com. Even if it is only a few sentences, it would be a huge help.